Course   Fundamentals of Chemistry
            David Goldberg
            University of Toledo
            Elementary Chemistry, Chem1090

http://create.mheducation.com

ISBN-10: 1259707547   ISBN-13: 9781259707544

Contents

Credits

Preface

Chemistry is a dynamic and rapidly changing field. It is an extraordinarily interesting subject to study and an intriguing one to teach. The diversity of knowledge of the beginning student presents a unique challenge to the student and to the teacher. This text is written primarily for use in courses designed to prepare students who wish to pursue a science major requiring a comprehensive course in general chemistry. These students, in most cases, have never taken a course in chemistry or have had limited instruction in the basic math necessary to solve chemistry problems, so a chemistry course can be very threatening to them.

To address this issue, this text has four major goals:

1. To provide a clear, consistent methodology that a student can follow to develop conceptual and quantitative problem-solving skills.

2. To engage the student by relying heavily on analogies that relate chemistry to daily life.

3. To anticipate the points where students are apt to have difficulty and to smooth the path to understanding by explaining in detail what the pitfalls are and how to avoid them.

4. To present, at one time, points that may be easily confused with one another so that students can avoid making the errors. For example, if a radioactive decay problem asks for the number of atoms that have *disintegrated* instead of the number *remaining* after a certain time, a student might easily make a mistake. If in one problem both the number disintegrated and the number remaining are required, the student can hardly make that same mistake. In a given chapter some early problems ask related questions together and later ones ask them separately to ensure that the differences are not forgotten.

Developing Problem-Solving Skills

ORGANIZING THEIR THOUGHTS

Students have numerous demands on their time, so helping them organize their thoughts and identifying the key concepts is important. This book has several ways to accomplish this task.

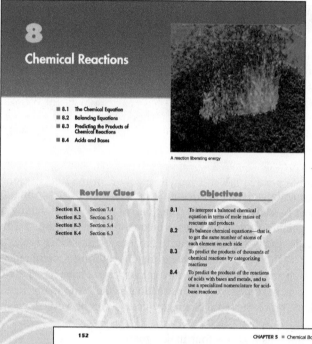

Chapter Outline   At the beginning of each chapter, the outline of the entire chapter is listed to introduce students to the topics presented in the chapter. This outline also provides the instructor with a quick topic summary for organizing lecture material.

Chapter Objectives   At the beginning of each chapter, the learning objectives are presented to alert the student to the key concepts covered in the chapter. These enable students to preview the material and become aware of the topics they are expected to master. These are also a valuable study tool for students when they are reviewing.

Review Clues   At the beginning of each chapter except the first, there is a list of Review Clues. These clues provide students the opportunity to go back to previous sections in the book or to Appendix 1 and review or relearn material pertinent to the present chapter.

Chapter Summary   At the end of each chapter is a summary designed to help the student identify important concepts and help them review for quizzes and tests.

Items for Special Attention   At the end of every chapter, this unique section highlights and emphasizes key concepts that often confuse students. This section anticipates students' questions and problem areas and helps them avoid many pitfalls.

Various Problem-Solving Methods

Many problems are worded to show students that very different questions may sound similar and that the same question may be presented in very different words. This will encourage students to try to understand concepts rather than to memorize solutions.

All Examples have the solutions following the stated problem. The solutions range from a simple statement (Example 1.4 on pages 6–7) to a short explanation (Example 3.1 on page 78) to a step-by-step solution (Example 7.13 on pages 194–195). Side-by-side examples are also presented with the general method for the technique presented on the left and a specific example of the method on the right (pages 193–194).

After most numbered examples, a practice problem is presented for the students to practice the problem-solving method. The complete answers are presented in Appendix 4. The students will then use these methods to solve the end-of-chapter problems.

The end-of-chapter problems have new variables while maintaining the same skill pattern. The end-of-chapter problems provide practice for the student using the skills presented in the chapter. Solutions to the problems numbered in red are provided in Appendix 5.

SELF-TESTING AND REVIEWING

Snapshot Review   At the end of each chapter section, a *Snapshot Review* appears. Students are provided a short synopsis of the section and then asked a question or two to test their comprehension of the concept(s). Answers to the *Snapshot Review* questions are provided at the end of each chapter.

ChemSkill Builder   At the end of chapter sections, where applicable, a ChemSkill Builder icon appears. ChemSkill Builder is an online electronic homework program that generates questions for students in a randomized fashion with a constant mix of variables. The icon lets the student know which sections of ChemSkill Builder to practice for the chemical skills relating to the specific content of the text. The correlation to ChemSkill Builder by James D. Spain and Harold J. Peters is enhanced by the increased number of topics covered there. Log on at www.mhhe.com/csb.

Self-Tutorial Problems   This end-of-chapter section presents problems in simple form designed as teaching devices. Many are from everyday life, and they emphasize the importance of identifying the information needed to answer questions, thus advancing analytical skills. By considering different terms that look or sound alike in a single problem, the students can more easily distinguish and learn both. (see Problems 5.1, 5.5, and 5.6 on pages 153–154)

Snapshot Review

ChemSkill Builder 3.6

❑ We classify matter so that we can learn the general properties of each type to enable us to answer specific questions about individual samples.

❑ All substances have definite compositions.

A. Does the compound baking soda have a definite composition?

Self-Tutorial Problems

8.1 Assign each of the following types to one of the five classes of reactions presented in Section 8.3:

Reactants	Products
(a) 2 elements	1 compound
(b) 1 compound	2 elements
(c) 2 compounds	2 different compounds
(d) 1 element + 1 compound	1 element + 1 compound
(e) 1 compound	1 element + 1 compound
(f) 1 compound + O_2	2 or more compounds
(g) 1 element + 1 compound	1 compound

8.2 Explain how to recognize that O_2 and MgO will not react with each other in a single substitution reaction.

8.3 Rewrite the following equations with integral coefficients:
(a) $CrF_2(s) + \frac{1}{2}F_2(g) \rightarrow CrF_3(s)$
(b) $CoCl_3(s) + \frac{1}{2}Co(s) \rightarrow \frac{3}{2}CoCl_2(s)$
(c) $CuCl(s) + \frac{1}{2}Cl_2(g) \rightarrow CuCl_2(s)$
(d) $\frac{2}{3}H_3PO_4(aq) + CaCO_3(s) \rightarrow$
  $\frac{1}{3}Ca_3(PO_4)_2(s) + H_2O(\ell) + CO_2(g)$
(e) $NH_3(g) + \frac{5}{4}O_2(g) \rightarrow NO(g) + \frac{3}{2}H_2O(g)$

8.4 Write a balanced chemical equation for each of the following reactions:
(a) $SO_2(g) + PCl_5(s) \rightarrow SOCl_2(\ell) + POCl_3(\ell)$
(b) $SO_2(g) + Cl_2(g) \rightarrow SO_2Cl_2(\ell)$

8.5 What is the difference, if any, among (a) the reaction of sodium with chlorine, (b) the combination of sodium and chlorine, and (c) the formation of sodium chloride from its elements?

8.6 Consider the reaction of aqueous chlorine with aqueous zinc iodide.
(a) Identify the reaction type.
(b) Write correct formulas for all reactants and products.
(c) Write a balanced equation.

8.7 Explain how a catalyst resembles a marriage broker.

8.8 A certain double substitution reaction produced silver chloride and potassium acetate. What were the reactants?

8.9 Can a single substitution reaction occur between an element and a compound of that same element?

8.10 Can a double substitution reaction occur between two compounds containing one ion in common?

8.11 Are oxides of reactive metals or oxides of unreactive metals more likely to decompose into their two elements when heated?

8.12 What type of reaction is the following? What are the products?
  $C_2H_6(g) + O_2(g, \text{excess}) \rightarrow$

8.13 In a certain double substitution reaction, $CrCl_3$ is a reactant. Is $Cr(NO_3)_3$ or $Cr(NO_3)_2$ more likely to be a product?

8.14 Do the classes of reactions described in Section 8.3 include all possible types of chemical reactions?

8.15 Which table in this chapter should be used when working with single substitution reaction, and which ones with double substitution reactions?

8.16 Which of the following compounds are acids?
  H_2O NH_3 C_4H_8 $HClO_3$
  AsH_3 LiH H_2O_2 H_3PO_4

8.17 Classify each of the following as an acidic anhydride, a basic anhydride, or neither:
  N_2O_5 CaO K_2O SO_3
  Cl_2O_7 N_2O

8.18 Which, if any, of the common acids exist completely in the form of ions (a) as a pure compound and (b) in aqueous solution?

8.19 What products are expected in each of the following cases?
(a) $KClO_3$ is heated in the presence of MnO_2 as a catalyst.
(b) $KClO_3$ is heated in the presence of MnO_2.
(c) $KClO_3$ and MnO_2 are heated together.
(d) $KClO_3$ is heated.

8.20 What type of substance can act as an acid but does not have hydrogen written first in its formula?

8.21 What is the difference between "acidic" and "acetic"?

8.22 Give two reasons why the following reaction produces products:
  $Ba(HCO_3)_2(aq) + H_2SO_4(aq) \rightarrow$
  $BaSO_4(s) + 2 H_2O(\ell) + 2 CO_2(g)$

Engaging Student Interest

ANALOGIES

Frequent use of analogies to daily life helps students understand that chemistry problems are not significantly different from everyday problems. For example, calculations involving dozens of pairs of socks and moles of diatomic molecules can be carried out by the same methods (see Problems 7.4 and 7.5 on page 201). Oxidizing and reducing agents can be compared conceptually to hand towels and wet hands (Example 16.11 on page 441). Specific heat calculations are like those involving room rates at a resort (Example 14.5 on page 384).

REAL-WORLD PROBLEMS

Students are engaged in the study of a topic by use of a real-world problem. The students easily understand by frequently using analogies to apply the scientific concept to a normal daily event. In working with conceptual problems, the use of chemistry in the real world is brought alive to the student. (See Problem 7.130 on page 205)

ITEMS OF INTEREST

Periodically throughout the book the students will find *Items of Interest* within the textual material. These items demonstrate the use of chemistry in the present and future. An example is the industrial Solvay process in Chapter 8 on page 222.

ART PROGRAM

Today's students are much more visually oriented than any previous generation and many are principally visual learners. We have attempted to develop this style of learning through the expanded use of color and illustrations. Each chapter is amply illustrated with accurate, colorful diagrams that clarify difficult concepts and enhance learning.

Content Changes in the Fifth Edition

Changes in the fifth edition include:

- The addition of a *NEW Chapter 17* on Electrochemistry, with calculation of potentials and of stoichiometric quantities from electrical quantities and vice versa. Six new in-chapter examples and *forty* end-of-chapter problems were added, as well as two tables, Table 17.1 "Electrical Variables and Units" and Table 17.2 "Standard Reduction Potentials."
- The addition of a *NEW Section 19.5* on Polyprotic Acids, with Table 19.4 on "Selected Dissociation Constants of Polyprotic Acids".
- Changes in positions of several sections for better flow of ideas:
  - Chapter 2: Presentation of Exponential Numbers before The Metric System
  - Chapter 12: Presentation of Dalton's Law immediately after Ideal Gas Law

Preface

- Five *new* Item of Interest additions:
  - Chapter 10: Ion mass in food chemistry
  - Chapter 14: High heat capacity and heat of vaporization of water
  - Chapter 17: Purification process for copper
    Galvanic cell reactions
  - Chapter 19: H_2S, a dangerous but useful gas
- *New* Enrichment Box on Controlled Experiments in Chapter 13
- The elimination of Section 16.6 on Equivalents and Normality form Chapter 16. These concepts are available online for instructors who want them; contact your McGraw-Hill Sales Representative.

In addition, the entire book has been examined for accuracy, and the problems and examples have been amended. More in-chapter examples and end-of-chapter problems have been added as well. The artwork has been upgraded to further student interest and understanding.

Major pedagogy retained by the author includes:

- Asking questions in a way so students can understand concepts rather than memorize has been retained and hopefully improved.
- Multiple-part questions that ask the same question in several different ways, or that ask quite different questions in similar-sounding ways, have been retained. (For example, see Problem 18.6 where equilibria involving solid and gaseous iodine are both presented in a single problem.)
- Increase in the number of problems and examples; full solutions are given, either in the appendices or the instructor's manual.

Supplemental Materials

INSTRUCTOR RESOURCES

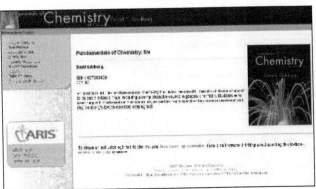

ARIS—Assessment, Review, and Instruction System. ARIS is a complete, online tutorial, electronic homework, and course management system, designed for greater ease of use than any other system available. Instructors can create and share course materials and assignments with colleagues with a few clicks of the mouse. All assignments, quizzes, and question tutorials are directly tied to text-specific materials, but instructors can also edit questions, import their own content, and create announcements and due dates for assignments. ARIS has automatic grading and reporting of homework, quizzing, and testing. All student activity within McGraw-Hill's ARIS is automatically recorded and available through a fully integrated gradebook that can be downloaded to Excel. Log on at www.mhhe.com/goldberg.

Instructor's Manual and Solution Manual is found in the *Fundamentals of Chemistry,* Fifth Edition ARIS website under the Instructor Center. The Instructor's Manual contains the test bank questions, suggestions on how to organize the course and answers to the end-of-chapter problems.

Instructor's Testing and Resource CD-ROM contains the electronic format for the test bank questions allowing the instructors to edit or create their own test templates. The Test Bank is formatted for easy integration into any course management system.

Digital Content Manager CD-ROM is a multimedia collection of visual resources allowing instructors to utilize artwork from the text in multiple formats to create customized classroom presentation, visually based tests and quizzes, dynamic course content, or attractive support materials. The Digital Content Manager is a cross-platform CD containing an image library, a photo library, and a table library.

ChemSkill Builder is an online tool containing more than 1500 algorithmically generated questions, each with tutorial feedback. There is a direct correlation between student time investment in this program and increased problem-solving ability. A record of student work is maintained in an online gradebook so that homework can be done at home, in a dorm room, or in a university lab. Log on at www.mhhe.com/csb

STUDENT RESOURCES

ARIS—Assessment, Review, and Instruction System. ARIS is a complete, online tutorial, and electronic homework system, designed for greater ease of use than any other system available. All assignments, quizzes, and question tutorials are directly tied to text-specific materials. ARIS has automatic grading and reporting of homework, quizzing, and testing. All student activity within ARIS is automatically recorded and available to the instructor. Log on at www.mhhe.com/goldberg.

ChemSkill Builder challenges the students' knowledge of introductory chemistry with an array of individualized problems. The ChemSkill

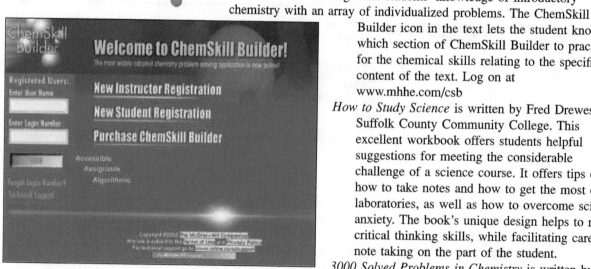

Builder icon in the text lets the student know which section of ChemSkill Builder to practice for the chemical skills relating to the specific content of the text. Log on at www.mhhe.com/csb

How to Study Science is written by Fred Drewes of Suffolk County Community College. This excellent workbook offers students helpful suggestions for meeting the considerable challenge of a science course. It offers tips on how to take notes and how to get the most out of laboratories, as well as how to overcome science anxiety. The book's unique design helps to rouse critical thinking skills, while facilitating careful note taking on the part of the student.

3000 Solved Problems in Chemistry is written by David E. Goldberg. This Schaum's solved problem manual provides 3000 solved problems. It provides problem-solving strategies and helpful hints in studying.

Acknowledgments

The preparation of a textbook is a family effort, and the quality of the final product is a reflection of the dedication of all the family members. First, I would like to thank my wife, without whose patience and support this project would not have been possible. Second, I would like to thank the scores of my fellow chemists and my students who have taught me much in the past and continue to do so. Learning is a never-ending process, and I continue to learn from my colleagues and students. Please let me know about any errors that I have not eliminated from this edition. I would also like to thank the members of my extended family at McGraw-Hill, without whom there would not have been a text: my developmental editor, Lorraine Buczek, my managing developmental editor, Shirley Oberbroeckling, my project manager, Jayne Klein, and my publisher, Thomas Timp. I gratefully acknowledge the invaluable help of the following dedicated reviewers, who provided expert suggestions and the needed encouragement to improve the text:

John R. Allen
Southeastern Louisiana University

Bob Blake
Texas Tech University

David A. Boyajian
Palomar College

Steve Gentemann
Southwestern Illinois College

Claudia M.S. Hein
Diablo Valley College

James R. Jeitler
North Idaho College

Marc Lord
Columbus State Community College

Lydia J. Martinez Rivera
University of Texas at San Antonio

Kirsten L Murphy
University of Wisconsin–Milwaukee

D.K. Philbin
Allan Hancock College

Elsa C. Santos
Colorado State University

Mark W. Schraf
West Virginia University

Mary C. Setzer
University of Alabama in Huntsville

Jeffrey S. Temple
Southeastern Louisiana University

Jacquelyn A. Thomas
Southwestern College

To the Student

This book is designed to help you learn the fundamentals of chemistry. To be successful, you must master the concepts of chemistry and acquire the mathematical skills necessary to solve problems in this quantitative science. If your algebra is rusty, you should polish it up. Appendix 1 reviews the algebra used in basic chemistry and also shows how to avoid mistakes while solving chemistry problems with your scientific calculator. The factor label method is introduced in Chapter 2 to show you how to use units to help with problem solutions. You can help yourself by using the standard symbols and abbreviations for various quantities (such as m for mass, m for meter, mol for moles, and M for molarity). Always use the proper units with your numerical answers; it makes a big difference whether your roommate's pet is 6 inches long or 6 feet long!

Many laws, generalizations, and rules are presented in the study of basic chemistry. Most students can master these. Successful students, however, not only know them but also know *when to use each one*. Word problems are the biggest hurdle for most students who do have difficulty with chemistry. The best way to learn to do word problems is to practice intensively. Review the Examples and do the Practice Problems until you feel confident that you understand the concepts and techniques involved. (Do not try to memorize solutions; there are too many different ways to ask the same questions, and many similar-sounding questions are actually quite different.) Do the Snapshot Review items at the end of each section. Do as many of the end-of-chapter problem as you possibly can to see whether you have mastered the material.

You should not try to speed-read chemistry. Mere reading of a section will not generally yield full comprehension of the material. You must be able to solve the problems to be sure that you have really mastered the concepts. Many of the problems sound alike but are very different (for example, Problems 5.10, 7.4, 7.5, and 11.9), and many others sound different but are essentially the same (for example, Problems 3.5, 5.16, 8.5, and 8.19). These will help you develop careful reading habits and prepare you for the questions asked on examinations.

Problems from everyday life that are analogous to scientific problems are included to help you understand certain points better (for example, Problems 7.4 and 7.5). Other problems are first presented in parts to help you work through the solution and later appear as a single question, as is more likely to occur on examinations. Some of the problems are very easy; these are generally intended to emphasize an important point. After solving one of these problems, ask yourself why such a question was asked. Make sure you understand the point.

Make sure you understand the scientific meaning of each new term introduced. For example, the word "significant" as used in Chapter 2 means something entirely different from its meaning in everyday conversation; be sure you understand the difference. Key terms are **boldfaced** when they are first introduced in the text. A list of these terms is given at the end of each chapter. A complete glossary of all important terms is provided at the end of the book.

Other materials to aid your study include lists of standard symbols and abbreviations for variables, units, and subatomic particles, found in Appendix 2. A summary of the mathematical equations used in the book is presented in Appendix 3. The solutions to all Practice Problems and selected end-of-chapter problems are provided in Appendices 4 and 5, respectively. The selected end-of-chapter problem numbers are printed in red. A periodic table is printed inside the front cover of the book, and a table of the elements appears inside the back cover. Let these tools help you succeed!

A representation of atoms bonded together

1

Basic Concepts

Objectives

1.1 To classify matter into types to make manageable the wealth of information about matter

1.2 To use properties to help identify substances

1.3 To distinguish among matter, mass, and weight, as well as between matter and energy

1.4 To write the symbols for the important elements and the names of these elements from the symbols

1.5 To begin to classify the elements in a systematic manner. To identify periods, groups, and sections of the periodic table by name and/or number

1.6 To distinguish among laws, hypotheses, and theories

Chemistry is the study of matter and energy. Matter includes all the material things in the universe. In Section 1.1, we will learn to classify matter into various types—elements, compounds, and mixtures—based on composition. Properties—the characteristics by which samples of matter may be identified—are discussed in Section 1.2.

Energy may be defined as the ability to do work. We often carry out chemical reactions for the sole purpose of changing energy from one form to another—for example, we pay large sums of money for fuels to burn in our homes or cars. The relationship between energy and matter, an important one for chemists, is explored in Section 1.3.

Symbols, introduced in Section 1.4, are used to represent the elements. The periodic table, introduced in Section 1.5, groups together elements with similar properties. Chemical symbols and the periodic table are both designed to decrease the effort required to learn a great deal of chemistry. Section 1.6 presents scientific laws, hypotheses, and theories that generalize and explain natural phenomena.

For convenience, chemistry is often divided into the following five subdisciplines: organic chemistry, inorganic chemistry, analytical chemistry, physical chemistry, and biochemistry. **Organic chemistry** deals with most compounds of carbon. These compounds are introduced systematically in Chapter 20. **Inorganic chemistry** deals with all the elements and with compounds that are not defined as organic. **Analytical chemistry** involves finding which elements or compounds are present in a sample or how much of each is present. **Physical chemistry** deals with the properties—especially quantitative (measurable) properties—of substances. **Biochemistry** deals with the chemistry of living things.

These subdivisions of chemistry are somewhat arbitrary. A chemist specializing in any one of the first four subdivisions uses all of them and often biochemistry as well. A biochemist uses all five specializations. For example, the modern organic chemist often uses inorganic compounds to convert starting materials to desired products and then analyzes the products and measures their properties. In addition, many organic chemists now are investigating compounds of biological interest.

The importance of science in general and of chemistry in particular in our everyday lives can hardly be overstated. For example, color television, computers, and modern copy machines all stem from chemical advances of the past few decades. (Color TV requires compounds that glow intensely in red, blue, or green when bombarded with electron beams. Computers work with "chips" made from specially treated metalloids. Copy machines require materials that "remember" how much light has fallen on them.) However, today's and tomorrow's chemists are still faced with monumental tasks—cleaning up the environment and providing sufficient food for an ever-growing world population to mention just two.

1.1 Classification of Matter

Matter is defined as anything that has mass and occupies space. All the materials in the world are composed of a few more than a hundred elements. **Elements** are the simplest form of matter and cannot be broken down chemically into simpler, stable substances. They can be thought of as building blocks for everything in the universe. The same elements that make up the Earth also make up the Moon, as shown by actual analysis of rock samples from the Moon. Moreover, indirect evidence obtained from analysis of light from stars shows that the rest of the universe is composed of the same elements.

Clearly the number of different combinations of elements must be huge to get all the varieties of matter in the universe. But elements can combine in only two fundamentally different ways: by physical changes to form mixtures or by chemical changes to produce compounds. **Chemical changes,** also called **chemical reactions,** change the composition (or structure) of a substance. **Physical changes** do not alter the composition. The breaking of glass into small pieces is an example of a physical change. The glass still has the same composition and the same properties as before, but its external form is changed. The burning of charcoal (mostly carbon) in air (or in pure oxygen) to get carbon dioxide, a colorless gas, is an example of a chemical reaction. Not only the form of the material but also its composition has changed. The gas has both carbon and oxygen in it, but the charcoal had no oxygen and the oxygen had no carbon.

If a sample of matter cannot be broken down into simpler substances by ordinary chemical means, the sample is an element. [Ordinary chemical means includes any methods except nuclear reactions (Chapter 21).] An element has a definite set of properties. A **compound** is a chemical combination of elements that has its own set of properties and a **definite composition.** For example, pure water obtained from any natural source contains 88.8% oxygen and 11.2% hydrogen by mass. Compounds can be separated into their constituent elements only by chemical reaction. Elements and compounds are the two types of **substances,** often referred to as pure substances.

EXAMPLE 1.1

The percentage of carbon in a small box of the pure substance sucrose (table sugar) is 42.1%. (a) Is sucrose an element or a compound? (b) What is the percentage of carbon in a large box of the same substance?

Solution

(a) Sucrose is a compound; it contains more than one element.

(b) The larger sample is also 42.1% carbon because a given compound always contains the same percentage of each of its elements, no matter what the size of the sample.

Two or more substances—elements, compounds, or both—can combine physically to produce a mixture. A mixture can be separated into its components by physical means. **Mixtures** are physical combinations of substances that have properties related to those of their components but that do not have definite compositions. They can be either **heterogeneous** or **homogeneous mixtures.** In heterogeneous mixtures, two or more different types of matter can be seen to be present with the naked eye or a good optical microscope. Homogeneous mixtures, also called **solutions,** look alike throughout, even under a microscope.

Both types of pure substances are usually homogeneous (but can be heterogeneous, as in ice water).

●●●●●●●●●●●●●●●●●●●●●●●●

ITEM OF INTEREST

The difference between elements and compounds is illustrated in human nutrition:

A. *Vitamins* are complex compounds of carbon, hydrogen, and several other elements. A vitamin owes its activity to the nature of the compound as a whole, and any slight change in it can destroy its nutritional value.

B. About 20 elements are called *minerals*. They also play a role in human nutrition. The minerals known to be essential for good health are calcium, phosphorus, potassium, sulfur, sodium, chlorine, magnesium, iron, manganese, copper, iodine, cobalt, fluorine, and zinc. Traces of silicon, boron, arsenic, strontium, aluminum, bromine, molybdenum, selenium, and nickel may also be required. These elements are eaten in the form of their compounds, but it does not matter much which compounds.

Heating a vitamin will destroy its potency by breaking the compound into other compounds. In contrast, heating a compound that contains one of the essential minerals might destroy the compound, but it will not change the mineral into another element. For example, calcium citrate can be changed into another calcium-containing compound, but the calcium is still present.

●●●●●●●●●●●●●●●●●●●●●●●●

ITEM OF INTEREST

The word *homogenize* is related to the term *homogeneous,* but as used in everyday conversation, it does not mean exactly the same thing. For example, homogenized milk is not really homogeneous; we can see individual particles of cream under a microscope. Truly homogeneous liquids are transparent (though not always colorless). If we cannot recognize objects viewed through a thin layer of liquid, the liquid is not homogeneous.

Table 1.1 Classification of Matter

Pure substances
   Elements
   Compounds
Mixtures
   Heterogeneous mixtures
   Homogeneous mixtures
    (solutions)

The entire classification scheme for matter discussed in this section is outlined in Table 1.1 and Figure 1.1.

EXAMPLE 1.2

If we stir a teaspoon of sugar into a glass of water and a teaspoon of mud into another glass of water, the sugar will disappear into the water (dissolve), but the mud will not (Figure 1.2). Which mixture is a solution?

Solution

The sugar forms a solution—a homogeneous mixture—with the water. The mud and water form a heterogeneous mixture. Particles of mud are easy to see in the mud-water mixture, but seeing any sugar particles in the sugar-water solution is impossible, no matter how hard we look (even with a microscope).

Practice Problem 1.2   When solid iodine is added to ethyl alcohol, a colorless liquid, it forms a uniform, transparent liquid mixture with a deep color. Is the mixture homogeneous or heterogeneous?

Figure 1.1 Classification of Matter

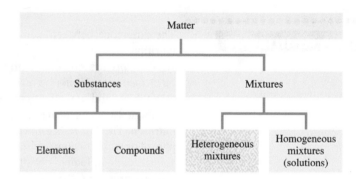

EXAMPLE 1.3

Classify each of the following statements as true or false:

(a) Every mixture contains two or more free elements.

(b) Every compound is a substance.

(c) Every compound contains two or more elements.

(d) Every mixture contains two or more compounds.

(e) Every substance is a compound.

(f) All mixtures are homogeneous.

(g) Every mixture contains two or more substances.

Solution

(a) False (They may contain compounds and only one or no free elements.)

(b) True

(c) True

(d) False (They may contain free elements or compounds or both.)

(e) False (Some are free elements.)

(f) False (Some are heterogeneous.)

(g) True

Figure 1.2 Sugar Plus Water, and Mud Plus Water

(a) Sugar dissolves in water and is not distinguishable from the water; a solution is formed. (b) Mud does not dissolve in water; a heterogeneous mixture is formed.

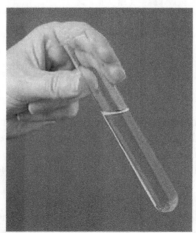

(a)   (b)

Practice Problem 1.3 Classify each of the following statements as true or false:

(a) Every mixture contains two or more elements.

(b) All mixtures are heterogeneous.

(c) Every substance contains two or more elements.

(d) All homogeneous samples are solutions.

Snapshot Review

ChemSkill Builder 3.6

❏ We classify matter so that we can learn the general properties of each type to enable us to answer specific questions about individual samples.

❏ All substances have definite compositions.

A. Does the compound baking soda have a definite composition?

1.2 Properties

Every substance has a definite set of properties. **Properties** are the characteristics by which we can identify something. For example, we know that pure water is a colorless, odorless, tasteless substance that is a liquid under the conditions usually found in an ordinary room. Water puts out fires, and it dissolves sugar and salt. Liquid water can be changed into a gas (called water vapor or steam) by heating it, or into a solid (ice) by cooling it. Salt has a different set of properties from water; sugar has yet another set.

Chemical properties are the characteristic ways a substance can react to produce other substances. **Physical properties** are the ways a substance can be identified without changing its characteristic composition. For example, water can react with very active metals to produce hydrogen and another compound. That reactivity is a chemical property of water. Water can also freeze to ice at 0°C (equal to 32°F) or it can evaporate to water vapor, neither of which changes it from H_2O. These are physical properties of water.

Some properties of a sample of a substance depend on the quantity of the sample. These properties are called **extensive properties.** For example, the weight of a solid sample depends on how much of the substance is present. Other properties, such as color and taste, do not depend on how much is present. These properties are known as **intensive properties.** Intensive properties are much more useful for identifying substances.

EXAMPLE 1.4

(a) Sample A weighs twice as much as sample B. Is it possible to tell which sample is iron and which is powdered sugar?

(b) Sample A is attracted by a magnet and sample B is a white powder. Is it possible to tell which sample is iron and which is powdered sugar?

Solution

(a) The weight of a sample is an extensive property that does not tell anything about the material's identity.

(b) The intensive properties described enable us to tell which of the two samples is iron (the magnetic one) and which is powdered sugar (the white one).

Practice Problem 1.4   Which is heavier, (a) bricks or straw? (b) one package of cheese or two of those packages of cheese? (c) Which of these uses of the word *heavier* describes an intensive property and which an extensive property?

Some of the most important intensive properties that chemists use to identify substances are ones that they measure; they are called **quantitative properties.** Two such properties are the freezing point and the normal boiling point of a substance, which are the temperatures at which a liquid freezes to form a solid and boils to form a gas under normal atmospheric conditions, respectively. We will discuss quantitative properties in more detail in Chapter 2.

We can distinguish compounds from mixtures because of the characteristic properties of compounds. Mixtures have properties like those of their constituents. The more of a given component present in a mixture, the more the properties of the mixture will resemble those of that component. For example, the more sugar we put into a glass of water, the sweeter is the solution that is produced.

An experiment will illustrate how properties are used to distinguish between a compound and a mixture. We place small samples of iron filings and powdered sulfur on separate watch glasses to investigate their properties (Figure 1.3a). We note that both are solids. We place the samples in separate test tubes and then hold a magnet beside the first tube (Figure 1.3b). We find that the iron is attracted to the magnet. When we hold the magnet next to the tube with the sulfur, nothing happens; the sulfur is not attracted by the magnet.

> Caution: Carbon disulfide is both explosive in air and poisonous.

When we pour carbon disulfide, a colorless, flammable liquid, on the sulfur sample, the solid sulfur disappears, and the liquid turns yellow. The sulfur has **dissolved,** forming a solution with the carbon disulfide. When we pour carbon disulfide on the iron, nothing happens; the iron stays solid, and the liquid stays colorless. If we had large pieces of each element, we could pound them with a hammer and find that the sulfur is brittle and easily powdered but that the iron does not easily break into small pieces. Iron is **malleable**—that is, it can be pounded into various shapes. Table 1.2 lists the properties discussed so far of the two elements.

Next we pour some iron filings and some powdered sulfur into a large test tube and stir them together. The sample appears to be a dirty yellow, but if we look closely, we can see yellow specks and black specks. If we hold a magnet next to the test tube (Figure 1.3c), the black particles (with some yellow particles clinging to them) are attracted by the magnet. When we pour some carbon disulfide on the sample, the liquid turns yellow. We pour off that liquid and pour on more carbon disulfide until no yellow solid remains in the sample. When we evaporate the carbon disulfide in a fume hood, we get a

Figure 1.3   *Iron, Sulfur, and a Mixture of the Two*
(a) Iron filings (black) and powdered sulfur (yellow).
(b) The iron is attracted by the magnet, but the sulfur is not.
(c) The iron filings in a mixture of iron and sulfur are still
attracted by the magnet. (Some of the powdered sulfur sticks to
the iron filings, but the sulfur is not attracted by the magnet.)

(a)

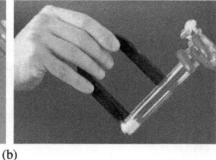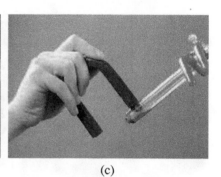

(b)   (c)

yellow solid again. If we place a magnet next to the black material left in the
large test tube, we find that it is attracted to the magnet. It seems that mixing
the two samples of elements has not changed their properties. The sulfur is still
yellow and still soluble in carbon disulfide; the iron is still black and still
attracted by a magnet. The two elements have retained their properties and their
identities; they are still elements. This combination of the two is a mixture. A
mixture does not have a definite composition, and it has properties related to
the properties of its components.

    Now we place two new, carefully measured samples of iron filings and
powdered sulfur in another large test tube and heat the mixture strongly
with a Bunsen burner. After a time, a red glow appears in the bottom of the
tube and gradually spreads throughout the sample. This is evidence of a

Table 1.2   Some Properties of Iron, Sulfur, and an
Iron-Sulfur Compound

Iron	Sulfur	Iron-Sulfur Compound
Solid	Solid	Solid
Shiny	Dull	Dull
Magnetic	Not magnetic	Not magnetic
Black	Yellow	Black
Malleable	Brittle	Brittle
Insoluble in carbon disulfide	Soluble in carbon disulfide	Insoluble in carbon disulfide

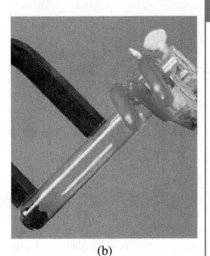

(a)

chemical reaction. Some sulfur escapes into the gas phase because of the heat and then deposits on the test tube wall (Figure 1.4a). A black solid results from the chemical reaction. When we remove the solid from the test tube (we may have to break the tube to get it out), we can pulverize the solid with a hammer—that is, it is brittle. If we try to dissolve the material in carbon disulfide, it does not dissolve. If we bring the magnet close to it, it is not attracted (Figure 1.4b). This material has its own set of properties: a dull black color, brittleness, insolubility in carbon disulfide, lack of attraction to a magnet (see Table 1.2). It is a compound—a chemical combination of iron and sulfur.

EXAMPLE 1.5

After a certain substance is heated in air until no further reaction takes place, a metal is left that has a mass 58.5% of that of the original substance. After another substance is heated in air, a white powder is left that has a mass of 138% of that of the original substance. Can you tell whether the reactants and the products are elements or compounds?

Solution

The first substance is a compound. When it is heated, it decomposes into a metallic material that is left behind and some gaseous product that escapes into the air. Because the metal has less mass than the original substance, it is simpler. The original substance is decomposable—it is not an element. The metal product might or might not be decomposable, so we cannot tell from the information given whether it is an element or a compound.

The second substance combined with something in the air; it gained mass. The powdery product is therefore a combination of substances and cannot be an element. We do not know if the original substance can be decomposed (it was not decomposed in this experiment), so we cannot tell if it is an element or a compound.

Practice Problem 1.5   A certain sample of a shiny substance is heated in air. Afterward, a white powder with twice the mass is present. Is the change a chemical reaction? Is the powder an element?

(b)

Figure 1.4   Reaction of Iron and Sulfur

(a) When a mixture of iron and sulfur is heated, the two elements react. Some sulfur is vaporized and then deposits on the test tube wall.
(b) The pulverized product of the reaction is not attracted by a magnet.

ChemSkill Builder 1.2

Snapshot Review

❐ Each substance has its own characteristic set of properties.
❐ Extensive properties depend on how much sample is present; intensive properties do not.
❐ Intensive properties are useful for identifying substances.

A. Consider the statement: "There is 1 liter (L) of colorless soda in the can." Which of the two properties is intensive and which is extensive?
B. A certain familiar substance freezes at 0°C. Does this property help identify the substance?

1.3   Matter and Energy

Matter is anything that has mass and occupies space. All the material things in the universe are composed of matter, including anything we can touch as well as the planets in the solar system and all the stars in the sky.

The **mass** of an object measures how much matter is in the object. Mass is directly proportional to weight at any given place in the universe. If we leave the surface of the Earth, our mass remains the same, but our weight changes. An astronaut positioned between two celestial bodies such that their gravitational attractions pull equally in opposite directions is weightless, but the astronaut's mass remains the same as it is on Earth. Because chemists ordinarily do their work on the Earth's surface and because mass and weight are directly proportional here, many chemists use the terms *mass* and *weight* interchangeably, but we must remember that they differ.

Energy is the capacity to do work. We cannot hold a sound or a beam of light in our hands; they are not forms of matter but forms of energy. Some of the many forms of energy are outlined in Table 1.3. Energy cannot be created or destroyed, but it can be converted from one form to another. This statement is known as the **law of conservation of energy.**

Table 1.3   Forms of Energy

Heat
Chemical
Nuclear
Mechanical
   Kinetic (energy of motion)
   Potential (energy of position)
Electrical
Sound
Electromagnetic (light)
   Visible light
   Ultraviolet
   X-rays
   Gamma rays
   Infrared
   Radio waves
   Microwaves
   Solar*

*Solar energy is a combination of several forms of light.

EXAMPLE 1.6

What desired energy conversion is exhibited by (a) use of a flashlight and (b) an automobile consuming gasoline?

Solution

(a) Chemical energy is converted to electrical energy, which is converted to light.

(b) Chemical energy is converted to kinetic energy.

Practice Problem 1.6   What desired energy conversion is exhibited by (a) an alternator in a car recharging the battery and (b) automobile brakes in use?

ENRICHMENT

In 1905, Albert Einstein (1879–1955) published his theory that the mass of a sample of matter is increased as the energy of the sample is increased. For example, a baseball in motion has a very slightly greater mass than the same baseball at rest. The difference in mass is given by the famous equation

$$E = mc^2$$

In this equation, E is the energy of the object, m is the *mass difference,* and c^2 is a very large constant—the square of the velocity of light:

$$c^2 = (300,000 \text{ kilometers/second})^2$$
$$= 90,000,000,000 \text{ kilometers}^2/\text{second}^2$$
$$= (186,000 \text{ miles/second})^2$$
$$= 34,600,000,000 \text{ miles}^2/\text{second}^2$$

For macroscopic bodies such as a baseball, the increase in mass because of the added energy is so small that it is not measurable. It was not even discovered until the beginning of the twentieth century. At atomic and subatomic levels, however, the conversion of a small quantity of matter into energy is very important. It is the energy source of the Sun and the stars, the atomic bomb, the hydrogen bomb, and nuclear power plants.

Chemistry is the study of the interaction of matter and energy and the changes that matter undergoes. (In nuclear reactions, tiny quantities of matter are actually converted to relatively large quantities of energy. See Chapter 21.)

 Snapshot Review

❏ Matter has mass and occupies space.
❏ Mass is a measure of the quantity of matter in a sample (but energy also has a mass equivalent).

A. Which has a greater mass—an automobile or a sewing thimble?

1.4 Chemical Symbols

Because the elements are the building blocks of all materials in the universe, we need an easy way to identify and refer to them. For this purpose, each chemical element is identified by an internationally used **symbol** consisting of one or two letters. The first letter of an element's symbol is always capitalized. If the symbol has a second letter, it is a lowercase (small) letter. The symbol is an abbreviation of the element's name, but some symbols represent names in languages other than English. The 10 elements whose symbols and names have different first letters are listed in Table 1.4. A list of the names and symbols of the first 109 elements, along with some other information, is presented in a table inside the back cover of this book. In that table, the elements are alphabetized according to their names, but duplicate entries appear under the initial letter of the symbols for the elements in Table 1.4.

The most important symbols for beginning students to learn are given in Figure 1.5. The names of these elements and their symbols must be memorized. The elements indicated by pink shading should be learned first. Don't bother to memorize the numbers shown in the boxes with the elements.

Chemists write symbols together in **formulas** to identify compounds. For example, the letters CO represent a compound of carbon and oxygen. Be careful to distinguish the formula CO from the symbol Co, which represents the element cobalt. The capitalization of letters is very important! Formulas are sometimes written with subscripts to tell the relative proportions of the elements present. For example, H_2O represents water, which has two atoms of hydrogen for every atom of oxygen present. More about formulas will be presented in Section 5.1.

Table 1.4 Elements Whose Names and Symbols Begin with Different Letters

Name	Symbol
Antimony	Sb
Gold	Au
Iron	Fe
Lead	Pb
Mercury	Hg
Potassium	K
Silver	Ag
Sodium	Na
Tin	Sn
Tungsten	W

EXAMPLE 1.7

Which of the elements of Table 1.4 are not among the most important elements to learn (see Figure 1.5)?

Solution

Antimony (Sb) and tungsten (W).

1 **H** Hydrogen																	2 **He** Helium
3 **Li** Lithium	4 **Be** Beryllium											5 **B** Boron	6 **C** Carbon	7 **N** Nitrogen	8 **O** Oxygen	9 **F** Fluorine	10 **Ne** Neon
11 **Na** Sodium	12 **Mg** Magnesium											13 **Al** Aluminum	14 **Si** Silicon	15 **P** Phosphorus	16 **S** Sulfur	17 **Cl** Chlorine	18 **Ar** Argon
19 **K** Potassium	20 **Ca** Calcium	21 **Sc** Scandium	22 **Ti** Titanium	23 **V** Vanadium	24 **Cr** Chromium	25 **Mn** Manganese	26 **Fe** Iron	27 **Co** Cobalt	28 **Ni** Nickel	29 **Cu** Copper	30 **Zn** Zinc	31 **Ga** Gallium	32 **Ge** Germanium	33 **As** Arsenic	34 **Se** Selenium	35 **Br** Bromine	36 **Kr** Krypton
37 **Rb** Rubidium	38 **Sr** Strontium								46 **Pd** Palladium	47 **Ag** Silver	48 **Cd** Cadmium		50 **Sn** Tin	51 **Sb** Antimony	52 **Te** Tellurium	53 **I** Iodine	54 **Xe** Xenon
55 **Cs** Cesium	56 **Ba** Barium			74 **W** Tungsten					78 **Pt** Platinum	79 **Au** Gold	80 **Hg** Mercury		82 **Pb** Lead	83 **Bi** Bismuth			86 **Rn** Radon
87 **Fr** Francium	88 **Ra** Radium																

Most important elements in this course

Other important elements in this course

		92 **U** Uranium										

Figure 1.5 Elements Whose Names and Symbols Should Be Learned

The elements shown with a pink background are most important in this course. Those with a blue background are also important. It is not necessary to memorize the (atomic) numbers.

Snapshot Review

ChemSkill Builder
1.4, 3.1

❑ The first letter in a symbol for an element is always capitalized; the second letter, if any, is small (lowercase).
❑ Memorize the names and symbols of the elements in Figure 1.5 by the end of the first few weeks of this course.

A. How many different elements are represented in the formula $CoCO_3$?

1.5 The Periodic Table

In Section 1.2, we learned a few of the properties of sulfur and of iron. Do we have to learn the properties of all 100 or so elements individually, or are there some ways to ease that burden? For over 140 years, chemists have arranged the elements into groups with similar chemical characteristics, which makes it easier to learn their properties. This grouping of the elements has been refined to a high degree, and the modern **periodic table** is the result. A full periodic table is shown inside the front cover of this book. The elements numbered 104 and up in that table have only recently been produced and in such infinitely small quantities that their chemical properties are unmeasured. Therefore, we will almost totally ignore them in the remainder of this book.

We will explore several uses for the periodic table in this section, as well as a number of terms associated with it. This table will be used extensively throughout the rest of this course and in subsequent chemistry courses.

All the elements in any horizontal row of the periodic table are said to be in the same **period.** There are seven periods, the first consisting of just two elements. The second and third periods contain 8 elements each, and the next two contain 18 elements each. The sixth period has 32 elements (including 14 inner transition elements numbered 57 through 71, located at the bottom of the table), and the last period is not yet complete. The periods are conventionally numbered with the Arabic numerals 1 through 7 (Figure 1.6).

EXAMPLE 1.8

Which element begins the fourth period of the periodic table? Which element ends it? How many elements are in that period?

Solution

Potassium (K) begins the period, Krypton (Kr) ends it, and there are 18 elements in the period.

Practice Problem 1.8   Which element begins the second period of the periodic table? Which element ends it? How many elements are in that period? ▌

The elements in any vertical column in the periodic table are in the same **group,** or **family.** They have similar chemical properties, which change gradually from each one to the one below it. In some groups, the elements are very

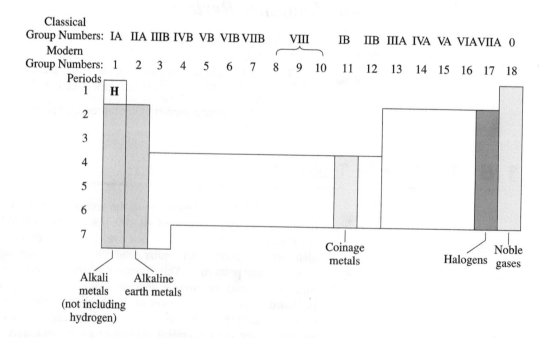

Figure 1.6   Groups and Periods

similar, in others, less so. The groups have been given two sets of group numbers (shown in Figure 1.6). The classical group numbers are Roman numerals followed by a letter A or B. These are more useful for beginning students in learning about atomic structure and bonding. The elements in two groups having the same number have some chemical similarities, especially in the formulas of some of their compounds. A chemical formula (Section 5.1) shows the ratio of atoms of each of its elements to every other element. For example, water, H_2O, has two hydrogen atoms for each of its oxygen atoms, and carbon dioxide, CO_2, has one carbon atom for every two atoms of oxygen. Examples of the periodic similarities of compounds are BaO and CdO, with barium in group IIA and cadmium in group IIB, as well as $KMnO_4$ and $KClO_4$, with manganese in group VIIB and chlorine in group VIIA. The modern group numbers are given as Arabic numerals. The classical group numbers will be used throughout this book, with the modern group numbers sometimes added in parentheses afterward.

Five groups have family names (see Figure 1.6). The **alkali metals** include all the elements of group IA (1) except hydrogen. The **alkaline earth metals** are the elements of periodic group IIA (2), and the **coinage metals** are those of group IB (11). The **halogens** form group VIIA (17), and the **noble gases** constitute group 0 (18).

> Be careful. Some periodic tables have hydrogen located above fluorine as well as above lithium. Hydrogen is neither an alkali metal nor a halogen.

EXAMPLE 1.9

Is each of the following sets of elements in the same period or in the same group? Which set has the more similar chemical properties?

(a) N, P, As   (b) Li, C, F

Solution

Set (b) is in the same period (2); set (a) is in the same group (VA). Set (a) has the more similar chemical properties.

Practice Problem 1.9 Is sulfur more likely to be similar to selenium (Se) or to chlorine in its chemical properties?

Another major classification of the elements in terms of the periodic table is shown in Figure 1.7. Three areas are defined and named the **main group elements,** the **transition elements,** and the **inner transition elements.** The main group elements are the simplest to learn about, and they will be studied first. The transition elements include some of the most important elements in our everyday lives, such as iron, nickel, chromium, zinc, and copper. The transition elements are often divided into four rows of elements, called the first, second, third, and fourth transition series. The elements of the fourth transition series except for actinium (Ac), and those of the main group elements above 112, are artificial; they are not found in nature. The two inner transition series fit into the periodic table in periods 6 and 7, right after lanthanum (La) and actinium (Ac), respectively. The inner transition elements include a few important elements, including uranium and plutonium. The first series of inner transition elements is called the lanthanide series, after lanthanum, the element that precedes

Figure 1.7 Main Group Elements, Transition Elements, and Inner Transition Elements

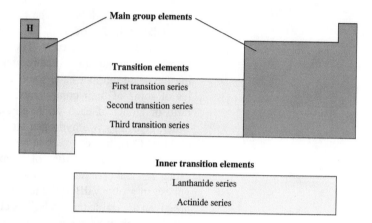

them; the second series is called the actinide series, after actinium, the element that precedes them. These elements are conventionally placed below the others so as not to make the periodic table too wide. None of the actinide elements to the right of uranium has been found in nature; they all are artificial. All of the elements in the actinide series are radioactive.

EXAMPLE 1.10

In what period are the actinide elements found?

Solution

The actinide elements, 90–103, follow element 89 and therefore are in period 7.

Practice Problem 1.10   In what period are the lanthanide elements found?

EXAMPLE 1.11

The symbols for how many transition elements are included in the periodic table inside the front cover of the text?

Solution

There are 37 (including the new artificial elements).

Practice Problem 1.11   How many inner transition elements are there?

We can also divide the elements into metals and nonmetals because each of these classes has some distinctive properties common to all their members. For example, metals generally have a metallic luster (a glossy or shiny appearance) and are generally malleable (can be pounded into thin sheets) and **ductile** (can be drawn into a wire); nonmetals are generally brittle. Metals conduct electricity; most nonmetals do not.

In the periodic table, the **metals** are to the left of a stepped line starting to the left of boron (B) and continuing downward and to the right, ending to the left of astatine (At) (Figure 1.8). Except for hydrogen, all the **nonmetals** are to the right of this line. As we can see, the metallic elements greatly outnumber the nonmetallic elements. The properties of the elements vary gradually across the periodic table. Several of the elements near the stepped line have some properties of metals and some properties of nonmetals; they are sometimes called **metalloids.**

EXAMPLE 1.12

Which of the following elements are metals, and which are nonmetals?

(a) Calcium   (b) Phosphorus

(c) Nickel   (d) The carbon in a diamond

Solution

(a) Calcium is a metal.   (b) Phosphorus is a nonmetal.

(c) Nickel is a metal.   (d) Carbon is a nonmetal.

Practice Problem 1.12 Classify each of the following as metal or nonmetal:

(a) The carbon in a "lead" pencil   (b) Silver

Hydrogen is unique in its properties. It is placed on the side of the stepped line with the metals because it has many chemical properties similar to those of metals. In some periodic tables, it is also placed in another position, above the halogens, because of its nonmetallic chemical and physical properties. It actually does not fit comfortably in either position because it is neither an alkali metal nor a halogen, it is placed in the center on still other periodic tables to reflect its unique properties.

Figure 1.8 Metals and Nonmetals

The symbols adjacent to the stepped line are the metalloids.

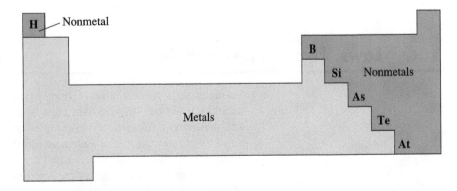

EXAMPLE 1.13

Use the periodic table to identify each of the following:

(a) The fifth element of the first transition series
(b) The element of the fourth period that is also in group VB
(c) The last lanthanide
(d) The seventh transition element   (e) The second actinide metal
(f) The first element of group VIII   (g) The third halogen
(h) The first alkaline earth metal   (i) The first coinage metal

Solution

(a) Mn   (b) V   (c) Lu   (d) Co   (e) Pa   (f) Fe
(g) Br   (h) Be   (i) Cu

Practice Problem 1.13   Identify the second noble gas.

Snapshot Review

❐ The elements are classified in the periodic table for much the same reasons that matter is classified as described in Section 1.1.
❐ Elements in the same periodic group have similar chemical properties.
❐ Learn the nomenclature of the table. For example, when the instructor states that "main group elements are easiest to understand," we must know which elements are in the main groups.

A. What are the atomic numbers (the integers) of the third transition series of elements?
B. What element that is not naturally occurring has the smallest atomic number?

1.6   Laws, Hypotheses, and Theories

So many facts are available to scientists as they do experiments and observe natural phenomena that the data must be classified so that they can be learned and understood. When a large group of scientific observations is generalized into a single statement, that statement is called a **law.** For example, when a pen drops, it falls downward. When a ball drops, it falls downward. These and millions of other such observations are grouped together and generalized as the law of gravity. A law is a general statement about observable facts.

After organizing observed data into a law, scientists try to explain the law. A statement that attempts to explain why a law is true is called a **hypothesis.** If the hypothesis becomes generally accepted, it becomes a **theory.** Einstein explained the law of gravity with his theory of relativity. Laws and theories are necessary because learning or remembering all the data that have been observed over the ages is impossible.

One of the most important laws in chemistry is the **law of conservation of mass.** This law states that, in any chemical reaction or physical change, the total mass present after the change is equal to the total mass present before the change. This law will be further explain in Section 3.1. Section 3.2 will present John Dalton's explanation of the law, in which he proposed that the particles that make up matter can rearrange themselves in various ways but cannot be created or destroyed. That explanation is a theory; it explains the law. If the particles that make up the materials before and after the change are the same, the total mass must also be the same.

The way new generalities are accepted by the scientific community as being true has been loosely codified into a system known as the **scientific method.** The steps of this method are

1. State the problem clearly.

2. Do further experiments. Many scientists test the generality with experiments, repeating each other's work and doing other experiments related to those.

3. Interpret the results. See if the generality explains all the results, new and old.

4. Accept the law. If all the data support the law, it is generally accepted by the scientific community as true. If later, further experiments are in conflict with the law, it is modified or abandoned altogether.

> All samples of a given compound have the same percentage of each of its elements.

An example of how the scientific method works is the establishment of the law of constant composition of compounds, also called the law of definite proportions. The initial statement, based on the work of Antoine Lavoisier (1743–1794), was that every sample of a given compound is composed of the same percentage of each of its elements as any other sample of the same compound. That concept was subjected to many tests, in which other scientists measured and remeasured the compositions of many samples of a wide range of compounds. Claude-Louis Berthollet (1748–1822) showed that gaseous combinations of carbon and oxygen had compositions ranging from 27.29% carbon to 42.88% carbon; and thus the composition was not definite. He therefore stated that the proposed law was incorrect. However, Joseph Louis Proust (1754–1826) found that Berthollet's samples were *mixtures* of *two* compounds—carbon monoxide and carbon dioxide—and that when either compound was analyzed by itself, it always had the same composition. The law of definite proportions was firmly established by his work. An explanation of the law of definite proportions was proposed by John Dalton in 1803 (Section 3.2). His hypothesis generated a great deal of additional work, all of which supported his ideas, which made the hypothesis into a theory.

Snapshot Review

❏ Generalities about empirical observations are called *laws;* accepted explanations of these laws are called *theories.*

A. Is the law of definite proportions (Chapter 3) an explanation or a collection of observations?

Key Terms

Key terms are defined in the Glossary.

alkali metal (1.5)
alkaline earth metal (1.5)
analytical chemistry (intro)
biochemistry (intro)
chemical change (1.1)
chemical property (1.2)
chemical reaction (1.1)
chemistry (1.3)
coinage metal (1.5)
compound (1.1)
definite composition (1.1)
dissolve (1.2)
ductile (1.5)
element (1.1)
energy (1.3)
extensive property (1.2)
family (1.5)
formula (1.4)

group (1.5)
halogen (1.5)
heterogeneous mixture (1.1)
homogeneous mixture (1.1)
hypothesis (1.6)
inner transition element (1.5)
inorganic chemistry (intro)
intensive property (1.2)
law (1.6)
law of conservation of energy (1.3)
law of conservation of mass (1.6)
main group element (1.5)
malleable (1.2)
mass (1.3)
matter (1.3)
metal (1.5)
metalloid (1.5)
mixture (1.1)

noble gas (1.5)
nonmetal (1.5)
organic chemistry (intro)
period (1.5)
periodic table (1.5)
physical change (1.1)
physical chemistry (intro)
physical property (1.2)
property (1.2)
quantitative property (1.2)
scientific method (1.6)
solution (1.1)
substance (1.1)
symbol (1.4)
theory (1.6)
transition element (1.5)

Summary

Matter includes every material thing in the universe. To be able to understand such a wide variety of items, we must classify matter. Matter is divided into pure substances and mixtures. Pure substances may be elements or compounds. Mixtures may be either heterogeneous or homogeneous. Elements are the fundamental building blocks of matter and cannot be broken down to simpler substances by chemical or physical means. Compounds are chemical combinations of elements; they have their own sets of properties and have definite compositions. A physical combination of substances results in a mixture, whose components retain most of their properties. Mixtures do not have definite compositions. Homogeneous mixtures, called solutions, look alike throughout, but some parts of a heterogeneous mixture can be seen to be different from other parts. (Section 1.1)

Properties are the characteristics by which we can identify samples of matter. Intensive properties, such as color and brittleness, do not depend on the size of the sample, but extensive properties, such as volume, do. Intensive properties are more important in identifying substances. We can determine whether a combination of substances is a mixture or a compound by its properties. When we combine samples of matter, the result has more matter present than any of the original samples. When we break down a sample, each of the resulting products is composed of less matter than the starting sample. (Section 1.2)

Matter is anything that has mass and occupies space. Mass is a measure of the quantity of matter in a sample. The mass of an object does not change with its position in the universe. On the surface of the Earth, mass is directly proportional to weight, and we determine the mass of an object by "weighing" it. Energy is the ability to do work and comes in many forms (Table 1.3). Energy cannot be created or destroyed, but it can be converted from one form to another. Chemistry is the study of the interaction of matter and energy and the changes that matter undergoes. (Section 1.3)

Each element has a chemical symbol consisting of one or two letters. The first letter (or the only one) is always written as a capital letter; the second, if present, is always written as a lowercase (small) letter. Associating the names of the most important elements (shown in Figure 1.5) with their symbols, and their symbols with their names, is a necessary skill. (Section 1.4)

The periodic table is a classification scheme for elements that is tremendously useful in learning the properties of the elements. It consists of seven periods and 16 classical groups, or families (18 in a more modern but less useful version). Several of the groups have names, which beginning students need to learn. The elements are separated into metals and nonmetals on the periodic table. They are also subdivided into main group elements, transition elements, and inner transition elements. (Section 1.5)

A statement that summarizes innumerable scientific facts and enables scientists to predict what will happen in a certain type of situation in the future is called a law. (For example, the law of gravity enables us to predict that if we drop something, it will fall downward. This law resulted from innumerable observations.) One of the most important laws in chemistry is the law of conservation of mass, which states that mass cannot be created or destroyed in any chemical reaction or physical change. An explanation that is proposed to explain why a law works is called a hypothesis. If the explanation is accepted by the scientific community, it is known as a theory. (Section 1.6)

Items for Special Attention

- Be sure to use the correct capitalization and abbreviations throughout the study of chemistry. Small differences can completely change the meaning of a term. For example, Co and CO are different substances.

- The word *homogeneous* does not necessarily refer to a homogeneous mixture. Most samples of pure substances are also homogeneous (but some, such as ice water, are heterogeneous).

- The elements in a given group of the periodic table have similar properties. This fact can help us learn a great deal of chemistry with less effort than would otherwise be required.

- Like some groups of the periodic table, some portions of periods have special names. For example, the first transition series (elements 21–30) is part of the fourth period.

Answers to Snapshot Reviews

1.1 A. Because all compounds (a type of substance) have definite compositions and baking soda is a compound, it must have a definite composition.

1.2 A. The lack of color is intensive; the volume, 1 liter (L), is extensive.

    B. The property certainly helps identify the substance. Many people would guess that it is water without further data, but that is risky.

1.3 A. The automobile has the greater mass—there is more matter present.

1.4 A. Three (Co, C, and O).

1.5 A. 57 and 72–80

    B. Po (84)

1.6 A. It is a collection of observations. That is why it is called a law.

Self-Tutorial Problems

1.1 A chemist in which branch of chemistry most often deals with the chemistry of compounds of carbon?

1.2 Would it be considered unusual for an organic chemist to analyze a new compound, even though analysis is considered to be the function of an analytical chemist?

1.3 Which of the following are samples of matter, and which are samples of energy?

    (a) A tree   (b) A beam of light

    (c) The exhaust gas   (d) The output of an electric
        from a car   heater

1.4 As seen in Figure 1.1, state which class of matter is *not* homogeneous.

1.5 All brands of pure aspirin are the same compound. If you need aspirin, how should you choose a brand to buy?

1.6 What property of water is most often desired to be affected by the presence in water solution of ethylene glycol, antifreeze?

1.7 Name as many properties of aluminum as you can think of. Indicate which ones are chemical properties.

1.8 Explain the difference between the results of hitting a piece of steel on a hard surface with a hammer and similarly hitting a pane of glass. Use the word *brittle* in your explanation.

1.9 How many elements are present in each of the following?

    (a) HF and Hf   (b) No and NO

    (c) Si and SI_2 (d) $PoCl_2$ and $POCl_3$

    (e) $Ni(CO)_4$ (f) $NiCO_3$

1.10 Cm is the chemical symbol for curium, named after the famous scientist Madam Curie. Why wasn't the symbol C, Cu, or Cr used instead?

1.11 Write the names from the symbols for the following:

    (a) The first 18 elements in the periodic table

    (b) The second 18 elements in the periodic table

    (c) The rest of the elements shown in Figure 1.5

1.12 Write the symbols from the names for the following:

(a) The first 18 elements in the periodic table

(b) The second 18 elements in the periodic table

(c) The rest of the elements shown in Figure 1.5

1.13 Which classical periodic group number is used for each of the following families?

(a) Alkali metals   (b) Alkaline earth metals

(c) Coinage metals   (d) Halogens

(e) Noble gases

1.14 Which classical transition group has the most elements?

1.15 Are the nonmetals main group elements, transition elements, or inner transition elements?

1.16 Do elements in the same period or elements in the same group have similar chemical properties?

1.17 Does each main group have more or fewer elements than a typical transition group?

1.18 (a) In which group of the periodic table is S?

(b) In which period is S?

(c) What type of element is S—a main group element, a transition element, or an inner transition element?

1.19 Why do scientists accept a new law?

(a) Scientific societies accept it.

(b) It explains most of the observations.

(c) The government says to accept it.

(d) Prominent scientists say to accept it.

(e) Many scientists check the law and find it correct.

1.20 Calculate the percentage of main group elements in the periodic table.

Problems

1.1 Classification of Matter

1.21 (a) When pure water is cooled below 0°C (32°F), it freezes (solidifies). When the solid is warmed above that temperature, it melts again. Its composition does not change during the entire process. Are these chemical or physical changes?

(b) When gaseous ethylene is treated with a tiny quantity of a certain other substance, it solidifies. It is difficult to cause the solid to re-form a gas. Is the solidification a chemical or a physical change?

1.22 What kind of change—chemical or physical—is the dissolving of sugar in (a) hot tea? (b) iced tea?

1.23 What kind of change—chemical or physical—accompanies each of the following?

(a) The conversion of two elements to a compound

(b) The conversion of two compounds into a solution

(c) The combination of an element and a compound into another compound

(d) The conversion of a compound to an element and another compound

(e) The separation of a mixture into its components

1.24 In a certain experiment, two separate samples of matter are mixed, and a great deal of heat is generated. Is this more likely to be a chemical or a physical change?

1.25 Classify each of the following as a compound or mixture. If it is impossible to tell, explain why.

(a) A solid combination of iron and oxygen, no part of which is attracted by a magnet

(b) A material containing 88.8% oxygen and 11.2% hydrogen

(c) A material that is explosive and that contains 88.8% oxygen and 11.2% hydrogen

(d) A material that consists of blue particles and red particles

(e) A material containing only hydrogen and oxygen that is a gas under ordinary room conditions

1.26 Classify each of the following as a compound or a mixture:

(a) Bubbling carbonated water

(b) Salt water

(c) Iced tea

(d) The liquid formed by a certain combination of oxygen and hydrogen gases

1.2 Properties

1.27 Bromine melts at −7.2°C; sodium melts at 97.81°C. A certain combination of the two melts at 747°C. Is the combination a mixture or a compound?

1.28 Classify each of the following as an element, a compound, or a mixture:

(a) Solid iodine (a dark violet solid)

(b) A homogeneous combination of sodium and iodine that is a white solid

(c) A homogeneous combination of iodine and alcohol (tincture of iodine), which retains a dark color and the liquid state of the alcohol

1.29 If 3 dozen donuts costs $10.50 and 10 dozen donuts costs $35.00, is the price of donuts intensive or extensive?

1.30 Classify the following materials as homogeneous or heterogeneous:

(a) White paint

(b) Milk

(c) Household ammonia (ammonia gas dissolved in water)

(d) A glass of pure water containing an ice cube (also pure water)

(e) A teaspoon of sugar in a glass of warm water after having been stirred thoroughly

(f) A cola drink with no bubbles visible

(g) A cola drink with bubbles

1.31 Electricity is passed through 14.40 grams (g) of a pure substance, and 5.66 grams of one material and 8.74 grams of another material are produced. Is the original substance an element or a compound?

1.32 Elemental nitrogen and hydrogen are both odorless.

(a) What is the odor of a mixture of the two gases?

(b) Explain why ammonia, a compound of nitrogen and hydrogen only, smells so strongly.

1.33 Which of the following properties are extensive and which are intensive?

(a) Length   (b) Color

(c) Price per unit (d) Total cost

(e) Volume   (f) Mass

(g) Boiling point   (h) Speed

1.34 Classify each of the following as a chemical change or a physical change:

(a) Melting ice by spreading salt on an icy sidewalk

(b) Striking a match

(c) Breaking a piece of metal by bending it back and forth

(d) Baking a cake

(e) Rubbing your hands together to get them warm

(f) Using a tea bag

(g) Cooking a hot dog

1.35 When some salt is added to water, a solution is formed. State several ways in which you can tell that the combination is a solution rather than a new compound.

1.36 List four or five properties you could use to distinguish between iron and aluminum. State which one(s) are chemical properties.

1.37 List four or five properties that enable us to distinguish between water and gasoline. State which one(s) are chemical properties.

1.38 A sample of a liquid is homogeneous. When it is cooled to 7°C, part of the liquid solidifies. The solid part is removed, and the liquid part is cooled further, but no other change takes place. Is the original liquid a compound or a solution?

1.39 A sample of a solid substance is heated under a stream of hydrogen gas, and a solid remains after the treatment that has a mass 63% of that of the original substance. Further treatment with hydrogen causes no further change. Is the original substance an element or a compound?

1.40 In the iron-sulfur experiment described in Section 1.2, heat was used to start a chemical reaction, which gave off more heat. Can you think of another example of a reaction that is started by heating and then gives off more heat?

1.41 When dinitrogen tetroxide, a colorless liquid, is warmed, a brown gas is formed. Is this change a chemical change or a physical change?

1.3 Matter and Energy

1.42 List as many kinds of energy as you can think of without consulting the text.

1.43 What is the mass of a 100-kilogram (kg) astronaut on the surface of the Moon, where gravity is 17% that on Earth?

1.44 For a given quantity of energy, the electricity produced by a battery is much more expensive than that provided by the electric company. Why do we still use batteries?

1.45 Explain the advantages and disadvantages of house current versus batteries for use in a home smoke detector.

1.46 How much energy is created when 1.00 kg of charcoal (mostly carbon) is burned in air?

1.47 What two changes in energy accompany the use of a flashlight?

1.48 Name a device commonly found on a car that changes:

(a) Chemical energy to electrical energy

(b) Electrical energy to sound

(c) Mechanical energy to heat

(d) Electrical energy to chemical energy

(e) Chemical energy to mechanical energy

(f) Electrical energy to mechanical energy

(g) Electrical energy to heat

1.49 Name one common device, not on a car, that performs each of the following conversions:

(a) Electrical energy to light

(b) Electrical energy to sound

(c) Chemical energy to heat

(d) Chemical energy to mechanical energy

1.4 Chemical Symbols

1.50 Calculate the percentage of all elements in the Table of the Elements (inside back cover) whose names start with the letter P.

1.51 How many elements are present in each of the following?

(a) $OsSO_4$ (b) BN   (c) NI_3

(d) $Sc(SCN)_3$ (e) HF   (f) Nb

(g) $CoCl_2$

1.52 Beginning students often mix up the following elements. Give the name for each element.

(a) Mg and Mn   (b) K and P

(c) Na and S   (d) Cu and Co

1.53 Write the symbol for each of the following elements:

(a) Mercury   (b) Copper   (c) Sodium

(d) Antimony   (e) Iron   (f) Lead

(g) Gold   (h) Tungsten   (i) Potassium

(j) Silver

1.54 Without consulting any tables, write the names of the following elements:

(a) Fe and F   (b) Ag and Au

(c) Na and Ne   (d) Sn and S

(e) P and K

1.55 Name each of the following elements:

(a) Ag   (b) Pb   (c) K

(d) W   (e) Fe   (f) Cu

(g) Au   (h) Na   (i) Sb

(j) Hg

1.56 Write the symbol for each of the following elements:

(a) Hydrogen   (b) Helium   (c) Lithium

(d) Carbon   (e) Nitrogen   (f) Oxygen

(g) Fluorine   (h) Neon   (i) Sodium

1.57 Without consulting any tables, write the symbols for the following elements:

(a) Potassium and phosphorus

(b) Carbon, cadmium, and calcium

(c) Boron, barium, and bismuth

(d) Sodium and sulfur

(e) Cobalt and copper

(f) Magnesium and manganese

(g) Iron and iodine

1.5 The Periodic Table

1.58 (a) What two elements are in group V of period 4?

(b) What element(s) is (are) in group V of period 2?

1.59 Which element of periodic group IA is *not* an alkali metal?

1.60 Which of the following neighbors of nitrogen in the periodic table has chemical properties most like those of nitrogen—oxygen, carbon, or phosphorus?

1.61 Would you expect vanadium (V) or sulfur to act more like a typical metal?

1.62 Which two elements are most like potassium in chemical properties?

1.63 How many elements are in the first period of the periodic table? the second? the third? the fourth?

1.64 Which element is in group IV of the second transition series?

1.65 The formula of an oxide of phosphorus is P_2O_5. Make an educated guess as to which one of the following formulas represents a real compound: S_2O_5 Ga_2O_5 As_2O_5

1.66 State the group number and period number of each of the following elements:

(a) Ca   (b) Cd   (c) Cl

1.67 Name the group and state the group number of each of the following elements:

(a) K   (b) Ne   (c) Be   (d) Cl

(e) Cu

1.68 Using the table inside the back cover of the text and the periodic table, determine:

(a) How many elements whose names start with the letter C are transition elements?

(b) How many elements whose symbols start with the letter P are transition elements?

1.69 Using the table inside the back cover of the text and/or the periodic table, determine:

(a) How many elements whose names start with the letter S are main group elements?

(b) How many elements whose symbols start with the letter P are inner transition elements?

1.6 Laws, Hypotheses, and Theories

1.70 Would an accepted generalization that explains why active metals react with acids be referred to as a law, hypothesis, or theory?

1.71 Suppose that you are a consultant to the National Science Foundation, an agency of the U.S. government. In a proposal for a $1 million grant, a claim is made that a method will be developed to make 20 ounces (oz) of gold from 10 oz of gold and no other ingredients. Would you recommend that government money be spent on this proposed research? Explain your reasoning.

1.72 Suppose that you are a consultant to the National Science Foundation. In a proposal for a $10 million grant, a claim is made that a method will be developed to make a machine that produces twice as much energy as it uses up, with no permanent changes in matter. Would you recommend that government money be spent on this proposed research? Explain your reasoning.

General Problems

1.73 (a) A chemist in which branch of chemistry is most likely to determine the number of parts per million of an impurity in a city's drinking water?

(b) A chemist in which branch of chemistry determines the electrical conductivity of a metal already prepared by another chemist?

(c) A chemist develops a pharmaceutical to help patients with thyroid problems. In what branch of chemistry is this chemist working?

1.74 Na_2SO_4 is the formula for a certain sulfur compound. Which of the following formulas is most likely to be the formula for a chromium compound?

(a) Na_3CrO_4 (b) Na_2CrO_4 (c) $NaCrO_4$

1.75 A chemist uses a compound of carbon, hydrogen, and oxygen to separate a metal from the rest of a sample to determine the metal's percentage in the sample. What branch of chemistry is the chemist practicing?

1.76 Ratios are generally intensive. Explain why.

1.77 (a) Predict the color of a solution of a blue substance dissolved in a yellow substance.

(b) Can you predict the color of a compound of a blue substance and a yellow substance?

(c) Explain your answers.

1.78 Explain the following statements sometimes made in everyday conversation:

(a) "Oil and water do not mix."

(b) "Gasoline and alcohol do not mix."

1.79 A nutritionist recommends more iron and less sodium in the diet of a patient with a blood problem. Does the nutritionist advocate eating iron metal, but not sodium metal? Explain.

1.80 What kind of electrical device has the advantage of portability like a dry cell but better economy?

1.81 (a) Count the number of each of the following types of elements in Figure 1.5: main group elements, transition elements, inner transition elements. Now calculate the percentage of each type important enough for you to learn of all the elements in that type. For example, what percentage of all the main group elements, is important for you to learn (from Figure 1.5)?

(b) Which type of element do you think will be most important in this course? Which will be second most important?

2

Measurement

Various types of laboratory glassware

- ■ 2.1 **Factor Label Method**
- ■ 2.2 **Exponential Numbers**
- ■ 2.3 **The Metric System**
- ■ 2.4 **Significant Digits**
- ■ 2.5 **Density**
- ■ 2.6 **Temperature Scales**

Review Clues

Objectives

2.1 To use the units of a measurement to help to do calculations involving that measurement

2.2 To use exponential notation to work with very large and very small numbers

2.3 To use the basic elements of the metric system—a system of units and prefixes designed to make scientific calculations as easy as possible

2.4 To use the correct number of digits to indicate the precision of a measurement or a calculated result

2.5 To calculate density, volume, or mass, given the other two, and to use density to identify substances

2.6 To distinguish among Fahrenheit, Celsius, and Kelvin temperature scales

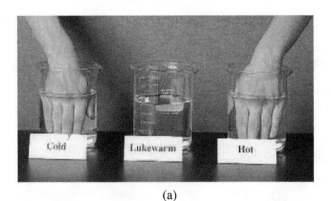

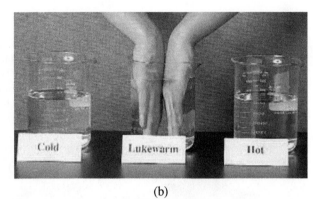

(a)

(b)

Figure 2.1 Hot and Cold Experiment

When the hands are moved from position (a) to position (b), the hand from the cold water feels hot and the hand from the hot water feels cold, even though they are both in water of the same lukewarm temperature. Try it.

Measurement is the heart of modern science, and even the social sciences are becoming more quantitative. Measurements make identifications of substances more precise and enable more scientific generalities to be made. For example, even ancient peoples knew that when objects were dropped, they fell downward. Measurements involving gravity enabled Sir Isaac Newton (1642–1727) to determine that the same laws of gravity that govern the fall of an object here on Earth also govern the motions of the Moon and the planets in the solar system.

A simple project will convince anyone that measuring things quantitatively tells more than qualitative estimates, especially those made using the human senses: Fill one beaker with cold water, a second beaker with hot water, and a third beaker with a mixture of equal amounts of hot and cold water. Place one hand in the cold water and the other hand in the hot water at the same time (Figure 2.1). Leave them there for 2 minutes (min). Then place both hands in the mixed water. That water will feel hot to the hand originally in the cold water but cold to the hand originally in the hot water, even though both hands are now in the same water!

There are a wide variety of things to measure in science, and many ways to make the measurements. For example, the volume of a rectangular box can be calculated by measuring its length, width, and height, and multiplying the values together. The volume of a sphere can be measured by determining its radius and using the equation $V = \frac{4}{3}\pi r^3$. Measuring the radius directly might not be feasible, as for example with a bowling ball, so we might measure the diameter by placing the ball between two parallel boards (Figure 2.2a) and taking half of the distance between them, because the radius is half the diameter. Alternatively, we might measure the circumference and find r from that, using the equation $c = 2\pi r$ (Figure 2.2b). The total volume of a bunch of small pieces of copper can be measured by measuring the volume of a sample of water, placing the copper in the water, and measuring the total volume. The difference between the volumes is the volume of the copper (Figure 2.2c). (This method works only with samples that do not dissolve to form a solution.) Quantities other than volume are measured in a variety of other ways.

Several aspects of measurement will be considered in this chapter. First, Section 2.1 presents the factor label method, which makes calculations with measured quantities easier. This method will be used in the sections that follow and throughout the book. Next, in Section 2.2, we consider how to calculate with extremely large and extremely small numbers, using exponential notation. Section 2.3 introduces the metric system, a system of weights and measures

Figure 2.2   Various Measurements

(a) Measuring the diameter of a bowling ball by placing it between two parallel boards and measuring the distance between the boards. (b) Measuring the circumference of a bowling ball, whereby the diameter may be calculated using $c = \pi d$. (c) Measuring the volume of irregularly shaped, insoluble objects by displacement of water. The volume of the copper shot is the total volume (shown) minus the volume of the water before the shot was added.

(a)

(b)

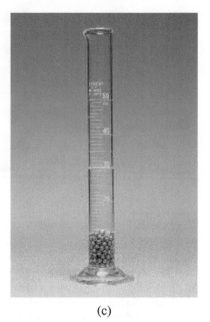

(c)

designed to make calculations as easy as possible. In Section 2.4, we discuss the accuracy and precision of measurements and how the precision should be reported, using the proper number of significant digits. The concept of density, considered in Section 2.5, not only is useful in itself, especially for identifying substances, but also enables us to apply the concepts presented in previous sections. Finally, Section 2.6 briefly discusses temperature scales.

The measurement of energy will be discussed in Section 14.3, and kinetic energy will be treated in Section 12.10.

2.1   Factor Label Method

> Use units in reporting all measurements and the results of calculations using them. Always use full spellings or standard abbreviations for all units.

Every measurement results in a number and a **unit.** Reporting the unit is just as important as reporting the number. For example, it makes quite a bit of difference whether a pet is 6 *inches* tall or 6 *feet* tall! The units are an integral part of any measurement, and from the outset, we must get used to stating the units for every measured quantity and for every quantity calculated from measured data. Always use full spellings or standard abbreviations for all units.

In a great many cases, we can use the units as a clue to which operation—multiplication or division—to perform in calculations with measured quantities. The units of measurement can be treated as algebraic quantities in calculations. For example, we can calculate the total wages of a student aide who has earned 9 dollars per hour for 30 hours of work, as follows:

$$\text{Total wages} = (\text{hours worked})(\text{hourly rate})$$

$$= 30 \text{ hours}\left(\frac{9 \text{ dollars}}{1 \text{ hour}}\right) = 270 \text{ dollars}$$

The unit *hours* (h) in the time cancels the unit *hour* in the rate, leaving the unit *dollars* in the answer. Each unit is treated as a whole, no matter how many letters it contains. Moreover, for the units to cancel, it does not matter if the unit is singular (such as hour) or plural (such as hours). If we did not know the equation to calculate the total wages, we could have put down the time with the unit *hours* and multiplied by the rate of pay, which has the unit *hour* in its denominator. The units tell us that we must multiply!

The previous calculation is an example of the use of the **factor label method,** also called **dimensional analysis,** in which a quantity is multiplied by a factor equal or equivalent to 1. The units included in the factor are the labels. In the previous example, $9 is equivalent to 1 hour (h), and the calculation changes the number of hours worked to the equivalent number of dollars. To use the factor label method, first put down the given quantity, then multiply by a **conversion factor** (a rate or ratio) that will change the units given to the units desired for the answer. The factor may be a known constant or a value given in the problem.

To summarize the steps of the factor label method:

1. Put down the *quantity* given (or, occasionally, a ratio to be converted).

2. Multiply the quantity by one or more factors—rates or ratios—which will change the units *given* to those *required* for the answer. The conversion factors may be given in the problems, or they may be constants of known value.

> To use the factor label method effectively, we must know the units of all the quantities being dealt with and write them down as part of the calculation.

To use the factor label method effectively, we must know the units of all the quantities involved.

Small diagrams that show the initial units and the final units connected by the conversion factor are used in many places in this book to show how to change a quantity from one of the units to the other. For example, for calculating the student aide's total wages, we can use the following diagram:

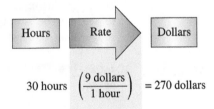

$$30 \text{ hours} \left(\frac{9 \text{ dollars}}{1 \text{ hour}} \right) = 270 \text{ dollars}$$

Diagrams like this will accompany many of the solutions to the in-text examples. To solve the practice problems and the problems at the end of the chapter, make your own diagrams if necessary.

EXAMPLE 2.1

Change 5445 minutes to hours.

Solution

Put down the quantity given and then multiply it by a factor (which in this case is known) that changes minutes to hours. The factor should have the unit

minutes in the denominator to cancel the *minutes* in the quantity given. It should also have the unit *hour* in the numerator so that the answer is in hours:

$$5445 \text{ minutes} \left(\frac{1 \text{ hour}}{60 \text{ minutes}} \right) = 90.75 \text{ hours}$$

Any units in the denominator are divided into units in the numerator, just as any number in the denominator is. Any units and any numbers in the numerator are multiplied. (If a quantity, such as 5445 minutes, is given with no denominator, the quantity is considered to be in a numerator.)

Practice Problem 2.1 Change 5445 minutes to seconds (s).

A ratio or rate may be inverted (turned upside down) if the units that need to be canceled call for that.

EXAMPLE 2.2

Calculate the time required for a student aide to earn $483 at $11.50 per hour.

Solution

First, put down the quantity given; then multiply it by a factor involving the rate:

$$483 \text{ dollars} \left(\frac{1 \text{ hour}}{11.50 \text{ dollars}} \right) = 42.0 \text{ hours}$$

In this case, the inverse of the rate of pay (the factor used previously to calculate total wages) is employed. Rates or ratios can be used either right side up or upside down; getting the units to cancel properly will indicate which form to use. Just be sure that the number in the rate (such as 11.50) stays with the proper unit (dollars).

Practice Problem 2.2 Calculate the time required to travel 15.0 miles at 60.0 miles per hour (mph).

EXAMPLE 2.3

Explain why the factor label method works, using the conversion of $2.67 to cents as an example.

Solution

Consider this equality:

$$1 \text{ dollar} = 100 \text{ cents}$$

Dividing both sides of this equation by $1 yields

$$1 = \frac{100 \text{ cents}}{1 \text{ dollar}}$$

Anything divided by itself is equal to 1, so the left side of this equation is 1. The right side of the equation is thus equal to 1 and therefore may be used to multiply any quantity to change its *form* without changing its *value*.

$$2.67 \text{ dollars} \left(\frac{100 \text{ cents}}{1 \text{ dollar}} \right) = 267 \text{ cents}$$

In any factor, the numerator is equal or equivalent to the denominator, so the value of the number multiplied is not changed, even though the units are.

EXAMPLE 2.4

In the United States, troy weight is used to measure gold and silver and avoirdupois weight is used for most other things. Given that

$$1 \text{ troy pound} = 12 \text{ troy ounces}$$

$$1 \text{ avoirdupois pound} = 16 \text{ avoirdupois ounces}$$

and that ounces in the two systems are *almost* the same weight, calculate the number of (a) troy ounces in 2.50 troy pounds. (b) the number of avoirdupois ounces in 2.50 avoirdupois pounds.

Solution

$$2.50 \text{ troy lb} \left(\frac{12 \text{ troy oz}}{1 \text{ troy lb}} \right) = 30.0 \text{ troy oz}$$

$$2.50 \text{ avoirdupois lb} \left(\frac{16 \text{ avoirdupois oz}}{1 \text{ avoirdupois lb}} \right) = 40.0 \text{ avoirdupois oz}$$

Practice Problem 2.4   (a) Which weighs more, a pound of bricks or a pound of lead. (b) Which weighs more, a pound of gold or a pound of lead.

It may be necessary to use more than one factor to get a desired answer. The factors may be used in separate steps or may be combined in a single step.

EXAMPLE 2.5

Calculate the number of seconds in 5.175 h.

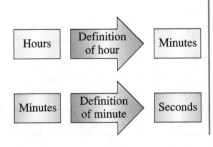

Solution

$$5.175 \text{ hours} \left(\frac{60 \text{ minutes}}{1 \text{ hour}} \right) = 310.5 \text{ minutes}$$

$$310.5 \text{ minutes} \left(\frac{60 \text{ seconds}}{1 \text{ minute}} \right) = 18,630 \text{ seconds}$$

Alternatively,

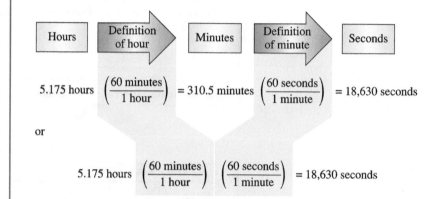

5.175 hours $\left(\dfrac{60 \text{ minutes}}{1 \text{ hour}}\right) = 310.5$ minutes $\left(\dfrac{60 \text{ seconds}}{1 \text{ minute}}\right) = 18{,}630$ seconds

or

5.175 hours $\left(\dfrac{60 \text{ minutes}}{1 \text{ hour}}\right)\left(\dfrac{60 \text{ seconds}}{1 \text{ minute}}\right) = 18{,}630$ seconds

In this particular problem, it does not matter if we press the equal key on the calculator after entering the first 60. Similarly, we can write down the 310.5 min or not write it down, as we please, but the final answer is still the same.

Practice Problem 2.5   Calculate the number of seconds in exactly 7 weeks.

A factor can be raised to a power if the units to be converted require that. Remember that when a ratio in parentheses is raised to a power, *all the numbers* and *all the units* within the parentheses must be raised to that power.

EXAMPLE 2.6

How many square feet (ft^2) are in 12.0 square yards (yd^2)?

Solution

$$12.0 \text{ yd}^2\left(\frac{3 \text{ ft}}{1 \text{ yd}}\right)^2$$

$$= 12.0 \text{ yd}^2\left(\frac{9 \text{ ft}^2}{1 \text{ yd}^2}\right) = 108 \text{ ft}^2$$

The second factor can be derived as follows:

$$3 \text{ ft} = 1 \text{ yd}$$
$$(3 \text{ ft})^2 = (1 \text{ yd})^2$$
$$3^2 \text{ ft}^2 = 1^2 \text{ yd}^2$$
$$9 \text{ ft}^2 = 1 \text{ yd}^2$$

Note that the number 3 is squared, the unit *feet* is squared, the number 1 is squared, and the unit *yard* is squared. There are 9 ft^2 in 1 yd^2 (Figure 2.3).

Practice Problem 2.6   How many cubic feet (ft^3) of cement can be held in a cement mixer with a capacity of 7.34 cubic yards (yd^3)?

32

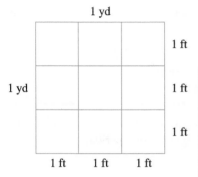

1 yd

1 yd

1 ft

1 ft

1 ft

1 ft   1 ft   1 ft

Figure 2.3 Number of Square Feet in a Square Yard

(not actual size) Each side of the square is 1 yard long or 3 feet long. The area is the square of these, 1 yd^2 or 9 ft^2.

A ratio may be changed to an equivalent ratio with different units by applying the factor label method.

EXAMPLE 2.7

Change 75 mph to feet per second.

Solution

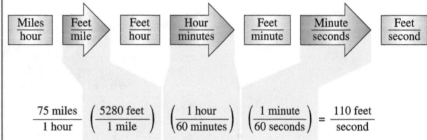

$$\frac{75 \text{ miles}}{1 \text{ hour}} \left(\frac{5280 \text{ feet}}{1 \text{ mile}} \right) \left(\frac{1 \text{ hour}}{60 \text{ minutes}} \right) \left(\frac{1 \text{ minute}}{60 \text{ seconds}} \right) = \frac{110 \text{ feet}}{\text{second}}$$

Practice Problem 2.7   Calculate the speed in miles per hour of a runner who runs the 100-yd dash in 8.53 s.

The use of percentages as factor labels is presented in Appendix 1.

Many more examples of the use of the factor label method will be presented in the sections that follow, where we will work problems involving quantities that are directly proportional to each other. The method can be expanded to quantities that are equivalent to each other. For example, its use with percentages is presented in Appendix 1 and with moles of substances in Section 7.3.

ChemSkill Builder 2.5

Snapshot Review

❐ In the factor label method, units may be canceled like variables (x, y) in algebra. Placement of the units so that they cancel to give the desired units is the essence of the method.

❐ Some factors are constant, such as the number of cents in a dollar; others are variable, such as the number of miles traveled by a car per hour, and these must be given in the statement of a problem.

A. (a) Calculate the number of quarters ($0.25) in $22.75. (b) Calculate the value in dollars of 144 quarters.

2.2   Exponential Numbers

Objects of scientific interest range from incredibly tiny to almost unimaginably large. The number of iron atoms that would fit side by side on a line 1 inch (2.54 cm) in length is about 100 million (Section 13.1). The number that could be packed into a volume of 1 inch^3 is 100 million cubed—about 1 million billion billion! Each iron atom is almost unimaginably small.

EXAMPLE 2.8

To get an idea of how large a number 1 billion is, calculate the number of years it would take to spend $1 billion if a person spent $1000 per day. (Assume that there is no interest or other addition to the $1 billion.)

Solution

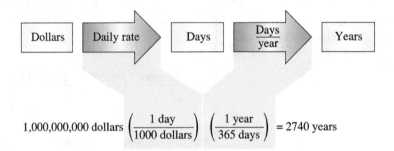

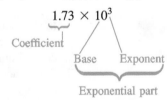

$$1{,}000{,}000{,}000 \text{ dollars} \left(\frac{1 \text{ day}}{1000 \text{ dollars}}\right)\left(\frac{1 \text{ year}}{365 \text{ days}}\right) = 2740 \text{ years}$$

It would take over 2700 years to spend $1 billion by spending $1000 a day! Just think how large the number 100 billion or 1 million billion billion is. Some numbers common in science are even larger than these.

Practice Problem 2.8 Calculate the amount of money that you would have to spend *per second* to use up $10 billion in 100 years.

Scientists handle large and small numbers using **exponential notation.** A number written in this format has the following parts:

$$\underbrace{1.73}_{\text{Coefficient}} \times \underbrace{10^{\overbrace{3}^{\text{Exponent}}}}_{}$$

Base   Exponent

Exponential part

The **coefficient** is an ordinary number that may or may not include a decimal point. It is multiplied by an **exponential part,** consisting of a **base** and an **exponent.** For numbers used in scientific work, the base is usually 10, and the exponent is usually an integer (a whole number). The coefficient is multiplied by the base the number of times given by the exponent. That is, the number in the example is 1.73 multiplied three times by 10:

$$1.73 \times 10^3 = 1.73 \times 10 \times 10 \times 10 = 1730$$

Table 2.1 lists important exponential parts and their meanings. Thus we can write 1 million in exponential notation as follows:

$$1{,}000{,}000 = 1 \times 10 \times 10 \times 10 \times 10 \times 10 \times 10 = 1 \times 10^6$$

Table 2.1 Important Exponential Parts and Their Meanings

Exponential Part	Value	Meaning
10^{-9}	0.000000001	One-billionth
10^{-6}	0.000001	One-millionth
10^{-3}	0.001	One-thousandth
10^{-2}	0.01	One-hundredth
10^{-1}	0.1	One-tenth
10^{0}	1	One
10^{1}	10	Ten
10^{2}	100	One hundred
10^{3}	1000	One thousand
10^{6}	1,000,000	One million
10^{9}	1,000,000,000	One billion

Scientists generally report numbers in exponential notation with coefficients that have one and only one integer digit, and that digit is not zero. That is, the coefficient is a number that is greater than or equal to 1 and less than 10. Numbers in this format are said to be written in **standard exponential form,** or **scientific notation.** A scientific calculator gives exponential numbers in this form, unless "engineering format" is selected. See Appendix 1 for methods of handling numbers in exponential format with a scientific calculator.

In standard exponential notation, the coefficient is 1 or more but less than 10.

EXAMPLE 2.9

Which one(s) of the following numbers is (are) written in scientific notation?
(a) 0.131×10^8 (b) 73×10^3 (c) 2.01×10^4 (d) 1.66×10^0
(e) $1.001 \times 10^{2.5}$

Solution

(a) The number 0.131×10^8 is not in scientific notation because the integer digit of its coefficient is zero.

(b) The number 73×10^3 is not in scientific notation because its coefficient is a two-digit integer.

(c) The number 2.01×10^4 is in scientific notation because the coefficient has only one integer digit and the exponent is an integer.

(d) The number 1.66×10^0 is in scientific notation. The zero exponent is permitted.

(e) The number $1.001 \times 10^{2.5}$ is not in scientific notation because the exponent is not an integer.

Practice Problem 2.9   Which of the following numbers is in scientific notation?
(a) $4.000 \times 10^{2.1}$ (b) 0.500×10^3 (c) 6.51×10^{-2}

To enter a number in exponential notation on an electronic calculator, enter the coefficient, press the EXP or EE key, then enter the exponent. *Do not* press the multiplication key ⊠ or the ⊡ and ⊡ keys. See Appendix 1. If a number is given in exponential notation without a coefficient, a coefficient of 1 is assumed. Thus, 10^6 is 1 million. (Some electronic calculators require a coefficient of 1 to be entered.)

EXAMPLE 2.10

How many times should the multiplication key be pressed to solve the following problem?

$$(2.9 \times 10^{12})/(1.71 \times 10^7)$$

Solution

None. (Press the EXP or EE key twice.)

Changing the Form of Exponential Numbers

The *form* of an exponential number may be changed without changing its *value*. For example, 1.25×10^4 can be changed to another coefficient times 10^3 or a different coefficient times 10^2, and so on:

$$1.25 \times 10^4 = 1.25 \times 10 \times 10 \times 10 \times 10$$
$$= 1.25 \times 10 \times (10 \times 10 \times 10) = 12.5 \times 10^3$$
$$= 1.25 \times 10 \times 10 \times (10 \times 10) = 125 \times 10^2$$
$$= 1.25 \times 10 \times 10 \times 10 \times (10) = 1250 \times 10^1$$
$$= 1.25 \times 10 \times 10 \times 10 \times 10 \quad = 12{,}500 \times 10^0 = 12{,}500$$

In the first conversion, we multiplied the coefficient by one of the tens and ended up with one fewer ten in the exponential portion of the number. The *values* of all these numbers are the same; only their *format* is different. We may need to change to different formats when we add or subtract exponential numbers, or we can use a scientific calculator.

We can *increase* either the coefficient or the exponential part of a number by any factor without changing the number's overall value if we *reduce* the other part by the same factor. A simple working rule allows changing the format of a number in exponential notation: Move the decimal point in the coefficient *to the right* n *places and reduce the exponent* n *units,* or move the decimal point in the coefficient *to the left* n *places and increase the exponent* n *units.*

> Move the decimal point in the coefficient to the right *n* places and reduce the exponent *n* units,
> or
> move the decimal point in the coefficient to the left *n* places and increase the exponent *n* units.

EXAMPLE 2.11

Change the format of each of the following numbers to scientific notation:

(a) 237×10^4 (b) 0.0141×10^{-1} (c) 300.3×10^0

Solution

(a) The decimal point must be moved two places to the *left*, so the exponent is *increased* by 2: 2.37×10^6.

(b) The decimal point has to be moved two places to the *right*, so the exponent is *reduced* by 2: 1.41×10^{-3}.

(c) The coefficient is reduced by a factor of 100 (equal to 10^2), and the exponential part is increased by the same factor: 3.003×10^2.

> Read the instruction manual for your calculator to learn to change numbers in decimal format to scientific notation.

Practice Problem 2.11 Change the format of each of the following numbers to scientific notation:

(a) 0.0110×10^7 (b) 240×10^3 (c) 0.000123×10^1

Multiplication and Division of Exponential Numbers

To multiply numbers in exponential format, we multiply the coefficients and the exponential parts separately. To multiply exponential parts, the exponents are *added*. For example, let's multiply 4.0×10^3 and 1.5×10^4:

$$(4.0 \times 10^3) \times (1.5 \times 10^4) = (4.0 \times 1.5) \times (10^3 \times 10^4)$$
$$= 6.0 \times 10^{3+4} = 6.0 \times 10^7$$

It's easy to see that if we multiply three tens by four tens, we get seven tens:

$$10^3 \times 10^4 = (10 \times 10 \times 10) \times (10 \times 10 \times 10 \times 10)$$
$$= 10 \times 10 \times 10 \times 10 \times 10 \times 10 \times 10 = 10^7$$

EXAMPLE 2.12

Multiply the following numbers, and express the answers in scientific notation:

(a) $(2.0 \times 10^3) \times (3.0 \times 10^4)$

(b) $(4.0 \times 10^3) \times (5.0 \times 10^5)$

(c) $(6.0 \times 10^7) \times (1.5 \times 10^4)$

Solution

(a) $(2.0 \times 10^3) \times (3.0 \times 10^4) = 6.0 \times 10^7$

(b) $(4.0 \times 10^3) \times (5.0 \times 10^5) = 20 \times 10^8 = 2.0 \times 10^9$

(c) $(6.0 \times 10^7) \times (1.5 \times 10^4) = 9.0 \times 10^{11}$

Practice Problem 2.12 Multiply the following numbers and express the answers in scientific notation:

(a) $(4.5 \times 10^7) \times (4.0 \times 10^7)$

(b) $(6.0 \times 10^3) \times (3.5 \times 10^4)$

(c) $(2.0 \times 10^8) \times (2.7 \times 10^7)$

To divide exponential numbers, we divide the coefficients and the exponential parts separately. To divide exponential parts, we subtract the exponents.

EXAMPLE 2.13

Divide 7.0×10^6 by 3.5×10^3.

Solution

$$(7.0 \times 10^6)/(3.5 \times 10^3) = (7.0/3.5) \times 10^{6-3} = 2.0 \times 10^3$$

We can see that this procedure is correct:

$$\frac{7.0 \times 10^6}{3.5 \times 10^3} = \frac{7.0 \times 10 \times 10 \times 10 \times 10 \times 10 \times 10}{3.5 \times 10 \times 10 \times 10}$$

$$= 2.0 \times 10 \times 10 \times 10 = 2.0 \times 10^3$$

Practice Problem 2.13   Divide 1.6×10^4 by 6.4×10^2.

We can apply this procedure to calculate the quotient of two exponential numbers even when the denominator has a larger magnitude than the numerator. For example, let's divide 8.0×10^5 by 4.0×10^7. The rule for dividing exponential numbers gives the following result:

$$(8.0 \times 10^5)/(4.0 \times 10^7) = 2.0 \times 10^{5-7} = 2.0 \times 10^{-2}$$

What does the negative exponent mean? Writing out all the expressions enables us to see:

$$\frac{8.0 \times 10^5}{4.0 \times 10^7} = \frac{8.0 \times 10 \times 10 \times 10 \times 10 \times 10}{2.0 \times 10 \times 10 \times 10 \times 10 \times 10 \times 10 \times 10}$$

$$= 2.0 \times \left(\frac{1}{10 \times 10}\right) = 0.020 = 2.0 \times 10^{-2}$$

The negative exponent means to *divide* the coefficient by the base a certain number of times.

EXAMPLE 2.14

Calculate the quotient of $(9.5 \times 10^3)/(5.0 \times 10^3)$.

Solution

By the rule for division of exponential numbers:

$$\frac{9.5 \times 10^3}{5.0 \times 10^3} = 1.9 \times 10^0$$

By cancellation:

$$\frac{9.5 \times 10^3}{5.0 \times 10^3} = \frac{9.5 \times 10 \times 10 \times 10}{5.0 \times 10 \times 10 \times 10} = 1.9$$

A positive exponent indicates that the exponential part of the number is greater than 1, a negative exponent indicates that it is less than 1, and a zero exponent indicates that it is equal to 1.

Because $1.9 = 1.9 \times 10^0$, it is apparent that 10^0 is equal to 1.

Practice Problem 2.14 What is the decimal value (the value with no power of 10 shown) of 6.13×10^0?

EXAMPLE 2.15

Change the format of each of the following numbers to scientific notation:

(a) 0.0050×10^{-4} (b) 100.0×10^{-2} (c) 30.03×10^{-5}

Solution

(a) The decimal point has to be moved three places to the *right,* so the exponent is *reduced* by 3: 5.0×10^{-7}.

(b) The decimal point must be moved two places to the *left,* so the exponent is *increased* by 2: 1.000×10^0.

(c) The coefficient is reduced by a factor of 10 (equal to 10^1), and the exponential part is increased by the same factor: 3.003×10^{-4}.

Practice Problem 2.15 Change the format of each of the following numbers to scientific notation:

(a) 0.101×10^{-6} (b) $200,000 \times 10^{-3}$ (c) 0.00300×10^0

The rules for multiplication and division need to be stated slightly differently to allow for negative exponents. To multiply exponential parts, add the exponents *algebraically.* To divide exponential parts, subtract the exponents *algebraically.* The word *algebraically* means "with due regard for the signs."

EXAMPLE 2.16

Divide 6.0×10^5 by 2.0×10^{-4}.

Solution

$$\frac{6.0 \times 10^5}{2.0 \times 10^{-4}} = 3.0 \times 10^{5-(-4)} = 3.0 \times 10^9$$

Instead of dividing a negative exponent by changing its sign and adding, we may transfer the *exponential part* of a number from numerator to denominator or from denominator to numerator if we simply change the sign of the exponent:

$$\frac{6.0 \times 10^5}{2.0 \times 10^{-4}} = \frac{6.0 \times 10^5 \times 10^{+4}}{2.0} = 3.0 \times 10^9$$

Practice Problem 2.16 Divide 3.0×10^{-5} by 7.5×10^{-3}.

Addition and Subtraction of Exponential Numbers

When we add or subtract numbers in exponential notation, *the exponents must be the same.* (This rule is related to the rule that requires numbers being added or subtracted to have their decimal points aligned.) The answer is then the sum or difference of the coefficients times the same exponential part as in each number being added or subtracted. (The calculator does this operation automatically, but we must know what is happening in order to report the proper number of significant digits [see Section 2.4].)

EXAMPLE 2.17

Add (a) $6.22 \times 10^4 + 2.13 \times 10^4$, (b) $6.00 \times 10^5 + 5.55 \times 10^5$, and (c) $9.13 \times 10^4 + 2.5 \times 10^3$.

Solution

(a)
$$
\begin{array}{r}
6.22 \times 10^4 \\
+\ 2.13 \times 10^4 \\
\hline
8.35 \times 10^4
\end{array}
\qquad \text{Same exponent}
$$

Sum of coefficients

Because the exponents are the same, the coefficients are simply added. The answer has the same exponential part as each number added.

(b)
$$
\begin{array}{r}
6.00 \times 10^5 \\
+\ 5.55 \times 10^5 \\
\hline
11.55 \times 10^5 = 1.155 \times 10^6
\end{array}
$$

Because the coefficient of the answer has a value greater than 10, the form must be changed to get the answer into scientific notation.

(c)
$$
\begin{array}{r}
9.13 \times 10^4 \\
+\ 0.25 \times 10^4 \\
\hline
9.38 \times 10^4
\end{array}
\qquad \text{Coefficient and exponent amended to allow addition}
$$

Because the exponents are not the same, one of them must be changed to equal the other. Of course, we cannot change only the exponent because that would change the value of the number. We can move the decimal point one place to the left in 2.5×10^3 (making the coefficient smaller) and increase the exponent by one (making the exponential part larger). The value of the number is unchanged, but its format is now suitable for the addition we want to do.

Practice Problem 2.17   Subtract (a) $6.11 \times 10^4 - 8.22 \times 10^4$ and (b) $6.43 \times 10^4 - 5.1 \times 10^3$.

40

Raising an Exponential Number to a Power

To raise an exponential number to a power, we raise both the coefficient and the exponential part to the power. We raise an exponential part to a power by *multiplying* the exponent by the power.

EXAMPLE 2.18

Calculate the cube of 2.0×10^5

Solution

$$(2.0 \times 10^5)^3 = (2.0)^3 \times (10^5)^3 = (2.0)^3 \times 10^{5 \times 3}$$
$$= 8.0 \times 10^{15}$$
$$(2.0 \times 10^5)^3 = (2.0 \times 10^5)(2.0 \times 10^5)(2.0 \times 10^5)$$
$$= 8.0 \times 10^{15}$$

Practice Problem 2.18   Calculate the value of $(3.0 \times 10^{-3})^2$.

Taking the square root of a number is equivalent to raising the number to the $\frac{1}{2}$ power. In general, the nth root of a number is the number to the $1/n$ power.

EXAMPLE 2.19

Calculate the square root of 2.25×10^{-4}.

Solution

$$\sqrt{2.25 \times 10^{-4}} = 1.50 \times \sqrt{10^{-4}} = 1.50 \times (10^{-4})^{1/2} = 1.50 \times 10^{-2}$$

Practice Problem 2.19   Calculate the cube root of 8.00×10^6.

Snapshot Review

ChemSkill Builder 2.1

❒ In addition or subtraction, the units must be the same and the exponents must be the same to merely add the coefficients for the proper result.

A. Report the following numbers in standard exponential form: (a) 1234, (b) 200.0, and (c) 0.0200.
B. Do the following calculations
   (a) $1.67 \times 10^3 + 4.2 \times 10^2$
   (b) $(1.25 \times 10^3)/(8.40 \times 10^2)$
   (c) $1.6 \times 10^{-3} - 4.20 \times 10^{-2}$

2.3 The Metric System

The **metric system** and its more modern counterpart **SI** (for S̲ystème I̲nternational d'Unités) are systems of units designed to make calculations as easy as possible. It was designed to make every word mean one and only one thing. Its subdivisions and multiples of units are powers of 10 times a primary unit. Each of its prefixes means the same thing, no matter what unit it is attached to. The abbreviations for the quantities and prefixes are easy to remember. All these features have been built into the metric system to make it easy. Contrast this lack of ambiguity with the ambiguity in the English system, as illustrated in Example 2.4.

Learning the following six words is essential to understanding the metric system:

1. meter   4. centi-
2. gram   5. milli-
3. liter   6. kilo-

(A few more words will be added as we progress.) Meter, gram, and liter are the units of length, mass, and volume, respectively, in the metric system. Just as the English system has subdivisions of its primary units (12 inches [in.] in a foot, for example), so does the metric system. But the metric system uses prefixes that mean the same thing no matter what primary unit they are used with. Centi-, milli-, and kilo- are prefixes that indicate certain multiples or divisions of any primary unit. Other less important prefixes are given along with these in Table 2.2.

The **meter** is the primary unit of length in the metric system. Its abbreviation is m. The meter is defined in such a way that it can be duplicated precisely in any well-equipped laboratory in the world. It had been defined as the distance between two marks on a metal bar kept at the Bureau of Weights and Measures in Paris. (It now has an even more precise definition.) A meter is 39.37 in. long—3.37 in. longer than a yard.

A **standard** is an agreed upon quantity with which like quantities can be compared. For example, the *meter* is the agreed standard of length, to which other lengths can be compared. In the measurement of most quantities, the

Table 2.2 Metric Prefixes*

Prefix	Abbreviation	Meaning	
Giga-	G	One billion	1,000,000,000
Mega-	M	One million	1,000,000
Kilo-	**k**	**One thousand**	**1000**
Deci-	d	One-tenth	0.1
Centi-	**c**	**One-hundredth**	**0.01**
Milli-	**m**	**One-thousandth**	**0.001**
Micro-	μ	One-millionth	0.000001
Nano-	n	One-billionth	0.000000001
Pico-	p	One-trillionth	0.000000000001

*The most important prefixes for most chemistry courses are given in **boldface** type.

Figure 2.4 One-Kilogram Samples

Note that the same masses of strawberries, water, cubes of sugar, iron, nails, and copper pennies have different volumes.

primary unit is also the standard. With mass, however, the standard is different from the unit. The **gram** is the primary unit of mass in the metric system. The gram, abbreviated g, is such a small mass that the kilogram has been chosen as the legal standard of mass in the United States and as the worldwide standard in SI. Mass is measured by comparison with standard masses. The kilogram (kg) is a mass equivalent to about 2.2 pounds (lb) (Figure 2.4).

The **cubic meter** (m^3) is the primary unit of volume in SI. A smaller unit, the **liter,** is the primary unit of volume in the metric system. The abbreviation for liter is L. We need to know both the cubic meter and the liter. Table 2.3 summarizes the primary metric units of distance, mass, and volume.

The prefix *centi-* means one-hundredth of any primary unit. For example, a centimeter (cm) is 0.01 m, and a centigram (cg) is 0.01 g.

The prefix *milli-* means one-thousandth. No matter which primary unit it is used with, it always means 0.001 times that unit. A millimeter (mm) is 0.001 m, a milliliter (mL) is 0.001 L, and so on.

The prefix *kilo-* means 1000 times the primary unit, no matter which primary unit it is used with. For example, a kilogram (kg) is 1000 g, and a kilometer (km) is 1000 m.

Table 2.3 Primary Metric Units

	Unit	Symbol	Equivalencies
Distance	Meter	m	
Mass	Gram	g	
Volume	Liter	L	
Volume	Cubic meter	m^3	$1000\,L = 1\,m^3$
Volume	Cubic centimeter	cm^3	$1000\,cm^3 = 1\,L$

EXAMPLE 2.20

Which is bigger—1 Mg or 1 mg?

Solution

$$1 \text{ Mg} = 1,000,000 \text{ g (see Table 2.2)}$$

$$1 \text{ mg} = 0.001 \text{ g}$$

A megagram (Mg), equal to a metric ton, is a billion times larger than a milligram (mg).

The metric system is easier to use than the English system.

EXAMPLE 2.21

(a) How many meters are in 5.200 km?

(b) How many yards are in 5.200 miles?

Solution

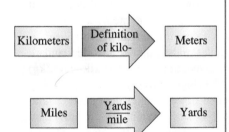

We can use the factor-label method (Section 2.1) to do these metric calculations.

(a) $5.200 \text{ km} \left(\dfrac{1000 \text{ m}}{1 \text{ km}} \right) = 5200 \text{ m}$

(b) $5.200 \text{ miles} \left(\dfrac{1760 \text{ yards}}{1 \text{ mile}} \right) = 9152 \text{ yards}$

The metric system problem, part (a), can be solved without paper and pencil—by moving the decimal point in 5.200 three places to the right. The English system conversion, part (b), requires that we remember the number of yards per mile (harder than the 1000 m/km metric conversion factor) and that we use pencil and paper or a calculator to do the arithmetic. The conversion factor 1000 is used for kilograms, kiloliters, kilowatts, and any other factor involving the prefix *kilo-*. The English conversion factor 1760 yd/mile is not used in any other conversion.

Practice Problem 2.21 (a) How many centimeters are in 2.370 m? (b) How many inches are in 2.370 ft? (c) For which of these two conversions do we need to use a calculator?

To convert a value expressed in a primary metric unit to its equivalent in a subunit, or vice versa, use a conversion factor with a 1 in front of the subunit and the equivalent value in front of the main unit. Note that either the prefix abbreviation or its equivalent is in front of the symbol for the primary unit:

Prefix	Equivalent value
Kilo	1000
Centi	0.01
Milli	0.001

For example, either of the following conversion factors is correct:

$$\left(\frac{1 \text{ centimeter}}{0.01 \text{ meter}}\right)\left(\frac{0.01 \text{ meter}}{1 \text{ centimeter}}\right)$$

Thus, to convert 729 cm to meters:

$$729 \text{ cm}\left(\frac{0.01 \text{ m}}{1 \text{ cm}}\right) = 7.29 \text{ m}$$

To convert 1.66 m to centimeters:

$$1.66 \text{ m}\left(\frac{1 \text{ cm}}{0.01 \text{ m}}\right) = 166 \text{ cm}$$

Note that **1 centi-** (1 c) means **0.01.**

EXAMPLE 2.22

Convert 75.0 g to (a) kilograms and (b) milligrams.

Solution

(a) $75.0 \text{ g}\left(\dfrac{1 \text{ kg}}{1000 \text{ g}}\right) = 0.0750 \text{ kg}$

(b) $75.0 \text{ g}\left(\dfrac{1 \text{ mg}}{0.001 \text{ g}}\right) = 75{,}000 \text{ mg}$

Practice Problem 2.22 Calculate the number of (a) meters in 6.66 km, (b) liters in 6.66 kL, and (c) grams in 6.66 kg. (d) Highlight the differences among these three problems and comment on the ease of the metric system.

Some conversions between metric and English system units are presented in Table 2.4. Engineers must know how to do such conversions because they still use some English system units. However, scientists rarely use English system units, and therefore, these conversions are less important for them. (The use of a metric unit that is slowly becoming familiar to the general public is shown in Figure 2.5. Note that 80 km/h is about 50 mph.)

Table 2.4 Metric-English Conversions

Length	Mass	Volume
1 m = 39.37 in.	1 kg = 2.2045 lb (avoirdupois)	1 L = 1.059 qt
2.540 cm = 1 in.	453.6 g = 1 lb (avoirdupois)	29.57 mL = 1 fl oz
1.609 km = 1 mile	28.35 g = 1 oz (avoirdupois)	3.777 L = 1 US gal
= 1760 yd	31.103 g = 1 oz (troy)*	0.472 L = 1 US pt
= 5280 ft	1 metric ton = 2204.5 lb (avoirdupois)	

*Troy weight is generally used for gold and silver.

> The units must be the same for the addition or subtraction of numbers that represent measurements.

When we add or subtract measured quantities, we treat the units just as we treat variables (such as x, y, and z) in algebraic manipulations (see Appendix 1). The units must be the same for the addition or subtraction of numbers that represent measurements. A sum or difference will have the same units as the quantities being added or subtracted.

Figure 2.5 *English and Metric Usage*

The metric system is increasingly being used in everyday life in the United States, as illustrated by the automobile speedometer. Kilometers per hour are shown in smaller yellow digits.

EXAMPLE 2.23

Add (a) 7.13 m + 0.45 m and (b) 7.13 m + 45 cm.

Solution

(a) The units are the same, so we simply add:

$$7.13 \text{ m} + 0.45 \text{ m} = 7.58 \text{ m}$$

(b) We must either change 7.13 m to centimeters or 45 cm to meters, and then add:

$$45 \text{ cm}\left(\frac{0.01 \text{ m}}{1 \text{ cm}}\right) = 0.45 \text{ m}$$

$$7.13 \text{ m} + 0.45 \text{ m} = 7.58 \text{ m}$$

Practice Problem 2.23   Add the following algebraic quantities:

(a) $179x + 22x$ (b) $179x + 33.00y$, where $x = 0.10y$

To multiply or divide measured quantities of the same type, such as two lengths, we may have to convert the units so that they are the same. For quantities of different types, the units cannot be the same.

EXAMPLE 2.24

Multiply (a) 1.08 cm × 6.50 cm and (b) 4.10 m × 32.5 cm.

Solution

(a) The units are already the same, so we just multiply:

$$1.08 \text{ cm} \times 6.50 \text{ cm} = 7.02 \text{ cm}^2$$

Note that both the numbers and the units are multiplied.

(b) The 4.10 m could be changed to centimeters, or the 32.5 cm could be changed to meters:

$$32.5 \text{ cm}\left(\frac{0.01 \text{ m}}{1 \text{ cm}}\right) = 0.325 \text{ m}$$

$$4.10 \text{ m} \times 0.325 \text{ m} = 1.33 \text{ m}^2$$

Centimeters → Definition of centi- → Meters

Practice Problem 2.24 Multiply the following algebraic quantities:

$$(1.08x)(6.50x)$$

How does the x in this problem resemble the unit in Example 2.24(a)?

EXAMPLE 2.25

The cost of a certain 75.00-cm gold chain is $975.00. What is the cost per centimeter?

Solution

$$\frac{\$975.00}{75.00 \text{ cm}} = \$13.00/\text{cm}$$

Practice Problem 2.25 Divide the algebraic quantities: $(195x)/(15y^3)$.

Length or Distance

The primary unit of **length** in the metric system is the meter, which is 3.37 in. longer than a yard. The same prefixes are used with the meter as with all other metric units.

EXAMPLE 2.26

Olympic divers use 3.00-m boards and 10.00-m boards. Calculate these heights in centimeters.

Solution

A centimeter is 0.01 m, just as a cent is 0.01 dollar. There are 100 cm in 1 m, so in exactly 3 m, there are 300 cm:

$$3.00 \text{ m}\left(\frac{1 \text{ cm}}{0.01 \text{ m}}\right) = 300 \text{ cm}$$

In exactly 10 m, there are 1000 cm:

$$10.00 \text{ m}\left(\frac{1 \text{ cm}}{0.01 \text{ m}}\right) = 1000 \text{ cm}$$

Practice Problem 2.26 Calculate the heights of these Olympic diving boards in millimeters.

EXAMPLE 2.27

How many kilometers are in 206 m?

Solution

There are 1000 m in 1 km, by definition.

$$206 \text{ m}\left(\frac{1 \text{ km}}{1000 \text{ m}}\right) = 0.206 \text{ km}$$

Practice Problem 2.27 How many millimeters are in 1.04 cm?

Mass

As stated earlier, the primary unit of mass in the metric system is the gram. Because the gram is so small, however, the standard mass in SI and the legal standard in the United States is the kilogram.

EXAMPLE 2.28

How many grams are in 1 kg?

Solution

The prefix *kilo-* means 1000 of whatever it is attached to. Therefore, 1 kg is 1000 g.

Practice Problem 2.28 How many grams are in 1 mg?

EXAMPLE 2.29

Airlines usually have a 15-kg free-baggage allowance for overseas travelers. (a) How many grams does this allowance represent? (b) How many pounds?

Solution

(a)

$$15 \text{ kg}\left(\frac{1000 \text{ g}}{1 \text{ kg}}\right) = 15,000 \text{ g}$$

(b) From Table 2.4, we see that 1 kg = 2.20 lb:

$$15 \text{ kg}\left(\frac{2.20 \text{ lb}}{1 \text{ kg}}\right) = 33 \text{ lb}$$

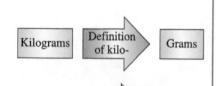

Practice Problem 2.29 Calculate the mass of a 207-lb person in kilograms.

EXAMPLE 2.30

(a) Using data from Table 2.4, calculate the number of troy ounces in 1.000 kg.

(b) Using data from Table 2.4, calculate the number of avoirdupois ounces in 1.000 kg.

Solution

(a) $1.000 \text{ kg} \left(\dfrac{1000 \text{ g}}{1 \text{ kg}} \right) \left(\dfrac{1 \text{ troy ounce}}{31.103 \text{ g}} \right) = 32.15$ troy ounces

(b) $1.000 \text{ kg} \left(\dfrac{1000 \text{ g}}{1 \text{ kg}} \right) \left(\dfrac{1 \text{ avoirdupois ounce}}{28.35 \text{ g}} \right) = 35.27$ avoirdupois ounces

Practice Problem 2.30 (a) Which is heavier, a pound of lead or a pound of bricks? (b) Which is heavier, a pound of lead or a pound of gold? (c) Calculate the mass of each in grams.

Volume

Volume can be measured in two ways (Figure 2.6): (1) using the capacity of a certain container, and (2) using the space defined by a cube of length l on each side. The second method uses the cube of a length (and thus one possible unit for volume is the cube of a length unit). The volume of a rectangular solid is given by

$$\text{Volume} = \text{length} \times \text{width} \times \text{height}$$

$$V = l \times w \times h$$

A cube is a special case for which $l = w = h$, so the volume of a cube is $V = l^3$.

The metric system unit of volume is the liter (L), originally defined as the volume occupied by a cube exactly 10 cm on each side (see Figure 2.6). In SI, the cubic meter is the standard. Because the cubic meter is a rather large

> The only metric *units* that are cubed are units of length—any unit ending in *m*—to give a unit of volume.

Figure 2.6 Two Methods to Determine Volume

(not drawn to scale)

Note that
$10 \text{ cm} \times 10 \text{ cm} \times 10 \text{ cm} = 1000 \text{ cm}^3$.

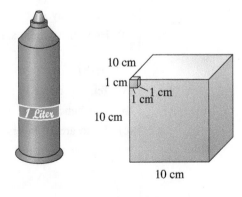

1-liter bottle   1-liter cube

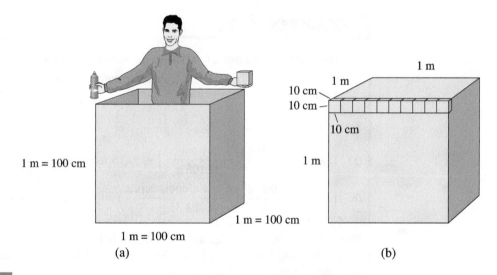

Figure 2.7 Cubic Meter and Liter

(a) The man in the cubic meter box is holding two objects, each of which is 1 L in volume. Note the difference in size between 1 L and 1 m³. (b) A cubic meter has edges that are 1 m = 100 cm long. Thus the 1 m³ cube is $(100 \text{ cm})^3 = 1{,}000{,}000 \text{ cm}^3$ in volume. Ten boxes with 10-cm edges fit along each such edge. Ten rows of those 10-cm boxes would fit in a layer covering the whole top surface of the cubic meter, and ten layers would fill the whole volume. There is 1000 liters in a cubic meter.

volume (about half the capacity of a small cement truck), the liter is favored by chemists (Figure 2.7).

$$1.00 \text{ L} = (10 \text{ cm})^3 = 1000 \text{ cm}^3 = 1000 \text{ mL}$$

Thus,

$$1.00 \text{ cm}^3 = 1.00 \text{ mL}$$

and

$$1.000 \text{ m}^3 = 1000 \text{ L}$$

EXAMPLE 2.31

(a) How many 1-L cubes fit along the top front edge of the cubic meter pictured in Figure 2.7?

(b) How many fit on the front face?

(c) How many such vertical layers are in the entire cube?

(d) How many liters are in 1 m³?

Solution

(a) Ten 1-L cubes fit along the edge.

(b) One hundred (10 × 10) 1-L cubes fit in the 10 rows on the front face.

(c) There are 10 layers from front to back.

(d) One thousand (10 × 10 × 10) 1-L cubes fit into 1 m³. Thus,

$$1 \text{ m}^3 = 1000 \text{ L} = 1 \text{ kL}$$

Practice Problem 2.31   How many cubic centimeters are in 1 L?

EXAMPLE 2.32

Calculate the number of centimeters in 7.13×10^{-2} km.

Solution

$$7.13 \times 10^{-2} \text{ km} \left(\frac{1000 \text{ m}}{1 \text{ km}} \right) \left(\frac{1 \text{ cm}}{0.01 \text{ m}} \right) = 7.13 \times 10^{3} \text{ cm}$$

Practice Problem 2.32 Calculate the number of kilograms in 1.77×10^{3} milligrams.

EXAMPLE 2.33

Calculate the volume of a 0.887 m^3 container in (a) liters and (b) cubic centimeters.

Solution

(a) $0.887 \text{ m}^3 \left(\frac{1000 \text{ L}}{1 \text{ m}^3} \right) = 887 \text{ L}$

(b) $0.887 \text{ m}^3 \left(\frac{1,000,000 \text{ cm}^3}{1 \text{ m}^3} \right) = 887,000 \text{ cm}^3 = 8.87 \times 10^{5} \text{ cm}^3$

Practice Problem 2.33 Calculate the volume of a 623-L container in cubic meters.

EXAMPLE 2.34

A *unit cell* is a small portion of a crystalline solid that, when repeated very many times, builds up an entire sample. A unit cell of a certain solid is cubic, with edge length 2.00×10^{-10} m. How many unit cells does it take to occupy 1.00 cm^3?

Solution

The volume of the unit cell is

$$(2.00 \times 10^{-10} \text{ m})^3 = (2.00 \times 10^{-8} \text{ cm})^3 = 8.00 \times 10^{-24} \text{ cm}^3$$

The number of unit cells is therefore

$$1.00 \text{ cm}^3 \left(\frac{1 \text{ unit cell}}{8.00 \times 10^{-24} \text{ cm}^3} \right) = 1.25 \times 10^{23} \text{ unit cells}$$

 Snapshot Review

ChemSkill Builder 2.4

❐ The metric system is easy because all the conversions are powers of 10, all the prefixes mean the same thing no matter what unit they are attached to, and all the symbols and abbreviations are meaningful.

❒ English-metric conversions are most often presented, if at all, to give an idea of the size of the metric unit. They are not used very much in this course.

❒ Volume can be presented in liters (or its subdivisions) or in the cube of a unit of length (such as m^3 or cm^3). The *centi-* in cm^3 does *not* mean one-hundredth of 1 m^3, because the 0.01 must be cubed.

A. Complete each of the following parts by inserting the correct metric unit:
   (a) Volume of a can of soda   0.366 _____
   (b) Height of a professional basketball player   1.9 _____
   (c) Volume of water in a backyard swimming pool   2.5 _____
   (d) Mass of a U.S. quarter (25¢)   5.7 _____

B. Calculate the number of (a) meters in 1234 mm, (b) liters in 1234 mL, and (c) grams in 1234 mg.

C. Calculate the number of (a) liters in 0.175 m^3 and (b) liters in 315 cm^3.

2.4   Significant Digits

Scientific measurements are usually repeated three or more times. The average value of the measurements is probably closer to the true value than any one of them. The **accuracy** is the closeness of the average of a set of measurements to the true value. The **precision** is the closeness of all of a set of measured values to one another. A set of measurements may be precise without being accurate or accurate without being precise (if the measurer is very lucky), but the best measurements are both accurate and precise.

No matter how accurate our measuring tool, the accuracy of our measurements is limited. For example, an automobile odometer has divisions of 0.1 mile (or 0.1 km), and we can estimate to one-tenth of that smallest scale division, but we cannot measure 1 in. or even 1 ft with an odometer. Similarly, we cannot measure the thickness of a piece of paper with a ruler marked in centimeters.

EXAMPLE 2.35

A set of weighings is done with a bathroom scale that registers 2 lb with no load (Figure 2.8). Each weighing results in a reading of 117 lb.

(a) Are the measurements precise?

(b) Are the measurements accurate?

(c) What is the probable true weight of the person?

Solution

(a) The weighings are precise, because exactly the same answer (to the precision of the device) was obtained each time.

(b) They are not accurate, because the no-load value was incorrect.

(c) The true weight is probably 115 lb.

Figure 2.8 Bathroom Scale

If a bathroom scale is not adjusted to read zero when no load is on it, the results it yields with a load may be precise but probably not accurate. For example, if it reads 2 lb with no load, each time a person uses the scale, it will probably read 2 lb heavier than his or her true weight.

Practice Problem 2.35   A machine wraps sticks of butter with paper that is printed with lines marking 1-oz portions. If the machine wraps the butter one-eighth of an inch away from the correct position (Figure 2.9), the first portion might be too small and the last too large. Having 12 sticks of butter all wrapped by the same machine in the same way: (a) Will there be the same mass of butter at the first mark each time? (b) Will each portion be 1 oz in mass? (c) Is the wrapping more precise than accurate or vice versa?

The precision with which we measure must be indicated when we report a measurement. When we use a measuring instrument, we must estimate to one digit beyond the smallest scale division, if possible. For example, see Figure 2.10. If we measure the length of the bar with the top ruler, calibrated in centimeters, we see that the bar is between 4 and 5 cm long and can estimate that it extends 0.1 cm past 4 cm, for a reading of 4.1 cm. In contrast, if we use the bottom ruler, calibrated in tenths of centimeters—that is, millimeters—we see that

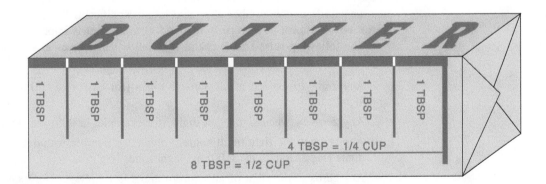

Figure 2.9   Precise but Inaccurate Measurement

If the wrapping machine regularly places the wrapper too close to one end of each stick of butter, the end piece might be the same weight in each stick but still be far from 1 tablespoon (TBSP).

Figure 2.10 *Measurements of Different Precision*

The smallest scale divisions on the bottom ruler are millimeters.

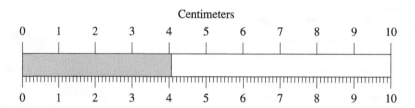

the length of the bar is between 4.0 and 4.1 cm. We estimate that it is 4.08 cm. We use the last digit to report that we used a ruler with a millimeter scale.

Suppose that the bar extended exactly to the 4.1 line on the millimeter ruler. How should we report the result? We should report 4.10 cm. If we omit the zero, someone reading the result will think that we used a ruler calibrated only in centimeters. The third digit indicates that the result was obtained on a more precise ruler, but just happened to be a value ending in zero.

EXAMPLE 2.36

About what fraction of measurements reported should be values ending in a zero?

Solution

About one time in 10 the last digit of a reported measurement should be a zero. (There is an equal possibility of each digit, 0–9, being the last, so one-tenth of the time it should be a zero, one-tenth of the time it should be a one, one-tenth of the time a two, and so on.)

Scientists report the precision of their measurements every time they write down a result. The number of digits they use consists of the absolutely certain digits plus one estimated digit. Every digit that reflects the precision of the measurement is called a **significant digit,** or **significant figure.** Note that the word *significant* has a different meaning here than in everyday conversation, where it means "important."

Sometimes, zeros are used merely to indicate the magnitude of a number (how big or small the number is). If the purpose of a zero is *only* to establish the magnitude of the number, that zero is not significant. Determining which zeros are significant in a properly reported measurement is important.

The following rules enable chemists to tell whether zeros in a number are significant or not:

1. Any zeros to the left of all nonzero digits (for example, in 0.03) are not significant.

2. Any zeros between significant digits (for example, in 903) are significant.

3. Any zeros to the right of all nonzero digits in a number with decimal place digits (for example, in 70.00) are significant.

4. Any zeros to the right of all nonzero digits in an integer (for example, in 4000) are uncertain. If they indicate only the magnitude of the measurement, they are not significant. However, if they also show something about the precision of the measurement, they are significant. We cannot tell whether they are significant merely by looking at the number.

EXAMPLE 2.37

A measurement of a bar yields a length of 4.84 cm. How many meters is that? How many significant digits are in the number of meters?

Solution

$$4.84 \text{ cm}\left(\frac{0.01 \text{ m}}{1 \text{ cm}}\right) = 0.0484 \text{ m}$$

Because the number of centimeters has three significant digits, there are three significant digits in the number of meters. The calculation changing the value from centimeters to meters does not change the precision with which the measurement was made. (That 0.01 m equals 1 cm is a *definition*, not a *measurement*.) The zeros in 0.0484 m are not significant; they merely show the magnitude of the number. (If they were not there, the value of the number would be different. They are *important*, but they are not *significant*; they do not tell anything about the precision of the measurement.)

Practice Problem 2.37 How many significant digits does the measurement 2.4 m have? If the measurement is changed to centimeters, how many significant digits will be in that value?

EXAMPLE 2.38

Underline the significant digits in each of the following measurements. If a digit is uncertain, place a question mark under it.

(a) 0.0020 m   (b) 1.200 m   (c) 10.002 m   (d) 6000 m

Solution

(a) 0.00<u>20</u> m
The zeros to the left of the two are not significant (rule 1), but the one to the right is (rule 3).

(b) <u>1.200</u> m
The zeros to the right of the two are significant (rule 3).

(c) <u>10.002</u> m
Zeros between significant digits are significant (rule 2).

(d) <u>6</u>000 m
   ???

The 6 is certainly significant. The zeros to the right of all other digits in an integer are uncertain; they may reflect the precision or just the magnitude of the number. Without further information, it is impossible to tell (rule 4).

Practice Problem 2.38 Underline the significant digits in each of the following measurements. If a digit is uncertain, place a question mark under it.

(a) 35.00 cm   (b) 203.50 cm   (c) 30.20 cm   (d) 30 cm

EXAMPLE 2.39

How many significant digits are in each of the following measurements?

(a) 3.5 m   (b) 3.50 m   (c) 3.500 m

Solution

(a) Two   (b) Three   (c) Four

The zeros in the numbers of parts (b) and (c) do not affect the magnitude; they must therefore show something about the precision of the measurements (rule 3).

EXAMPLE 2.40

Change each of the measurements given in meters in Example 2.39 to millimeters. How is it possible to tell how many significant digits are in each result?

Solution

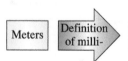

(a) $3.5 \text{ m} \left(\dfrac{1 \text{ mm}}{0.001 \text{ m}} \right) = 3500 \text{ mm}$

(b) $3.50 \text{ m} \left(\dfrac{1 \text{ mm}}{0.001 \text{ m}} \right) = 3500 \text{ mm}$

(c) $3.500 \text{ m} \left(\dfrac{1 \text{ mm}}{0.001 \text{ m}} \right) = 3500 \text{ mm}$

There are two significant digits in the result for part (a), three in the result for part (b), and four in the result for part (c). We know these numbers of significant digits only because we know the numbers of significant digits in the original numbers of meters given in Example 2.39. However, if we just look at the results, they all look the same! We cannot tell just by looking whether the zeros reflect the precision of the measurement or not.

Significant Digits in Calculated Results

In this electronic age, we have come to depend on our electronic calculators for solving arithmetic problems. However, electronic calculators usually do not give the correct number of significant digits. (A calculator may give the correct number of significant digits just by chance.) Each of us is responsible for making sure that the number of significant digits in a calculated answer is correct.

Not only must our recorded data reflect the precision of the measurements, but any results calculated from the data must also reflect that precision. Two rules govern how many significant digits are permitted in calculated results and how to get that many digits.

ADDITION AND SUBTRACTION

In the answers to addition and subtraction problems, the estimated digit that is farthest to the left is the last digit that can be retained. For example, let's add 6.2 cm and 9.203 cm:

$$
\begin{array}{r}
\text{Estimated digits}\\
6.2 \ \text{cm}\\
+\ 9.203 \ \text{cm}\\
\hline
15.403 \ \text{cm} \rightarrow 15.4 \ \text{cm}
\end{array}
$$

The leftmost estimated digit is the last digit that can be retained in the answer.

The digit 2 in 6.2 cm is an estimated digit; it has some uncertainty in it. Therefore, the digit 4 in the answer is also uncertain, and 0 and 3 are completely unknown. We cannot report the value 15.403 cm, or the reader will believe that 3 is the only uncertain digit. We must reduce the number of digits to leave 4 as the last digit. In general, we increase the last digit retained if the first digit to be dropped is 5 or greater; otherwise we leave that last digit unchanged.

Thus, for addition or subtraction, we retain digits in an answer only as far to the right as the leftmost uncertain digit in any of the numbers being added or subtracted. Note that the *number* of significant digits does not matter for addition or subtraction; what matters is *where the last digits lie*. In the previous calculation, there are two significant digits in the first number and four in the second, but the answer has three.

EXAMPLE 2.41

Calculate the sum of 10.10 cm + 1.332 cm + 6.4 cm.

Solution

$$
\begin{array}{r}
10.10 \ \text{cm}\\
1.332 \ \text{cm}\\
6.4 \ \ \ \text{cm}\\
\hline
17.832 \ \text{cm} \rightarrow 17.8 \ \text{cm}
\end{array}
$$

Practice Problem 2.41   Calculate the answer to the proper precision:

62.44 cm − 7.145 cm + 27.7 cm

MULTIPLICATION AND DIVISION

For multiplication and division, the number of significant digits in the factor with the fewest significant digits limits the number of significant digits in the answer. For example, let's multiply 4.1 cm by 21.07 cm:

4.1 cm × 21.07 cm = 86.387 cm^2 (Incorrect number of significant digits)

If we just leave the answer the way our electronic calculator gives it to us, anyone could assume that the measurement had been carried out with a precision of 1 part in 86,387, which is not true. We must reduce the number of significant digits in the answer to two because the factor with fewer significant digits has two. Thus, we change the answer to 86 cm^2.

EXAMPLE 2.42

Do the following calculations, and report the answers to the correct number of significant digits:

(a) 2.171 cm $\times$ 4.20 cm   (b) 4.92 g/1.64 cm^3

Solution

(a) The answer is 9.12 cm^2. We have to reduce the number of digits in 9.1182 cm^2 to three significant digits, because the second factor has only three significant digits.

(b) The answer is 3.00 g/cm^3. It must have three significant digits because both the dividend (4.92) and the divisor (1.64) have three significant digits. In this case, *add two zeros* to the answer given by the electronic calculator (3) to get the correct number of significant digits.

Practice Problem 2.42   Perform the following calculations and limit the answers to the correct number of significant digits:

(a) 1.27 cm $\times$ 6.220 cm $\times$ 4.10 cm
(b) 9.030 g/(3.01 cm $\times$ 1.414 cm $\times$ 7.500 cm)

Numbers that are definitions and not measurements, such as the number of centimeters in a meter (100) or the number of radii in the diameter of a circle (2), are exact numbers. They do not limit the number of significant digits in a calculated result.

EXAMPLE 2.43

The radius of a circle is 13.7 cm. Calculate the diameter of the circle to the correct number of significant digits.

Solution

$$d = 2r = 2(13.7 \text{ cm}) = 27.4 \text{ cm}$$

The *measurement* with the fewest significant digits is 13.7 cm. (It is the only measurement in the problem.)

Practice Problem 2.43   Calculate the number of milligrams in 8.011 g.

The usual rules for handling significant figures are often not used with sums of money because (1) dollars and cents are counting numbers rather than measurements (for example, a price of $7.15 means exactly $7.15 and not a value nearer to $7.15 than to $7.14 or $7.16); and (2) amounts in dollars are customarily stated with two decimal places or none, but not with other numbers of decimal places. Very large or very small costs may be stated using the usual rules for significant digits. Because money calculations are seldom used in chemistry courses (they are used in this chapter to introduce the factor label method with familiar examples), the student need not be concerned with these exceptions from the usual rules.

Rounding Off

Reducing the number of digits to the number permitted involves a process called *rounding off*, often referred to simply as **rounding.** The process most often involves dropping one or more digits to the right of the decimal point and adjusting the last remaining digit if necessary.

Rule	Example
	Round each of the following measurements to two *decimal places:*

1. If the leftmost digit to be dropped is greater than or equal to 5, we increase the last retained digit by 1 without regard to the sign of the number.

(a)   8.5561 cm   8.56 cm
(b)   8.5550 cm   8.56 cm
(c)   −8.5561 cm   −8.56 cm

2. If the leftmost digit to be dropped is less than 5, we do not change the final digit that is retained.

(a)   8.5543 cm   8.55 cm
(b)   −8.5543 cm   −8.55 cm

EXAMPLE 2.44

Round off each of the following lengths to retain two significant digits:

(a) 2.68 m   (b) 2.62 m   (c) 2.65 m

Solution

(a) 2.7 m   (b) 2.6 m   (c) 2.7 m

Where a rounded digit lies in relation to the decimal point is immaterial, as long as it is to the right of the decimal point.

Practice Problem 2.44   Round off each of the following lengths to retain three significant digits:

(a) 1.177 m   (b) 1.173 m   (c) 1.175 m

Rounding of integer digits is a little different!

Sometimes integral digits must be dropped. If the digits to be rounded are to the left of the decimal point rather than to the right, they are changed to (nonsignificant) zeros rather than being dropped. However, quantities greater than 10 are better expressed in scientific notation (Section 2.2).

EXAMPLE 2.45

Round off each of the following values to two significant digits:

(a) 6742 cm   (b) 6773 cm   (c) 6750 cm

Solution

(a) 6700 cm   (b) 6800 cm   (c) 6800 cm

In each case, the digits rounded are changed to nonsignificant zeros, not dropped.

Practice Problem 2.45   The state of Colorado is essentially a rectangle, measuring 623 km from east to west and 444 km from north to south. Calculate the area of Colorado to three significant digits.

If a problem has both addition or subtraction and multiplication or division, the part that is done first must have its significant digits noted before the next operation is performed, because the rules are different for determining which digits are retained.

If addition or subtraction is done first, the *number* of significant digits in the sum or difference is used to determine the number in the operation to follow. If multiplication or division is done first, the *position* of the last significant digit is noted to help determine the last significant digit in the next answer. In multipart problems in the rest of this text, to avoid excessive round off errors, at least one extra digit will be retained (if it is nonzero) until the final answer. Those digits will be written in *italic* type.

EXAMPLE 2.46

Find the result of each of the following calculations to the proper number of significant digits:

(a) $\dfrac{(80.21 \text{ g} - 79.93 \text{ g})}{65.22 \text{ cm}^3}$ (b) $(92.12 \text{ mL})(0.912 \text{ g/mL}) + 223.02 \text{ g}$

Solution

(a) The subtraction is done first, yielding an answer that has only two significant digits:

$$
\begin{array}{r}
80.21 \text{ g} \\
-79.93 \text{ g} \\
\hline
0.28 \text{ g}
\end{array}
$$

That value is divided by 65.22 cm^3, yielding an answer with two significant digits: 0.0043 g/cm^3.

(b) The multiplication is done first, yielding a value with one significant digit after the decimal point.

$$(92.12 \text{ mL})(0.912 \text{ g/mL}) + 223.02 \text{ g}$$
$$= 84.0l \text{ g} + 223.02 \text{ g} = 307.0 \text{ g}$$

The final answer thus is limited to one significant digit after the decimal point.

Practice Problem 2.46   Find the result of the following calculation to the proper number of significant digits:

$$(21.33 \text{ cm})(4.44 \text{ cm})(1.91 \text{ cm}) + 3.12 \text{ cm}^3$$

The rules for significant digits in logarithms are presented in Appendix 1.

Another advantage to scientific notation is that all digits of the coefficient of a number in scientific notation are significant. The exponent determines the magnitude of the number, so any zeros present in the coefficient must be significant.

EXAMPLE 2.47

How can we resolve the difficulty presented in Example 2.40?

Solution

One way to resolve this problem is to report the values in scientific notation, where all digits of the coefficient are significant: (a) 3.5×10^3 mm, (b) 3.50×10^3 mm, (c) 3.500×10^3 mm.

Practice Problem 2.47 Report the number of grams in each of the following quantities in such a way that the proper number of significant digits is obvious:

(a) 1.2 kg   (b) 1.20 kg   (c) 1.200 kg

EXAMPLE 2.48

Calculate the result of each of the following problems to the correct number of significant digits:

(a) 1.41×10^7 g $- 5.98 \times 10^6$ g

(b) $\dfrac{1.41 \times 10^7 \text{ g} - 5.98 \times 10^6 \text{ g}}{6.35 \times 10^4 \text{ cm}^3}$

Solution

(a) 14.1×10^6 g $- 5.98 \times 10^6$ g $= 8.12 \times 10^6$ g $= 8.1 \times 10^6$ g

(b) $\dfrac{1.41 \times 10^7 \text{ g} - 5.98 \times 10^6 \text{ g}}{6.35 \times 10^4 \text{ cm}^3} = 1.3 \times 10^2 \text{ g/cm}^3$

Because two different rules are used for the subtraction and division, note that the numerator of part (b) has only two significant digits, as shown in part (a). Therefore the quotient has only two significant digits.

Practice Problem 2.48 Calculate the result of each of the following problems to the proper numbers of significant digits:

(a) 3.8×10^4 cm $- 5.55 \times 10^3$ cm

(b) $(3.8 \times 10^4 \text{ cm})(5.55 \times 10^3 \text{ cm})$

(c) 3.8×10^{-4} cm $- 5.55 \times 10^{-3}$ cm

ChemSkill Builder 2.2

Snapshot Review

❐ The precision that was used in a measurement is reflected in the number of significant digits reported.

❐ The rules for significant digits in addition and subtraction are different from those in multiplication and division.

❐ Significant digits and decimal place digits are not the same. There is no necessary relationship between the two.

❐ In general, electronic calculators do not give the proper number of significant digits.

❐ All the digits in the coefficient of a number in standard exponential form are significant.

❐ Do exponential calculations on the calculator to get the proper magnitude, then redo them mentally to get the proper number of significant digits.

A. How many significant digits and how many decimal place digits are present in each of the following? (a) 0.041 cm (b) 140.2 cm (c) 20.02 cm (d) 3.110×10^3 cm

B. Do the following calculations to the proper numbers of significant digits:
(a) 4.96 cm − 0.1919 cm (b) (4.96 cm)(0.1919 cm)
(c) 8.03×10^3 cm − 2.42×10^2 cm

2.5 Density

Density is defined as *mass per unit volume:*

$$\text{Density} = \frac{\text{mass}}{\text{volume}}$$

In symbols,

$$d = \frac{m}{V}$$

The dimensions (combination of units) of density involve a mass unit divided by a volume unit, such as grams per milliliter (g/mL) or grams per cubic centimeter (g/cm^3). Thus, to get the density of an object, we simply divide the mass of the object by its volume. Problems involving density usually involve finding one of the variables—d, m, or V—having been given the other two. Either the equation or the factor label method can be used to solve density problems. The equation is most often used when mass and volume are given. The factor label method is perhaps easier when density and one of the other two variables are given and the third variable is sought.

Densities of some common substances are given in Table 2.5. Note that scientists generally put the units at the heads of the columns when reporting data in a table. The only density to remember is the density of liquid water, about 1.00 g/mL = 1.00 g/cm^3.

Table 2.5 Densities of Some Common Substances

Substance	Density (g/mL)
Aluminum	2.702
Copper	8.92
Gold	19.3
Iron	7.86
Lead	11.3
Magnesium	1.74
Mercury	13.6
Platinum	21.45
Silver	10.5
Tin	5.75
Octane	0.7025
Salt (NaCl)	2.165
Sugar (sucrose)	1.56
Water (at 4°C)	1.000

EXAMPLE 2.49

Calculate the density of the wood in a certain desk if its mass is 41.6 kg and its volume is 51.3 L.

Solution

$$d = \frac{m}{V} = \frac{(41.6 \text{ kg})}{(51.3 \text{ L})} = 0.811 \text{ kg/L}$$

Practice Problem 2.49 Calculate the density of a rectangular metal bar that is 7.00 cm long, 4.00 cm wide, and 1.00 cm thick and has a mass of 352 g.

EXAMPLE 2.50

(a) Two objects have the same volume, but the first has a greater mass. Which is more dense?

(b) Two objects have the same mass, but the first is larger. Which is more dense?

Solution

(a) The first is more dense.

(b) The first is less dense because it has less mass per unit volume.

EXAMPLE 2.51

Calculate the mass of 41.0 mL of mercury (density = 13.6 g/mL).

Solution

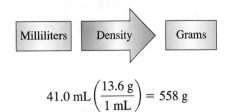

$$41.0 \text{ mL} \left(\frac{13.6 \text{ g}}{1 \text{ mL}} \right) = 558 \text{ g}$$

Practice Problem 2.51 Calculate the volume of 12.7 g of mercury (density = 13.6 g/mL).

EXAMPLE 2.52

Calculate the volume in liters of 1719 g of mercury. (*Hint:* see Table 2.5.)

Solution

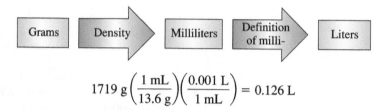

$$1719 \text{ g} \left(\frac{1 \text{ mL}}{13.6 \text{ g}} \right) \left(\frac{0.001 \text{ L}}{1 \text{ mL}} \right) = 0.126 \text{ L}$$

Practice Problem 2.52   Calculate the mass of 1.000 L of magnesium.

Substances expand when heated, and the resulting change in volume causes some change in density. Within reasonable temperature ranges, the density of a substance is relatively constant. For example, water varies from 0.99979 g/mL at 0°C to 1.0000 g/mL at 4°C to 0.95838 g/mL at 100°C. We will usually ignore such slight differences, especially since we will work most often with densities measured to only three significant digits.

Density is an intensive property, useful in identifying substances. For example, gold can be distinguished from iron pyrite by their greatly differing densities— 19.3 g/cm³ for gold and 5.0 g/cm³ for iron pyrite. Iron pyrite is known as "fool's gold" because of its striking visual resemblance to gold. Many prospectors in the western United States in gold-rush days were terribly disappointed when the test in the assay office showed that they had found iron pyrite rather than gold.

Relative densities determine whether an object will float in a given liquid in which it does not dissolve. An object will float if its density is less than the density of the liquid. For example, the density of liquid water is 1.00 g/mL and that of a particular kind of wood is 0.831 g/mL. The wood will float in water because it has a lower density.

EXAMPLE 2.53

A 7.00 cm × 3.00 cm × 2.50 cm rectangular metal bar has a mass of 593 g. Will the bar float in water or in mercury (density = 13.6 g/mL)?

Solution

The volume of the bar is $l \times w \times h = 52.5 \text{ cm}^3$, and its density is therefore

$$d = \frac{593 \text{ g}}{52.5 \text{ cm}^3} = 11.3 \text{ g/cm}^3$$

The bar will sink in water (density = 1.00 g/cm³), but it will float in mercury.

Practice Problem 2.53   A 5.03 cm × 3.11 cm × 1.22 cm rectangular solid has a mass of 51.5 g. Will the object float in mercury?

EXAMPLE 2.54

Identify the metal in the bar of Example 2.53.

Solution

The density is that of lead (see Table 2.5).

Practice Problem 2.54 Identify the substance in Practice Problem 2.53.

ChemSkill Builder 2.6

Snapshot Review

❏ Density is an important property, useful in identifying substances and other things, but it is used here mainly to tie together and review all the prior sections of this chapter.
❏ Any units of mass divided by any units of volume are acceptable for density.
❏ Density may be used as a factor, with either mass units or volume units in the numerator.

A. Calculate the volume of a 191 g object with density 5.75 g/mL.
B. Calculate the mass of a 191 mL object with density 5.75 g/mL.

2.6 Temperature Scales

In the United States, it is necessary for scientists to know three different temperature scales. The scale used in everyday American life is the **Fahrenheit scale,** on which the temperature of freezing water is defined as 32°F, and the temperature of water boiling under normal conditions is defined as 212°F. Scientists do not use the Fahrenheit scale (although American engineers sometimes do). Instead, they use the **Celsius scale,** the metric scale for temperature, which was formerly called the **centigrade scale.** On the Celsius scale, the temperature of freezing water is defined as 0°C, and the temperature of water boiling under normal conditions is defined as 100°C. The Celsius scale is used in most other countries of the world for everyday measurements as well as scientific ones. The **Kelvin scale** for measuring temperatures is important for work with gases (Chapter 12) and in other advanced work. On the Kelvin scale, the temperature of freezing water is 273 K, and the temperature of water boiling under normal conditions is 373 K. The degree sign (°) is not used with the Kelvin scale, and the units are called kelvins rather than degrees. The three scales are pictured in Figure 2.11.

To convert from degrees Fahrenheit (t_F) to degrees Celsius (t), or vice versa, we use the following equations:

$$t = \tfrac{5}{9}(t_F - 32°) \qquad \text{and} \qquad t_F = \tfrac{9}{5}t + 32°$$

The 32° is a definition and can be expanded to 32.0°, 32.00°, and so on. To convert from degrees Celsius to kelvins (T), we use the following equation:

$$T = t + 273$$

■ Key Terms   **65**

Figure 2.11 Comparison of
Temperature Scales

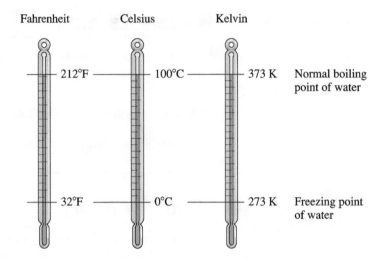

212°F	100°C	373 K	Normal boiling point of water
32°F	0°C	273 K	Freezing point of water

EXAMPLE 2.55

Convert 98.6°F (normal body temperature) to a Celsius temperature.

Solution

$$t = \tfrac{5}{9}(t_{\mathrm{F}} - 32.0°) = \tfrac{5}{9}(98.6° - 32.0°) = 37.0°C$$

 Snapshot Review

ChemSkill Builder 1.6

❑ The symbols for Celsius temperature and Kelvin temperature are lowercase t and capital T, respectively. Be careful to use the proper one.

A. What is the normal boiling point of water on the (a) Fahrenheit scale? (b) Celsius scale? (c) Kelvin scale?

B. Convert 30°C (a) to degrees Fahrenheit. (b) to kelvins.

Key Terms

Key terms are defined in the Glossary.

accuracy (2.4)	exponential notation (2.2)	precision (2.4)
base (2.2)	exponential part (2.2)	rounding (2.4)
Celsius scale (2.6)	factor label method (2.1)	scientific notation (2.2)
centigrade scale (2.6)	Fahrenheit scale (2.6)	SI (2.3)
coefficient (2.2)	gram (2.3)	significant digit (2.4)
conversion factor (2.1)	Kelvin scale (2.6)	significant figure (2.4)
cubic meter (2.3)	length (2.3)	standard (2.3)
density (2.5)	liter (2.3)	standard exponential form (2.2)
dimensional analysis (2.1)	meter (2.3)	unit (2.1)
exponent (2.2)	metric system (2.3)	volume (2.3)

Symbols/Abbreviations

c (centi-) (2.3)

d (density) (2.5)

g (gram) (2.3)

k (kilo-) (2.3)

h (hour) (2.1)

L (liter) (2.3)

m (mass) (2.3)

m (meter) (2.3)

m (milli-) (2.3)

min (minute) (2.1)

s (second) (2.1)

t (Celsius temperature) (2.6)

T (Kelvin temperature) (2.6)

t_F (Fahrenheit temperature) (2.6)

V (volume) (2.3)

Summary

Measurement is the key to quantitative physical science. The results of every measurement must include both a numeric value and a unit (or set of units). Be sure to use standard abbreviations for all units. The factor label method is used to convert a quantity from one set of units to another without changing its value. The original quantity is multiplied by a factor equal to 1. (The numerator and denominator of the factor are equal to each other in value but different in form.) To use the factor label method: (1) write down the quantity given, (2) multiply by a factor that will yield the desired units, (3) cancel the units, (4) multiply all numbers in the numerators and divide by the number(s) in the denominator(s). Sometimes, it is necessary to multiply by more than one factor. We may solve for the intermediate answers, but we do not have to. (Section 2.1)

Exponential notation enables easy reporting of extremely large and extremely small numbers. A number in scientific notation consists of a coefficient times 10 to an integral power, where the coefficient is equal to or greater than 1 but less than 10. Learn how to convert numbers from exponential notation to ordinary decimal values, and vice versa, and also how to use exponential numbers in calculations. Also learn to use effectively an electronic calculator with exponential capability (see Appendix 1). (Section 2.2)

The metric system and its newer counterpart, SI, use subunits and multiples of units that are equal to powers of 10, and they also use the same prefixes to mean certain fractions or multiples, no matter what primary unit is being modified. The meter is the primary unit of length; the gram is the primary unit of mass; and the liter (the cubic meter in SI) is the primary unit of volume. The prefixes centi- (0.01), milli- (0.001), and kilo- (1000) are used with any of these or with any other metric unit. Conversions between English and metric units are necessary for American engineers and may help us get familiar with the relative sizes of the metric units. To add, subtract, multiply, or divide measured quantities of the same type, first be sure that they all have the same units as far as possible. (Section 2.3)

The number of digits reported for a measurement or for the result of a calculation involving measurements is a means of showing how precisely the measurement(s) was (were) made. The last digit of reported measurements is usually an estimate based on tenths of the smallest scale division of the measuring instrument. Any digit from 1 through 9 in a properly reported result is significant. (The word *significant* as used here refers to the precision of the measurement and does not mean "important.") Zeros may or may not be significant; if they merely show the magnitude of the number, they are not significant.

When measurements are added or subtracted, the one that has significant digits least far to the right is the one that limits the number of significant digits in the answer. When measurements are multiplied or divided, the one with the fewest significant digits limits the number of significant digits in the answer. If too many digits are present in a calculated answer, the answer is rounded off: Some digits are dropped if they occur to the right of the decimal point or changed to nonsignificant zeros if they occur to the left of the decimal point. If too few digits are present, significant zeros are added. Note that, although a calculator gives the correct magnitude when used properly, we must understand the calculation processes to be able to determine the number of significant figures to report. All digits in the coefficients of numbers in scientific notation are significant. (Section 2.4)

Density, an intensive property, is defined as mass per unit volume. It can be calculated by dividing the mass of a sample by its volume. If a density is given, it may be used as a factor to solve for mass or volume. Density, may be used to help identify a substance. Samples of lower density float in fluids of higher density. (Section 2.5)

Scientists use two different temperature scales: Celsius and Kelvin. Their relationship to each other and to the more familiar Fahrenheit scale is shown in Figure 2.11. (Section 2.6)

Items for Special Attention

■ The metric units used to report volumes may involve liters or the cube of a length unit.

■ Adding a positive number to a negative exponent either makes the exponent positive or makes the exponent less negative (gives the exponent a smaller magnitude).

■ Do not key in 10 for the base of a number in scientific notation on your electronic calculator. The EXP or EE key means " × 10 to a power." See Appendix 1.

■ Significant digits and decimal place digits are two different things. Do not confuse them. For example, 4.53 has three significant digits and two decimal place digits.

■ The expressions that follow are simplified in the same way. That is, the algebraic quantities x and y and the units such

as meters and seconds (m and s) or miles and hours (h) are treated the same:

$$5y\left(\frac{60x}{y}\right) = 300x \qquad 5\text{ s}\left(\frac{60\text{ m}}{1\text{ s}}\right) = 300\text{ m}$$

$$5\text{ h}\left(\frac{60\text{ miles}}{1\text{ h}}\right) = 300\text{ miles}$$

■ When measurements expressed in exponential notation are added or subtracted, both the units and the exponents must be the same. When such measurements are multiplied or divided, units and exponents can be different.

Answers to Snapshot Reviews

2.1 A. (a) $22.75\text{ dollars}\left(\dfrac{4\text{ quarters}}{1\text{ dollar}}\right) = 91\text{ quarters}$

(b) $144\text{ quarters}\left(\dfrac{1\text{ dollar}}{4\text{ quarters}}\right) = 36.00\text{ dollars}$

2.2 A. (a) 1.234×10^3 (b) 2.000×10^2
(c) 2.00×10^{-2}

B. (a) 2.09×10^3 (b) 1.49×10^0
(c) -4.04×10^{-2}

2.3 A. (a) L   (b) m   (c) m^3 (d) g

B. (a) $1.234\text{ mm}\left(\dfrac{0.001\text{ m}}{1\text{ mm}}\right) = 1.234\text{ m}$

(b) $1234\text{ mL}\left(\dfrac{0.001\text{ L}}{1\text{ mL}}\right) = 1.234\text{ L}$

(c) $1234\text{ mg}\left(\dfrac{0.001\text{ g}}{1\text{ mg}}\right) = 1.234\text{ g}$

C. (a) $0.175\text{ m}^3\left(\dfrac{1000\text{ L}}{1\text{ m}^3}\right) = 175\text{ L}$

(b) $315\text{ cm}^3\left(\dfrac{1\text{ L}}{1000\text{ cm}^3}\right) = 0.315\text{ L}$

2.4 A. (a) Two significant digits, three decimal place digits
(b) Four significant digits, one decimal place digit
(c) Four significant digits, two decimal place digits
(d) Four significant digits, three decimal place digits

B. (a)   4.96   cm
$\underline{-0.1919\text{ cm}}$
     4.7681 cm → 4.77 cm^2
(b) $(4.96\text{ cm})(0.1919\text{ cm}) = 0.952\text{ cm}^2$
(Three significant digits)
(c) $8.03 \times 10^3\text{ cm} - 2.42 \times 10^2\text{ cm}$
$= 7.79 \times 10^3\text{ cm}$

2.5 A. $191\text{ g}\left(\dfrac{1\text{ mL}}{5.75\text{ g}}\right) = 33.2\text{ mL}$

B. $191\text{ mL}\left(\dfrac{5.75\text{ g}}{1\text{ mL}}\right) = 1100\text{ g} = 1.10\text{ kg}$

2.6 A. (a) 212°F   (b) 100°C   (c) 373 K

B. (a) $t_F = \frac{9}{5}(30°C) + 32° = 86°F$ (b) 303 K

Self-Tutorial Problems

2.1 Identify each of the following as a quantity or rate or ratio:

(a) Cost to fill a gas tank   (b) Amount of pay

(c) Number of hours worked   (d) Price of gasoline

(e) Minimum wage

2.2 (a) If we multiply a certain number by 1000 and then divide the result by 1000, what is the relationship of the final answer to the original number?

(b) If we multiply the coefficient of an exponential number by 1000 and divide the exponential part by 1000, what is the effect?

2.3 Find the value of this expression on an electronic calculator:

$$2 \times 10^0 + 0$$

2.4 Write each of the following numbers in exponential notation:

(a) 6 thousandths   (b) 4.2 million

(c) 195 billion   (d) 12.3 million

(e) 11 thousand   (f) 17 millionths

2.5 Use your electronic calculator to do the following calculation to check your calculator procedure:

$$\frac{12 \times 6}{4 \times 9}$$

2.6 Which of the following numbers have values less than zero? Which have magnitudes less than one? Which have values less than one?

(a) -1.8×10^{-3} (b) 7.5×10^{-2}

(c) 3.2×10^{6} (d) -2.3×10^{4}

2.7 What is the exponential equivalent of each of the following metric prefixes?

(a) kilo-   (b) centi-   (c) milli-

2.8 (a) Which is bigger, a cent or a dollar? Which would you need more of to buy a certain textbook?

(b) Which is bigger, a centimeter or a meter? Which does it take more of to measure the length of a certain textbook?

2.9 Which is bigger: 1 kg or 1 mg? Which would there be more of in a measurement of your own mass?

2.10 What is the difference between the masses 7 mg and 7 Mg?

2.11 Which of the following are units of volume?

L   Mg m^3 mm^3 g   m   kg   mg   mL

2.12 Which of the following animals is most likely to have a mass of 30 kg?

(a) Elephant   (b) Chicken

(c) Saint Bernard dog   (d) Fly

2.13 The author of this text is of average build. Fill in the metric units in the following description:

Height: 171 _____

Mass: 64 _____

Total volume of blood in his system: 4 _____

2.14 What factor is used to convert a measurement in grams to kilograms?

2.15 (a) How many square centimeters are in a square measuring 3.0 cm along each edge? (b) How many cubic centimeters are in a cube 3.0 cm on each edge?

2.16 Which of the following is the most probable distance between a dormitory room and the chemistry lecture room?

(a) 0.5 km   (b) 0.5 m

(c) 0.5 cm   (d) 0.5 mm

2.17 The population of New York City is 7 million people. A lottery advertises a $7 million jackpot. How many significant digits are probably in each number?

2.18 Refer to the more precise ruler in Figure 2.10. Count the number of smaller scale divisions in each 1 cm. How many would there be in 1 m (100 cm)? What unit represents the value of each small scale division?

2.19 Which metals in Table 2.5 will not float in mercury?

2.20 What is the difference in density, if any, among the following?

6.73 g in 1.00 mL

6.73 g divided by 1.00 mL

6.73 grams per milliliter

6.73 g/mL

6.73 g in exactly 1 mL

2.21 (a) How can we reduce the sweetness of a cup of coffee without taking out any sugar?

(b) How can a company raise the price of coffee at the supermarket without charging more for each can?

(c) What happens to the average speed for a trip if the time spent traveling remains unchanged but the distance is decreased?

(d) What happens to the density of an object if its volume is increased but its mass remains the same?

Problems

2.1 Factor Label Method

2.22 Calculate the number of minutes in 5.150 h.

2.23 Assume that donuts are $5.00 per dozen. Use the factor label method to answer each of the following:

(a) How much do 2.50 dozen cost?

(b) How many dozens can you buy with $32.50?

(c) How many donuts can you buy with $32.50?

2.24 Determine the cost of 540 pencils if the price is $1.15 per dozen.

2.25 Calculate the pay earned by a student who worked 18 h per week for 32 weeks at $9.00 per hour.

2.26 Calculate the pay received for 1.00 h of work by a junior executive who works 40 h per week and earns $48,250 per year for 50 weeks of work.

2.27 There is 60.0% oxygen by mass in a compound of sulfur and oxygen. Percent by mass is a ratio of the number of grams of a particular component to 100 g of the total sample. How many grams of sulfur are in a 14.6-g sample of the compound?

2.28 Calculate the number of hours in 8676 seconds.

2.29 Calculate the cost of a rug required to cover a living-room floor that is 15.3 ft wide and 18.3 ft long if the price is $29.00 yd^2.

2.2 Exponential Numbers

2.30 Which one(s) of the following is (are) in standard exponential notation?

(a) $2.5 \times 10^{2.5}$ (b) 0.123×10^4

(c) 1.23×10^{-4} (d) 62×10^{15}

(e) 7.1×10^0 (f) 8×10^{-23}

2.31 Convert each of the following numbers to standard exponential notation:

(a) 621   (b) 0.1033

(c) 100.001   (d) 0.011

2.32 Convert each of the following numbers to decimal format:

(a) 2.25×10^2 (b) 2.18×10^{-1}

(c) 4.56×10^{-2} (d) 6.31×10^0

2.33 Write each of the following numbers in scientific notation:

(a) 103.7

(b) 0.00200

(c) 602,000,000,000,000,000,000,000

(d) 0.00000000080

2.34 Express each of the following answers in scientific notation:

(a) $(4.0 \times 10^4)/(2.50 \times 10^4)$

(b) $(3.0 \times 10^2) + (3.72 \times 10^3)$

(c) $(2.0 \times 10^{-5}) - (2.0 \times 10^{-4})$

(d) $(6.0 \times 10^2)(3.06 \times 10^3)$

(e) $(7.0 \times 10^4)(3.5 \times 10^1)$

2.35 Subtract:

$$(7.0 \times 10^{-3}) - (-8.0 \times 10^{-2})$$

2.3 The Metric System

2.36 (a) How many milligrams are in 6.21 g?

(b) How many centimeters are in 6.21 m?

(c) How many kilograms are in 6.21 g?

2.37 How many milligrams are in 12.1 kg?

2.38 Convert

(a) 6.96 m to millimeters

(b) 6.96 L to milliliters

(c) 6.96 g to milligrams

(d) 6.96 watts to milliwatts

2.39 Convert:

(a) 21.3 m to centimeters

(b) 21.3 m to millimeters

(c) 21.3 m to kilometers

2.40 Calculate the number of

(a) millimeters in 6.03 m

(b) milliliters in 6.03 L

(c) milligrams in 6.03 g

2.41 Calculate the number of

(a) feet in 6.03 miles

(b) English tons (2000 lb per ton) in 6.03 lb

(c) fluid ounces in 6.03 gal

(d) Compare the difficulty of these calculations to those in the prior problem.

2.42 Express each of the following measurements as a decimal value:

(a) 7.00×10^{-3} L   (b) 7.0×10^{-3} L

(c) 7×10^{-3} L

2.43 Calculate the number of cubic centimeters in a rectangular box 0.0722 m by 3.39 cm by 7.013 mm. Be sure to use the proper units.

2.44 Calculate the length of each edge of a cube that has a volume of 2.57 cm^3.

2.45 The edge of a cube is 3.000×10^{-1} cm. What is the volume of the cube in cubic meters?

2.46 Which of the following is the smallest container that could hold 1 m^3 of liquid?

(a) Swimming pool   (b) Drinking glass

(c) Soda bottle   (d) Thimble

2.47 Convert

(a) 1.09×10^{-4} kg to milligrams

(b) 6.03×10^{-4} m^3 to milliliters, and express the answer in standard exponential notation

2.48 Calculate the number of liters in

(a) 0.0117 m^3 (b) 808 cm^3

(c) 290.2 mL   (d) 1.43×10^3 mm^3

2.49 How many liters are in 6.11×10^{-2} m^3?

2.50 How many cubic millimeters are in 0.117 mL?

2.51 What is the volume of a rectangular solid that is 0.0622 m wide, 7.15 cm long, and 0.0000560 km thick?

2.52 Calculate the number of liters in 7.05×10^{-2} m^3.

2.53 Convert each of the following numbers to centimeters, and express the answer in standard exponential notation:

(a) 6133 mm   (b) 1.733 m

(c) 20.2 km   (d) 6.191×10^4 mm

2.54 Change 3.50×10^4 cm to:

(a) meters   (b) millimeters   (c) kilometers

70

2.4 Significant Digits

2.55 Underline the significant digits in each of the following measurements. If any digit is uncertain, place a question mark below it.

(a) 67.00 km   (b) 0.0013 kg   (c) 690 m

(d) 209 L

2.56 Underline the significant digits in each of the following measurements. If a digit is uncertain, place a question mark below it.

(a) 5.0×10^2 cm   (b) 5.02×10^2 cm

(c) 7.00×10^2 cm   (d) 5.000×10^{-2} m

2.57 Convert each of the following values to ordinary (decimal) notation:

(a) 6.000×10^3 cm   (b) 6.00×10^3 cm

(c) 6.0×10^3 cm   (d) 6×10^3 cm

2.58 Express each of the following volumes in milliliters:

(a) 7.00×10^{-3} L   (b) 7.0×10^{-3} L

(c) 7×10^{-3} L

2.59 Express each of the following measurements in liters:

(a) 3.00×10^3 mL   (b) 3.0×10^3 mL

(c) 3×10^3 mL

2.60 Underline the significant digits in each of the following measurements. If a digit is uncertain, place a question mark below it.

(a) 4.000 mm   (b) 0.0040 cm

(c) 4000 m   (d) 40.00 km

2.61 Round off each of the following measurements to three significant digits:

(a) 0.0637425 cm

(b) 0.637425 cm

(c) 6.37425 cm

(d) 63.7425 cm

(e) 6374.25 cm

2.62 Round off each of the following measurements to three significant digits:

(a) 0.02316 cm

(b) 0.2316 cm

(c) 23.16 cm

(d) 2316 cm

2.63 Do the following calculations to the proper number of significant digits:

(a) 6.17 cm $\times$ 3.722 cm

(b) 3.09 cm $-$ 122.7 cm

(c) 7.07 g/1.81 mL

2.64 Express each of the following lengths in centimeters (to the proper number of significant digits):

(a) 4×10^{-3} m   (b) 4.0×10^{-3} m

(c) 4.00×10^{-3} m   (d) 4.000×10^{-3} m

2.65 Convert each of the following distances to meters, and express the results as ordinary numbers (not in exponential notation).

(a) 1.00×10^5 mm

(b) 1.00×10^5 cm

(c) 1.00×10^{-3} km

2.66 How many significant digits are present in each of the following measurements? How many decimal place digits?

(a) 127.900 kg   (b) 12.88 cm^3

(c) 0.3930 mL   (d) 2.002 m

2.67 Underline the significant digits in each of the following measurements. If a digit is uncertain, place a question mark under it.

(a) 1.630 cm   (b) 8.090 cm

(c) 0.022 cm   (d) 4000 cm

2.68 Underline the significant digits in each of the following measurements. If a digit is uncertain, place a question mark below it.

(a) 41.07 cm   (b) 6050 cm

(c) 400.0 cm   (d) 0.00120 m

(e) 220 mm

2.69 How many significant digits are present in each of the following measurements? How many decimal place digits?

(a) 0.020 kg   (b) 33.0 cm^3

(c) 403 mL   (d) 1.0 m

2.70 Report the length of the shaded bar, using each of the rulers shown:

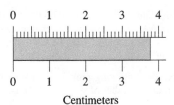

Centimeters

2.71 Add the following quantities, and report the answers to the proper number of significant digits:

(a) 219 g + 17.39 g

(b) 6.11 mL + 0.012 mL

(c) 1.102 mL + 0.013 mL

(d) 42.7 km + 61.4 km

2.72 Round off the following measurements to three significant digits:

(a) 110.9 mL   (b) 1109 mL

(c) Are the answers the same?

2.73 Express each of the following measurements as a decimal value. State how many significant digits are in each result. Could we tell just from looking at the results without knowing the original values?

(a) 9.00×10^3 mL   (b) 9.0×10^3 mL

(c) 9×10^3 mL

2.74 Divide the following quantities, and report the answers to the proper number of significant digits:

(a) $(3.08 \times 10^3 \text{ g})/(6.912 \text{ m}^3)$

(b) $(9.39 \text{ cm}^2)/(3.13 \times 10^{-1} \text{ cm})$

(c) $(6.93 \times 10^3 \text{ cm}^3)/(30.0 \text{ cm})$

(d) $(6.66 \times 10^4 \text{ g})/(2.22 \times 10^1 \text{ cm})^3$

2.75 Multiply the following quantities, and report the answers to the correct number of significant digits:

(a) $5.10 \text{ cm} \times (1.40 \times 10^2 \text{ cm})$

(b) $0.0115 \text{ cm} \times (9.2 \times 10^{-2} \text{ cm})$

(c) $(2.505 \times 10^{-2} \text{ cm}) \times 40.00 \text{ cm}$

(d) $(1.03 \times 10^3 \text{ cm})(6.88 \times 10^2 \text{ cm})$

2.76 Perform the following additions and explain the results:

(a) $(4.000 \times 10^{-3} \text{ mm}) + (2.0 \times 10^{-1} \text{ cm})$

(b) $(7.44 \times 10^2 \text{ g}) + 9.31 \text{ mg}$

2.77 In Problem 2.73, how can we report the proper number of significant digits in the results without using exponential notation?

2.78 Add the following quantities, and report the answers to the proper number of significant digits:

(a) $(3.000 \times 10^{-3} \text{ g}) + (7.0 \times 10^1 \text{ mg})$

(b) $(4.00 \times 10^{-1} \text{ g}) + (8.88 \times 10^{-4} \text{ kg})$

2.79 In Problem 2.58, can we tell how many significant digits are in each measurement as it is given in exponential form in the problem? Can we tell in decimal form in the answer?

2.80 Solve the following problem and state the answer with the proper number of significant digits:

$$\frac{101.1 \text{ g} - 98.31 \text{ g}}{38.92 \text{ mL} - 0.97 \text{ mL}}$$

2.81 Calculate the answer to each of the following problems to the proper number of significant digits:

(a) $(7.11 \times 10^3 \text{ cm})(23.7 \text{ cm})$

(b) $(9.02 \times 10^{-6} \text{ m})(4.9 \times 10^{-3} \text{ mm})$

(c) $(6.13 \text{ kg})/(6.8 \times 10^3 \text{ mL})$

(d) $(1.627 \text{ g})/(0.1122 \text{ L})$

(e) $(2.004 \times 10^4 \text{ mm})(6.97 \times 10^4 \text{ cm})$

(f) $(22.3 \text{ g}) + (1.0 \times 10^{-4} \text{ g})$

2.82 Calculate the answer to each of the following problems to the proper number of significant digits:

(a) $(4.66 \times 10^2 \text{ cm}^2)/(23.3 \text{ cm})$

(b) $(3.18 \times 10^{-5} \text{ cm}^3)/(6.929 \times 10^{-3} \text{ cm})$

(c) $(215 \text{ g})/(3.5 \times 10^2 \text{ mL})$

(d) $(19.55 \text{ g})/(21.21 \text{ mL})$

(e) $(6.172 \times 10^5 \text{ cm}^2)(7.17 \times 10^2 \text{ cm})$

(f) $(6.33 \text{ g}) + (2.3 \times 10^{-2} \text{ g})$

2.83 Do the following calculations to the proper number of significant digits:

(a) $(8.14 \times 10^3 \text{ cm})^3$

(b) $3.38 \times 10^{-3} \text{ g} - 1.902 \times 10^{-1} \text{ g}$

(c) $1.173 \times 10^6 \text{ cm} - 9.09 \times 10^4 \text{ cm}$

2.84 Add the following quantities, and report the answers to the correct number of significant digits:

(a) $1.72 \text{ kg} + (3.44 \times 10^2 \text{ g})$

(b) $0.0115 \text{ kg} + (6.96 \times 10^{-1} \text{ g})$

(c) $9.42 \text{ kg} + (3.72 \times 10^5 \text{ g})$

(d) $(9.00 \times 10^4 \text{ cm}^2) + (1.14 \times 10^4 \text{ cm})^2$

2.5 Density

2.85 What quantity is obtained in each of the following cases?

(a) Density is multiplied by volume.

(b) Mass is divided by density.

(c) Mass is divided by volume.

2.86 Calculate the number of milliliters of lead (density = 11.3 g/mL) having a mass of 4.145 kg.

2.87 Calculate the mass of water that occupies 9.10 L.

2.88 Calculate the density of an object that has a volume of 7.05 L and a mass of 52.6 kg.

2.89 (a) Calculate the volume of a rectangular box 42.6 cm by 4.41 cm by 1.932 cm.

(b) Calculate the number of kilograms of mercury (density = 13.6 g/mL) that can fit in that box.

2.90 Using the data of Table 2.5, explain why magnesium is preferable to steel (mostly iron) for building airplanes. What other metal might be useful for this purpose?

2.91 Using the densities in Table 2.5, identify the metal in a 30.38 cm³ solid of mass 319 g.

2.92 Calculate the number of milliliters of mercury (density = 13.6 g/mL) having a mass of 1.213 kg.

2.93 Does lead float in mercury? (*Hint:* See Table 2.5 if necessary.)

2.94 Explain why gasoline floats on water. Is water good for putting out gasoline fires?

2.95 Calculate the density of a rectangular 42.3-g piece of wood 12.2 cm long, 3.05 cm wide, and 1.43 cm thick.

2.96 Calculate the density of a rectangular solid of mass 716.0 g and dimensions:

(a) 20.21 cm × 3.163 cm × 2.321 cm

(b) 0.2021 m × 31.63 mm × 23.21 mm

2.97 Calculate the mass of mercury (density = 13.6 g/mL) that fills a rectangular box 23.0 cm by 3.06 cm by 1.551 cm.

2.98 Calculate the volume in cubic centimeters of an object with a density of 4.15 g/mL and a mass of 673 g.

2.99 Express the density 11.7 kg/L in grams per cubic centimeter.

2.100 Convert the density 2.05×10^3 kg/m^3 to grams per cubic centimeter.

2.101 Calculate the number of kilograms of mercury (density = 13.6 g/mL) occupying 747 mL.

2.102 An object has a density of 3.55 g/mL. Convert this density to kilograms per cubic meter.

2.103 Calculate the density in grams per milliliter of an object that has a volume of 7.81 cm^3 and a mass of 44.9 g.

2.6 Temperature Scales

2.104 Calculate the temperature in degrees Celsius of each of the following:

(a) 212°F   (b) 32.0°F   (c) 60°F   (d) 98.6°F

(e) 0°F   (f) −40.0°F   (g) 35.0°F

2.105 Calculate the temperature in degrees Fahrenheit of each of the following:

(a) 0°C   (b) 100°C   (c) 27.0°C   (d) 50.0°C

(e) −15°C   (f) 75°C   (g) −273°C

2.106 Calculate the temperature in kelvins of each of the following:

(a) 25°C   (b) 19.2°C   (c) −273°C

(d) 42°C   (e) 100°C

2.107 Calculate the temperature in degrees Celsius of each of the following:

(a) 295 K   (b) 373 K   (c) 273 K   (d) 0 K

General Problems

2.108 Calculate the answer to each of the following expressions to the correct number of significant digits:

(a) (6.33 cm + 7.2 cm) × 5.00 cm

(b) 1.37 cm × (9.05 cm − 4.782 cm)

(c) (6.11 cm × 1.4 cm) + 3.09 cm^2

(d) $(3.89 \times 10^3$ cm) − 4.46 cm

(e) 3.34 cm × $(6.12 \times 10^3$ cm)

(f) 2.10×10^{-3} cm + 6.90×10^{-2} cm

2.109 Calculate the answer to each of the following expressions to the correct number of significant digits:

(a) 6.33 cm × 7.2 cm − 5.00 cm^2

(b) 137 cm^2 − 9.05 cm × 4.782 cm

(c) 6.11 cm^2 + 1.4 cm × 3.09 cm

(d) $(3.89 \times 10^3$ cm)^2 − 4.46×10^5 cm^2

(e) 3.34 cm × $(6.12 \times 10^2$ cm)^2

(f) $(2.10 \times 10^{-3}$ cm) × $(6.90 \times 10^{-2}$ cm)

2.110 Convert

(a) 4.82 km to millimeters

(b) 4.82 L to cubic meters

(c) 4.82 mg to kilograms

2.111 Convert

(a) 6.14 cm to millimeters

(b) 6.14 m^3 to milliliters

(c) 6.14 cm^3 to milliliters

2.112 Calculate the number of cubic millimeters in 1.00 L.

2.113 How many cubic millimeters are there in 5.00 mL?

2.114 Convert

(a) 7.56×10^4 mm to kilometers

(b) 2.58×10^{-2} m^3 to liters

(c) 7.18×10^{-3} L to milliliters

2.115 Calculate the sum of 6.90×10^3 cm and 7.10×10^{-3} km.

2.116 Calculate the sum of 6.90×10^3 cm and 7.10×10^{-3} cm. Explain your result.

2.117 Calculate the price of a 3.00-kg bar of gold if the price of gold is $600 per troy ounce.

2.118 Calculate the cost of a bar of gold 110.0 cm by 10.0 cm by 10.0 cm if the price of gold is $600 per troy ounce.

2.119 Calculate the length of each edge of a 7.440-kg cube of gold.

2.120 Calculate the density of a cube with each edge 3.93 cm and mass 171 g.

2.121 Calculate the density of a cube with each edge 0.0393 m and mass 0.171 kg.

2.122 Compare the sizes, masses, and densities of the cubes in Problems 2.120 and 2.121.

2.123 Calculate the number of particles of volume 2.0×10^{-22} cm^3 that can fit into a cubic box of edge length 1.00 m.

2.124 Calculate the density in grams per milliliter of a cubic unit cell (see Example 2.34) of edge 6.63×10^{-8} cm and mass 5.09×10^{-25} kg.

2.125 Calculate the mass of one unit cell (see Example 2.34) of a substance with density 2.50 g/mL if its cubic unit cell has an edge 9.10×10^{-10} m.

2.126 A unit cell of a substance has a mass of 1.98×10^{-22} g. One particle of the substance has a mass of 4.94×10^{-23} g. How many particles are in each unit cell?

2.127 Calculate the number of cubic centimeters in a rectangular box

$$1.21 \times 10^{-1} \text{ m by } 12.2 \text{ cm by } 6.01 \times 10^2 \text{ mm}$$

2.128 Calculate the density in grams per milliliter of an object with a volume of 0.6912 L and a mass of 460.7 g.

2.129 How many 3.44×10^{-28} m^3 particles will fit into a 4.00-mL vessel?

2.130 Explain how it is possible to calculate an answer having five significant digits using two measurements having two significant digits each and two having four significant digits each.

2.131 A certain atom is spherical with radius 2.2×10^{-10} m, and its mass is 7.3×10^{-23} g. Calculate its density.

2.132 Perform the following calculations, and report the results to the proper number of significant digits:

(a) (6.53 cm)(7.113 cm)(1.9 cm)

(b) (7.19 kg)/[(6.12 × 10^2 cm)(25.7 cm)(3.3 cm)]

(c) (6.9021 g − 0.016 g)/(5.1274 cm^3)

2.133 Using the densities in Table 2.5, identify the metal in a cube with 3.00-cm edges and a mass of 579 g.

2.134 A certain road map of Maine shows part of Canada. The distances in Canada are shown in kilometers, and the legend states: "To convert kilometers to miles, multiply by 0.62." What is actually being converted?

2.135 Calculate the results of the following calculations to the proper number of significant digits:

(a) 1.36×10^{24} g − 6.17×10^{23} g

(b) $\dfrac{1.36 \times 10^{24} \text{ g} - 6.17 \times 10^{23} \text{ g}}{4.05 \times 10^9 \text{ cm} \times 4.11 \times 10^8 \text{ cm}^2}$

2.136 Calculate the number of

(a) Millimeters in 1.21×10^{-3} m

(b) Milliliters in 5.09×10^{-6} m^3

(c) Milligrams in 3.12×10^{-3} kg

2.137 Calculate the results of the following calculations to the proper number of significant digits:

(a) $(9.99 \times 10^7 \text{ mg}) + (3.36 \times 10^3 \text{ g})$

(b) $(2.49 \times 10^{-3} \text{ kg})/(7.31 \times 10^{-1} \text{ cm})^3$

(c) $(50.334 \text{ g} - 49.01 \text{ g})/(39.11 \text{ cm}^3)$

2.138 A certain brand of vitamin pill contains 346.0 μg of the vitamin per pill; another brand has 0.3460 mg of the vitamin per pill. Which is the better buy, all other factors being equal?

2.139 A nurse who is directed to give a patient a pill that has 0.150 cg of active ingredients has no pills with centigrams as units. What pill labeled in milligrams should the nurse administer?

2.140 Under a certain set of conditions, the density of water is 1.00 g/mL and that of oxygen gas is 1.30 g/L. Which will float on the other?

2.141 Calculate the number of liters in

(a) 62.1 mL   (b) 0.0293 m^3

(c) 703 cm^3 (d) 2.28×10^5 mm^3

2.142 Calculate the sum of 1.71×10^8 cm + 7.09×10^6 mm.

2.143 Calculate the result of the following calculation:

$$\frac{2.103 \times 10^{-22} \text{ g} - 6.18 \times 10^{-23} \text{ g}}{2.11 \times 10^{-9} \text{ cm} \times 8.10 \times 10^{-12} \text{ cm}^2}$$

2.144 Convert the density of air in a portion of the upper atmosphere, 2.78×10^{-4} kg/m^3, to grams per milliliter.

2.145 Calculate the sum of 2.00 m and 0.200 mm. Attempt to draw a picture of this sum to the proper scale. Explain the effect in terms of significant digits.

2.146 Calculate the density of a 25.0% by mass sodium chloride solution in water if 253 g of sodium chloride is used to make 850 mL of the solution.

2.147 Explain why a football referee, after two successive defensive offside penalties on a first down, rules *without a measurement* that a new first down has been achieved, but does not do so after a first-down running play for no gain followed by two offside penalties.

2.148 The density of a solution 25.0% by mass sodium chloride (table salt) in water is 1.19 g/mL. Calculate the mass of sodium chloride in 842 mL of the solution.

2.149 Calculate the approximate height in meters of the man in the cubic meter box (Figure 2.7). Use a ratio of the height of the man to the height of the box in the figure, which is equal to the ratio of the heights in real life.

(a) Use a metric ruler to measure the figure.

(b) Use an inch ruler.

(c) State another reason why the metric system is easier to use than the English system of measurement.

2.150 Repeat Problem 2.149 but estimate the man's width at his waist instead of his height.

2.151 Calculate the value of "72.90 ks" in (a) minutes and (b) hours.

2.152 If a patient has a blood count of 835 white corpuscles per cubic millimeter, what is the number of white corpuscles per milliliter?

2.153 (a) Draw a figure showing the addition of the lengths of two line segments, 20.0 cm and 0.20 cm.

(b) Can you do the same with 20.0 cm and 0.0020 cm? Explain.

2.154 How many grains of sand, each with a volume of 1.0 mm^3, could be held in a volume approximately equal to that of the Earth? (The Earth's radius is 6.4 $\times$ 10^3 km. For a sphere, $V = \frac{4}{3} \pi r^3$)

2.155 (a) A bank usually charges 16.0% interest for a certain type of loan. If the bank advertises a special 15.0% discount for that type of loan, what is the actual rate?

(b) The percentage of a certain ore in the rock from a mine is 19%. The percentage of iron in the ore is 69%. What is the percentage of iron in the rock?

2.156 Calculate the length in meters of each side of a cube that has a volume of 6.92 $\times$ 10^7 cm^3.

2.157 Calculate the radius of a sphere of volume 9.02 cm^3.

2.158 Equal volumes of water (density 1.00 g/mL) and ethyl alcohol (density 0.789 g/mL) are combined. If the total volume is 190% of the volume of each component, what is the density of the solution?

2.159 Calculate the length of each side of a cube that has a volume of 74.3 cm^3. (Be sure to use the proper units and the proper number of significant digits.)

2.160 Calculate the temperature in kelvins of each of the following:

(a) 98.6°F   (b) −40°F

(c) 37°F   (d) 212°F

2.161 Calculate the mass of gold in a bracelet that contains 66.7% gold by mass and that has a volume of 17.9 mL and a density of 14.9 g/mL.

2.162 How many significant digits are in the value 0°F? (The zero is not left of all other digits, right of all other digits, or between all other digits.) How many are there in its Celsius equivalent?

2.163 Calculate the depth of water in centimeters in a cubic box (not full) with 40.0-cm edges if the mass of the contents is 25.6 kg.

2.164 Calculate the length of a rectangular solid if its density is 6.12 g/cm^3, its mass is 512 g, its width is 9.12 cm, and its thickness is 0.250 cm.

2.165 A vitamin pill maker produces pills with a mass of 1.00 g each. If each of the following indicates the mass of active ingredient, what percentage of the pill is active in each case?

(a) 3.00 mg   (b) 0.300 mg   (c) 300 mg

2.166 What is the volume of a cube whose edge measures:

(a) 4.99 cm   (b) 6.13 $\times$ 10^{-8} cm

2.167 Using the densities in Table 2.5, identify the substance in a sphere with a 3.00-cm radius and a mass of 177 g. ($V = \frac{4}{3} \pi r^3$)

2.168 Calculate the average density of the Earth, assuming it to be spherical with radius 6400 km and mass 6.1 $\times$ 10^{24} kg. ($V = \frac{4}{3} \pi r^3$)

2.169 Calculate the temperature in degrees Fahrenheit of each of the following:

(a) 250 K   (b) 0 K   (c) 273 K   (d) 329 K

2.170 Which of the following amounts of money would more likely be rounded by a merchant to the nearest $10?

(a) $1303.22 or   (b) $13.22

2.171 (a) Calculate the price of an average grain of a certain type of rice if a pound of this rice costs $2.12 and there are 4.1 $\times$ 10^4 grains of rice per pound.

(b) How many significant digits should be reported in this calculation?

2.172 Calculate the mass of a sphere of radius 2.75 cm and density 0.382 g/cm^3. ($V = \frac{4}{3} \pi r^3$)

2.173 Calculate the density of a sphere of radius 5.12 cm and mass 441 g. ($V = \frac{4}{3} \pi r^3$)

2.174 Calculate the density in grams per cubic centimeter of an average chlorine atom, which has a radius of 1.05 $\times$ 10^{-10} m and a mass of 5.89 $\times$ 10^{-23} g. ($V = \frac{4}{3} \pi r^3$)

2.175 Equal volumes of water (density 1.00 g/mL) and ethyl alcohol (density 0.789 g/mL) are combined. If the density of the resulting solution is 0.942 g/mL, what is the volume of the solution compared to that of the water?

2.176 Calculate the volume of a (spherical) atom of chlorine, which has a radius of 1.05 $\times$ 10^{-10} m. ($V = \frac{4}{3} \pi r^3$)

2.177 Calculate the temperature in Celsius of each of the following: (a) 19°F, (b) 19.0°F, and (c) 0.0°F. How many significant digits should be reported for each?

2.178 Calculate the reduction in volume after 99.00 g of sulfuric acid is added to 1.000 g of water. The density of water is 1.000 g/mL, that of sulfuric acid is 1.8305 g/mL, and that of 99.00% sulfuric acid in water is 1.8342 g/mL.

2.179 Calculate the density of a solution prepared with 54.08 mL of sulfuric acid and 1.00 mL of water. The density of water is 1.00 g/mL and that of sulfuric acid is 1.8305 g/mL. The volume of the solution is 54.52 mL.

2.180 Calculate the reduction in volume after 30.00 g of sulfuric acid is added to 70.00 g of water. Assume that the density of water is 1.000 g/mL, that of sulfuric acid is 1.8305 g/mL, and that of 30.00% by mass sulfuric acid in water is 1.2185 g/mL.

2.181 Calculate the density of a solution prepared with 16.39 mL of sulfuric acid and 70.00 mL of water. Assume that the density of water is 1.000 g/mL and that of sulfuric acid is 1.8305 g/mL. The volume of the solution is 82.068 mL.

2.182 In light of the answers to the Problems 2.178–2.181, state why the method of determining volume of irregularly shaped objects in Figure 2.2 would not work for sugar crystals.

2.183 Calculate the number of microliters in 2.55×10^{-2} m^3.

3

Atoms and Atomic Masses

- 3.1 Laws of Chemical Combination
- 3.2 Dalton's Atomic Theory
- 3.3 Subatomic Particles
- 3.4 Atomic Mass
- 3.5 Development of the Periodic Table

White light broken into its spectrum of colors by a prism

Review Clues

Section 3.1	Section 1.1, Chapter 2
Section 3.2	Section 1.6
Section 3.3	Sections 1.4, 1.5
Section 3.5	Section 1.5

Objectives

3.1 To calculate some of the quantities involved in chemical combinations of elements, using the classical laws known at Dalton's time

3.2 To interpret the classical laws of chemical combination using Dalton's atomic theory

3.3 To use the properties of subatomic particles—protons, electrons, and neutrons—to determine atomic structure

3.4 To calculate the atomic mass of any element—the average mass of its atoms on a relative scale—two ways: (1) from the ratios of masses of equal numbers of atoms, as was done historically, and (2) from masses and abundances of its naturally occurring mixture of isotopes, the more modern method

3.5 To repeat the thought processes of Mendeleyev and Meyer in the development of the periodic table

The theory of the atom has had a long history. The ancient Greeks postulated that matter exists in the form of atoms, but they did not base their theory on experiments, nor did they use it to develop additional ideas about atoms. In 1803, John Dalton proposed the first modern theory of the atom, which was based on the experimentally determined laws of conservation of mass, definite proportions, and multiple proportions. Dalton suggested for the first time that atoms of different elements are different from each other. His theory generated a great deal of research activity, which brought forth additional laws and knowledge about atoms, and he is recognized as the father of the atomic theory.

Section 3.1 takes up the experimental laws on which Dalton based his atomic theory, and Section 3.2 discusses that theory itself. Some modern extensions of the theory, including subatomic particles and isotopes, are presented in Section 3.3. The concept of the masses of atoms of the individual elements is presented in Section 3.4, and the development of the periodic table is traced in Section 3.5. A much more sophisticated theory of the atom will be presented in Chapter 4.

3.1   Laws of Chemical Combination

Antoine Lavoisier (1743–1794), called the father of modern chemistry, discovered the law of conservation of mass (Section 1.6) by showing that during a chemical reaction, mass is neither gained nor lost. His quantitative work (work involving measurements) enabled him to conclude that the mass of the products generated during a chemical reaction is the same as the mass of the reactants used up (Figure 3.1). This was not an easy conclusion because "anyone could see that the ashes left after a large log burned did not weigh as much as the log itself." However, when the oxygen from the air (also a reactant in the burning of wood) and the carbon dioxide, water vapor, and other products formed (in addition to the ash) were considered, the total mass of the reactants and the total mass of the products were found to be equal. Lavoisier's work led other chemists to measure their reactants and products to confirm his conclusions and to see if they could make other quantitative observations.

The **law of definite proportions,** also known as the **law of constant composition,** emerged after careful work by many investigators. This law states that any given compound is composed of definite proportions by mass of its elements. For example, every sample of sucrose (table sugar) contains 6.55 times the mass of carbon as hydrogen and 8.00 times the mass of oxygen as hydrogen. This law was difficult to prove because many samples of compounds contain impurities of other compounds that have the same elements. For example, dinitrogen monoxide (N_2O), known as laughing gas, and nitrogen monoxide (NO), an air pollutant, are two different compounds, but each is composed of only nitrogen and oxygen. The two compounds can form a homogeneous mixture in any proportions. Analysis of an impure sample of either gas could lead to a percentage of nitrogen anywhere between that in pure dinitrogen monoxide and that in pure nitrogen monoxide. A pure sample of dinitrogen monoxide or nitrogen monoxide, not an arbitrary mixture of the two, is necessary to insure a definite percent composition. Once chemists isolated and worked on pure compounds, it was apparent that the law of definite proportions was valid (Section 1.6).

> The **proportion** of an element in a compound is the ratio of the mass of the element to the total mass of the compound. The **percent** of the element in the compound is just the proportion of the element times 100%.

Figure 3.1 Illustration of the Law of Conservation of Mass

In an eighteenth-century experiment, phosphorus in air is ignited by sunlight focused with a magnifying glass. The phosphorus reacts with the oxygen present in the air to produce an oxide of phosphorus, which dissolves in the water. The mass of the system after the reaction is the same as it was before, but the volume of gas trapped in the bell jar has obviously been reduced.

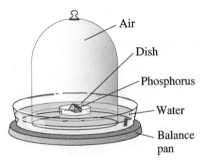

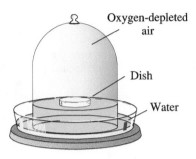

Before reaction: phosphorus in air trapped in bell jar

After reaction: an oxide of phosphorus dissolved in water

EXAMPLE 3.1

A 4.33-g sample of dinitrogen monoxide is composed of 63.65% nitrogen and 36.35% oxygen by mass. What is the percent composition of a 14.9-g sample of dinitrogen monoxide?

Solution

The 14.9-g sample is 63.65% nitrogen and 36.35% oxygen also. *All* samples of dinitrogen monoxide have the same percent composition, as required by the law of definite proportions.

Practice Problem 3.1 Nitrogen monoxide has a percent composition of 46.68% nitrogen and 53.32% oxygen. What possible percentages of nitrogen could be in a *mixture* of dinitrogen monoxide and nitrogen monoxide?

EXAMPLE 3.2

Calculate the mass of nitrogen in a 4.75-g sample of nitrogen monoxide, using the percentages in Practice Problem 3.1.

Solution

$$4.75 \text{ g NO} \left(\frac{46.68 \text{ g N}}{100.0 \text{ g NO}} \right) = 2.22 \text{ g N}$$

From the percent composition

Total mass → Percentage → Mass of component

Practice Problem 3.2 Calculate the mass of nitrogen monoxide that contains 100.0 g of nitrogen.

The **law of multiple proportions** states that for two (or more) compounds composed of the same elements, for a given mass of one of the elements, the ratio of masses of any other element in the compounds is a small, whole-number

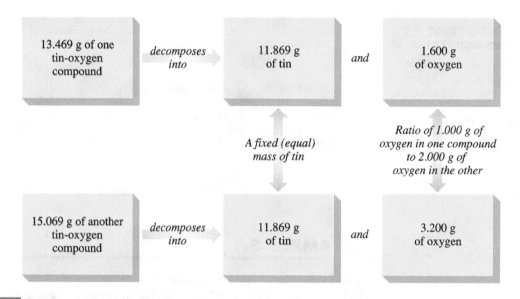

Figure 3.2   Example Illustrating the Law of Multiple Proportions

ratio (Figure 3.2). For example, hydrogen peroxide contains 0.06300 g of hydrogen for each gram of oxygen present. Water contains 0.1260 g of hydrogen for each gram of oxygen present. For the fixed mass of oxygen (1 g in each case), the ratio of masses of hydrogen is (0.1260 g)/(0.06300 g) = 2/1.

Sometimes, the ratio does not appear to be integral at first, but it can be converted to an integral ratio while keeping the value the same by multiplying both numerator and denominator by the same small integer. For example, a compound of chromium and oxygen contains 3.2499 g of chromium per gram of oxygen, while a second compound of these elements contains 2.1666 g of chromium per gram of oxygen. Per gram of oxygen, the ratio of masses of chromium is (3.2499 g)/(2.1666 g) = 1.5000/1. We can convert that ratio to an integral ratio by multiplying both numerator and denominator by 2:

$$\frac{1.5000 \times 2}{1 \quad \times 2} = \frac{3}{2}$$

Converting ratios to integral ratios is discussed further in Appendix 1.

EXAMPLE 3.3

The percent compositions of nitrogen dioxide and dinitrogen trioxide are as follows:

Nitrogen dioxide	*Dinitrogen trioxide*
30.45% nitrogen	36.85% nitrogen
69.55% oxygen	63.15% oxygen

Show that these data follow the law of multiple proportions.

Solution

Per gram of nitrogen, the following mass of oxygen is present in each of the two compounds:

In nitrogen dioxide

$$\frac{69.55 \text{ g O}}{30.45 \text{ g N}} = \frac{2.284 \text{ g O}}{1 \text{ g N}}$$

In dinitrogen trioxide

$$\frac{63.15 \text{ g O}}{36.85 \text{ g N}} = \frac{1.714 \text{ g O}}{1 \text{ g N}}$$

The ratio of grams of oxygen in nitrogen dioxide (per gram of nitrogen) to grams of oxygen in dinitrogen trioxide (per gram of nitrogen) is

$$\frac{2.284 \text{ g O}}{1.714 \text{ g O}} = \frac{1.333}{1.000} = \frac{3.999}{3.000} = \frac{4}{3}$$

This ratio is, within limits of experimental error, equal to a small, whole-number ratio.

Note that it is *not* the ratio of mass of nitrogen to mass of oxygen that must be an integral ratio, according to the law of multiple proportions, but the ratio of the mass of oxygen in one compound to the mass of oxygen in the other compound (for the same mass of nitrogen in the two compounds).

Practice Problem 3.3 The percent compositions of two oxides of iron are 77.73% Fe and 22.27% O for one oxide and 69.94% Fe and 30.06% O for the other. Show that these compounds obey the law of multiple proportions.

How did the chemists of 1800 explain *why* compounds obeyed the law of definite proportions and the law of multiple proportions? They didn't. A theory to explain these and many other phenomena was just about to be proposed.

 Snapshot Review

❑ The empirical laws governing the masses of reactants and products of chemical reactions formed the basis for the theoretical development of chemistry.

A. What is the total mass of the mercury and oxygen produced from the decomposition of 25.0 g of HgO?

B. Barium and chlorine combine in a ratio of 137.3 g of barium to 70.90 g of chlorine. What is the percent chlorine in (a) a 5.00-g sample of the compound? (b) a 10.0-g sample of the compound?

C. One compound of iron and chlorine contains 1.269 g of chlorine for each gram of iron. A second compound of these elements contains 1.907 g of chlorine for each gram of iron. Calculate the mass of iron per gram of chlorine in each compound, and show that the masses obey the law of multiple proportions.

3.2   Dalton's Atomic Theory

Figure 3.3   John Dalton

In 1803, John Dalton (1766–1844) (Figure 3.3) proposed his atomic theory, including the following **postulates,** to explain the laws of chemical combination discussed in Section 3.1:

1. Matter is made up of very tiny, indivisible particles called **atoms.**

2. The atoms of each element all have the same mass, but the mass of the atoms of one element is different from the mass of the atoms of every other element.

3. Atoms combine to form **molecules.** When they do so, they combine in small, whole-number ratios.

4. Atoms of some pairs of elements can combine with each other in different small, whole-number ratios to form different compounds.

5. If atoms of two elements can combine to form more than one compound, the most stable compound has the atoms in a 1 : 1 ratio. (This postulate was quickly shown to be incorrect.)

The first three postulates have had to be amended, and the fifth was quickly abandoned altogether. But the postulates explained the laws of chemical combination known at the time, and they caused great activity among chemists, which led to more generalizations and further advances in chemistry.

The postulates of **Dalton's atomic theory** explained the laws of chemical combination very readily.

1. The law of conservation of mass is explained as follows: Because atoms merely exchange "partners" during a chemical reaction and are not created or destroyed, their mass is also neither created nor destroyed. Thus, mass is conserved during a chemical reaction.

2. The law of definite proportions is explained as follows: Because *atoms* react in definite integral ratios (postulate 3), and atoms of each element have a definite *mass* (postulate 2), the *mass* ratio of one element to the other(s) must also be definite.

3. The law of multiple proportions is explained as follows: Because atoms combine in different ratios of small whole numbers (postulate 4), for a given number of atoms of one element, the number of atoms of the other element is in a small, whole-number ratio. A given number of atoms of the first element implies a given mass of that element, and a small, whole-number ratio for the atoms of the second element (each of the same mass) implies a small, whole-number ratio of masses of the second element (Figure 3.4). For example, consider water (H_2O) and hydrogen peroxide (H_2O_2), two compounds of hydrogen and oxygen. For a given number of hydrogen atoms (2), the numbers of oxygen atoms in the two compounds are 1 and 2. Stated another way, for a given mass of hydrogen (2.0160 g), the ratio of masses of oxygen in the two compounds is 15.9994 g to 31.9988 g, a ratio of 1 to 2—a small, whole-number ratio.

We will discuss the ways in which the first three of Dalton's postulates have had to be amended after we learn more about the atom.

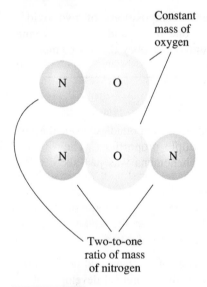

Figure 3.4   Dalton's Explanation of the Law of Multiple Proportions

Because the atoms of each element have a given mass, the fact that the atomic ratio is two atoms of nitrogen in one compound to one atom of nitrogen in the other (for one atom of oxygen in each) means that there is a 2 : 1 ratio of masses of nitrogen in the two compounds (for a given mass of oxygen).

Snapshot Review

❏ Dalton's theory explained why the classical laws of chemical combination worked and provided the theoretical background for the entire future development of chemistry.

A. If elements A and B react in a 1-to-2 atom ratio, yielding a compound with 4.80 g of B per gram of A, what is the mass ratio in a compound with a ratio of two atoms of A to three atoms of B?

3.3 Subatomic Particles

Since Dalton proposed his atomic theory, many types of experiments have been performed and many discoveries made that have led to the inescapable conclusion that the atom is *not* indivisible. Experiments with electricity in the 1850s showed that chemical reactions can be caused by the passage of electricity (a process called electrolysis) and that electricity can be generated by chemical reactions (as in batteries). (See Chapter 17.) The discovery of radioactivity, in which atoms of an element are changed into atoms of other elements, was another source of evidence (see Chapter 21). The fact that the placement of three pairs of elements in the periodic table are not in order of atomic mass (Sections 3.4 and 3.5) throws doubt on Dalton's theory. The interaction of light with matter gives further evidence that the atom is not indivisible. Absorption of specific wavelengths of light, meaning specific energies of light, led to the conclusion that atoms have certain energy levels in them. (See the following enrichment section.) Many other discoveries have been made that are beyond the scope of this text. If atoms are not indivisible, then what are the particles that constitute them?

The atom is composed of many types of **subatomic particles,** but only three types will be important in this course. **Protons** and **neutrons** exist in the atom's **nucleus,** and **electrons** exist outside the nucleus. The nucleus (plural, *nuclei*) is incredibly small, with a radius about one ten-thousandth of the radius of the atom itself. (If the atom were the size of a car, the nucleus would be about the size of the period at the end of this sentence.) The nucleus does not change during any ordinary chemical reaction. (Nuclear reactions are described in Chapter 21.) The protons, neutrons, and electrons have the properties listed in Table 3.1. These properties are independent of the atom of which the subatomic particles are a part. Thus, the atom is the smallest unit that has the characteristic composition of an element, and in that sense, it is the smallest particle of an element.

An uncombined atom is neither positive nor negative but electrically **neutral,** and thus the number of protons (p) must equal the number of electrons:

Number of protons = number of electrons   (For a neutral atom)

Because neutrons are neutral (see Table 3.1), the number of neutrons (n) does not affect the charge on the atom. The number of protons in an atom determines the element's identity. All atoms having the same number of protons are atoms of the same element. Atoms with different numbers of protons are atoms of different elements. The number of protons in an atom is what

> The nucleus does not change during any ordinary chemical reaction.

ENRICHMENT

Visible light (in fact all portions of the electromagnetic spectrum—microwaves, infrared radiation, visible light, ultraviolet light, X-rays, gamma rays) can be described in terms of wave motion. Each wavelength of visible light has a particular color, and a suitable combination of all the wavelengths of visible light produces white light. White light can be broken into its *spectrum* (a rainbow) by passing it through a prism (Figure 3.5).

When white light is passed through a sample of *gaseous* atoms, the atoms absorb some of the wavelengths of light. A given wavelength implies a given energy. Different elements absorb different sets of wavelengths, so an element can be identified by the wavelengths of white light that it absorbs. Helium was first discovered in the Sun because sunlight has a set of absorbed wavelengths that did not match the set of any element known on Earth (Figure 3.6). It was found on Earth shortly afterward.

Figure 3.5 Components of White Light
Visible light is broken up into all the colors of the rainbow by passing it through a prism.

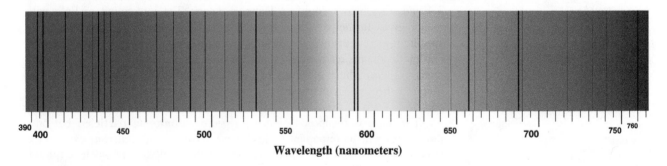

Wavelength (nanometers)

Figure 3.6 Spectral Lines in Sunlight
The dark lines on the visible spectrum of sunlight are due to energies of precise wavelengths of light being absorbed by atoms of elements in the outer layers of the Sun. Bright lines of the same wavelengths are emitted when gaseous samples of those elements are excited electrically.

Table 3.1 Properties of Subatomic Particles

Particle	Charge (e)*	Mass (amu)†	Location in the Atom
Proton	1+	1.0073	In the nucleus
Neutron	0	1.0087	In the nucleus
Electron	1−	0.000549	Outside the nucleus

*The charges given are relative charges, based on the charge on the electron, e, as the fundamental unit of charge (1 e = 1.60 × 10^{-19} coulomb).
†The masses are given in atomic mass units (amu), described in Section 3.4.

> The atomic number (Z) is equal to the number of protons (p) in the atom, and determines its identity.

> The mass number (A) is equal to the sum of the numbers of protons (p) and neutrons (n) in the atom. The number of neutrons is thus the difference between the mass number and the atomic number:
>
> $$n = A - Z$$

$$p + n = A$$
$${}_{1}^{1}H$$
(Optional) $p = Z$

differentiates each element from all others. It is called the **atomic number** (Z) of the element:

$$Z = p$$

The number of neutrons in the nuclei of atoms of the same element can differ. If two atoms have the same number of protons and different numbers of neutrons, they are atoms of the same element (they have the same atomic number). However, they have different masses because of the different numbers of neutrons. Such atoms are said to be **isotopes** of each other. Each isotope of an element is usually identified by its **mass number** (A), which is defined as the sum of the number of protons and the number of neutrons in the atom:

$$A = p + n = Z + n$$

Generally, the mass number for the isotopes rises as the atomic number rises, but the two are *not* directly proportional.

Symbols for the elements were introduced in Chapter 1. In addition, each of those symbols can be used to represent an atom of the element. Moreover, an isotope is identified by the symbol of the element, with the mass number added as a superscript on the left side. For example, the isotope of hydrogen with mass number of 1 is designated as ${}^{1}H$. (Its name is hydrogen-1.) Note that the number of neutrons is not given; the mass number is. The number of protons (the atomic number) may be shown as a subscript on the left, if desired, as in ${}_{1}^{1}H$. However, because the element's identity determines the atomic number, and vice versa, giving both the symbol and the atomic number is redundant—it identifies the element twice. Except for ${}^{1}H$, the number of neutrons equals or exceeds the number of protons in the nucleus of every isotope.

EXAMPLE 3.4

17p
18n

17p
20n

Two atoms have 17 protons each, but the first atom contains 18 neutrons and the second contains 20 neutrons. Show that their atomic numbers are the same but that their mass numbers differ.

Solution

The atomic numbers are the numbers of protons, in each case 17, so the atoms are both atoms of the same element—chlorine. (See the periodic table inside the front cover.) The mass number of the first atom is $17 + 18 = 35$, and the mass number of the second is $17 + 20 = 37$. Thus, the atoms have the same atomic number but different mass numbers. Their properties are essentially the same because they are the same element, but their masses are somewhat different. They are isotopes of each other: ${}^{35}Cl$ and ${}^{37}Cl$.

Practice Problem 3.4 Two atoms have mass number 119, but one has 69 neutrons and the other 70 neutrons. Are they isotopes of each other?

EXAMPLE 3.5

How many electrons are associated with each of the uncombined atoms in Example 3.4?

Solution

Each atom has 17 protons in its nucleus, so there is a 17+ charge on each nucleus. Because uncombined atoms are neutral, there must be 17 electrons, each with a 1− charge, to exactly balance the nuclear charge.

Practice Problem 3.5   How many electrons does each of the atoms in Practice Problem 3.4 have?

Dalton's first three postulates have had to be amended in light of information discovered after his work. The existence of subatomic particles means that atoms are not indivisible (postulate 1). Dalton thought that the mass differentiated the atoms of one element from those of another (postulate 2) because he believed that atoms were indivisible. However, atoms of *different* elements can have the *same mass number*. Atoms of each element have a distinctive atomic number—the number of protons in the nucleus—to distinguish them from atoms of other elements. In Chapter 5, postulate 3 will be shown to be only partially true. Only some combinations of atoms form molecules; other combinations form ionic compounds.

Snapshot Review

ChemSkill Builder 9.1

❑ The atom is not indivisible, but consists of protons and neutrons within a nucleus and electrons outside the nucleus.
❑ Atoms with different numbers of neutrons but the same number of protons are isotopes of each other.
❑ The atomic number determines the element of which the atom is a part.

A. How many protons are in an atom X that is an isotope of an atom Q that has 16 protons and 18 neutrons?
B. What are the atomic number and the mass number of atom Q of Problem A?
C. For what isotope is the mass number less than double the atomic number?

3.4   Atomic Mass

Atoms are so tiny that, until recently, the masses of individual atoms could not be measured directly (Figure 3.7). However, because mass was so important in Dalton's theory, some measure of atomic masses was necessary. Therefore, a **relative scale**—the **atomic mass scale**—is used. This scale is sometimes called the **atomic weight scale.** On this scale, an average of the masses of all the atoms of the naturally occurring mixture of isotopes of a given element is measured relative to the mass of an atom of a *standard*.

Figure 3.7 The Problem with Weighing Atoms

If we try to weigh one grain of rice on a bathroom scale, we get an inkling of the very much more difficult task of weighing atoms. (The ratio of the mass of an atom to that of the smallest mass weighable on any balance is about 10^{-22} g/10^{-6} g, or 10^{-16}. This is much lower than the ratio of the mass of a grain of rice to that of a person, which is about 10^{-3} g/10^{5} g, or 10^{-8}.)

Historic Determination of Atomic Mass

The early pioneers of chemistry, trying to verify Dalton's atomic theory, could not measure the mass of individual atoms. The best they could do was to measure the masses of equal numbers of atoms (or other known ratios of atoms) of two (or more) elements at a time, to determine their relative masses. They established one element as a standard, gave it an arbitrary value of atomic mass, and used that value to establish the atomic mass scale. The last naturally occurring mixture of isotopes that was used as a standard was oxygen, defined as having an atomic mass of exactly 16 **atomic mass units** (amu). That standard has been replaced; see the next subsection. The atomic mass unit is tiny; it takes 6.02×10^{23} amu to make 1.00 g. We can see how **atomic masses,** sometimes called **atomic weights,** were determined historically by using the analogy presented in Example 3.6.

EXAMPLE 3.6

A student buys beverages for a party. He buys an equal number of bottles of two sizes. The total volume of all the bottles of the first size is 27.5 L and the total volume of the second size is 16.5 L. What is the ratio of volumes of the first size of beverage to the second?

Solution

Let x equal the number of bottles of each size. The volume of each bottle of the first size is thus (27.5 L)/x. The volume of a bottle of the second size is (16.5 L)/x. The ratio of the two is thus

$$\frac{(27.5 \text{ L})/x}{(16.5 \text{ L})/x} = 1.67$$

Practice Problem 3.6 A student buys twice the number of bottles of one size of beverage than bottles of a second for a party for his group. The total volume of all the bottles of the first size is 6.50 L, and the total volume of the second size is 13.0 L. What is the ratio of volumes of each bottle of the first size of beverage to that of each bottle of the second?

This method is illustrated for elements in Example 3.7.

EXAMPLE 3.7

A compound contains equal numbers of nickel atoms and oxygen atoms. A sample of this compound contains 8.15 g of nickel and 2.22 g of oxygen. Calculate the atomic mass of nickel from this information.

Solution

Let x = the number of atoms of each element

Then

$$\frac{(8.15\ g)}{x} = \text{the mass of each nickel atom, and}$$

$$\frac{(2.22\ g)}{x} = \text{the mass of each oxygen atom}$$

Thus the ratio of masses is

$$\frac{(8.15\ g)/x}{(2.22\ g)/x} = 3.67$$

Since the atomic mass of oxygen is 16.0 amu, the atomic mass of nickel is 3.67(16.0 amu) = 58.7 amu.

After it has been determined as shown, the atomic mass of nickel can be used to determine the atomic masses of other elements.

Practice Problem 3.7   Oxygen and selenium form a compound containing twice as many oxygen atoms as selenium atoms. In a sample of the compound, the ratio of masses of selenium to oxygen is 2.47 to 1.00. Calculate the atomic mass of selenium.

How could the early chemists be sure that their samples of two elements had equal numbers of atoms? They made a compound of the elements in which the atomic ratio was 1 : 1. They did not need to know the exact number of atoms of each element, only that the atoms were present in a 1 : 1 ratio.

Modern Determination of Atomic Mass

The modern method of determining atomic mass uses the ^{12}C isotope as the standard, with a mass defined as exactly 12 amu. (The atomic mass of carbon on this scale is 12.011 amu, and that of oxygen is 15.9994 amu.) The atomic mass of an element is defined as the **weighted average** of the actual masses of its naturally occurring isotopes (not the mass numbers of the isotopes). A weighted average is the average taking into account the relative numbers of atoms of each type of isotope. The concept of weighted average may be understood using an analogy to a situation in everyday life, presented in Examples 3.8 and 3.9.

EXAMPLE 3.8

A supermarket is having a special, selling a package of seven 2.00-L bottles of soda at regular price and including three 1.00-L bottles free. (a) What is the average volume of two bottles—one bottle of each size? (b) What is the average volume of all 10 bottles together? (c) Explain the meaning of the term *weighted average.*

Solution

(a) The average of one bottle of each size is

$$\frac{2.00 \text{ L} + 1.00 \text{ L}}{2} = 1.50 \text{ L}$$

(b) The average of all the bottles is

$$\frac{7(2.00 \text{ L}) + 3(1.00 \text{ L})}{10} = 1.70 \text{ L}$$

(c) This weighted average calculated in part (b) takes into account the number of each size bottle.

EXAMPLE 3.9

(a) Calculate the percentage of 2-L bottles in Example 3.8. (b) Calculate the percentage of 1-L bottles in Example 3.8. (c) Determine the weighted average using the percentages rather than the actual numbers of bottles.

Solution

(a) $\dfrac{7 \text{ two-liter bottles}}{10 \text{ bottles total}} = 70\%$

(b) $\dfrac{3 \text{ one-liter bottles}}{10 \text{ bottles total}} = 30\%$

(c) $\dfrac{70\%(2.00 \text{ L}) + 30\%(1.00 \text{ L})}{100\%} = 1.7 \text{ L}$

EXAMPLE 3.10

Naturally occurring copper consists of 69.17% ^{63}Cu, which has a mass of 62.9396 amu, and 30.83% ^{65}Cu, which has a mass of 64.9278 amu. Calculate the atomic mass of copper.

Solution

The weighted average is given by the sum of the fraction of ^{63}Cu times its mass and the fraction of ^{65}Cu times its mass:

$$(0.6917)(62.9396 \text{ amu}) + (0.3083)(64.9278 \text{ amu}) = 63.55 \text{ amu}$$

Practice Problem 3.10 Naturally occurring gallium consists of 60.108% ^{69}Ga, with a mass of 68.9256 amu, and 39.892% ^{71}Ga, with a mass of 70.9247 amu. Calculate the atomic mass of gallium.

Atomic masses of naturally occurring elements are listed in the periodic table. (Because atomic mass is the weighted average of *naturally occurring* isotopes, artificial elements by definition do not have atomic masses. The mass number of the most stable isotope of each artificial element is placed in parentheses in the box for the element in the table.) Naturally occurring samples of an element have almost exactly the same mixture of isotopes, no matter what the source. For example, water from the rain forest of the Amazon, from an iceberg in the Arctic Ocean, or from the combustion of an oak tree in New York contains oxygen that is 99.759% ^{16}O, 0.037% ^{17}O, and 0.204% ^{18}O. Because the relative percentages of the isotopes in any naturally occurring element are remarkably constant, the average of the isotopic masses is also constant (to four, five, or even six significant digits). Thus, Dalton's postulate of a constant mass for the atoms of an element explained the laws of chemical combination because there is a constant *average* mass.

Snapshot Review

❑ Atomic mass is *defined* as the weighted average of the masses of the naturally occurring mixture of isotopes of an element. Be careful to distinguish it from *mass number* and the *mass of a particular atom*.

❑ Historically, atomic mass was determined from mass ratios, such as were used to develop the law of definite proportions. Now, the mass and percentage of each isotope is used.

A. In a compound containing one atom of X for every atom of oxygen, the ratio of masses is 8.58 g X per gram of oxygen. Identify element X.

B. Element X consists of 78.99% of atoms with mass 23.985 amu, 10.00% of atoms with mass 24.986 amu, and the rest of the atoms of mass 25.983 amu. Identify element X.

3.5 Development of the Periodic Table

Many atomic masses were determined as a direct result of Dalton's postulates and the work that they stimulated, and scientists attempted to relate the atomic masses of the elements to the elements' properties. This work culminated in the development of the periodic table by Dmitri Mendeleyev (1834-1907) (Figure 3.8) and independently by Lothar Meyer (1830-1895). Because Mendeleyev did more with his periodic table, he is often given sole credit for its development.

Mendeleyev put the elements known in the 1860s in ascending order according to their atomic masses (atomic numbers had not yet been defined) and noticed that the properties of every seventh element were similar. He arranged the elements in a table, with elements having similar properties in the same group. At several points where an element did not fit well in the position its atomic mass called for, he postulated that the next known element for that position. For example, the next known discovered element for was arsenic (As). However, because arsenic's properties are more similar to those of phosphorus (P) than to those of aluminum by atomic mass Mendeleyev predicted that two elements that fit the positions that fit the positions silicon in the periodic table had not yet been discovered. Silicon (Si), described their expected properties from those of the elements above them in the table. His predictions helped other chemists discover these now known as gallium (Ga) and germanium (Ge).

Figure 3.8 Dmitri Mendeleyev

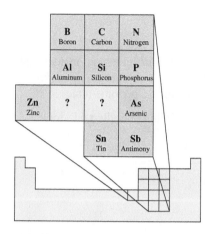

Figure 3.9 A Portion of Mendeleyev's Periodic Table

The periodic table is based on the atomic numbers of the elements, not the atomic masses.

Several other elements seemed out of order. For example, their atomic masses placed iodine (I) before tellurium (Te), but their chemical properties required the opposite order. Mendeleyev concluded that the atomic masses must have been determined incorrectly and put these two elements in positions reflecting their properties. We now know that the periodic properties of the elements are based on their atomic numbers, not their atomic masses, which explains Mendeleyev's difficulty with the placement of certain elements.

EXAMPLE 3.11

In the periodic table, locate two pairs of elements besides iodine and tellurium that are out of order, based on their atomic masses.

Solution

The elements argon and potassium and the elements cobalt and nickel are in reverse order with respect to their atomic masses.

Practice Problem 3.11 Are any elements in the periodic table out of order according to their atomic numbers?

An entire group of elements—the noble gases—was discovered after the periodic table was first formulated. These elements are colorless, odorless gases and almost totally inert. Their lack of combining capacity means that they are not found in any naturally occurring compound. If some compound had had a percentage of its mass unaccounted for, chemists would have known to look for the missing elements, but because the noble gases do not combine spontaneously with substances that they come into contact with in nature, there was no clue to their existence.

That each element fits properly into place in a vertical column proves the fundamental correctness of arranging the elements according to their atomic numbers and chemical properties. Henry Moseley (1887-1915) discovered a quantitative relationship between the wavelength of X-rays emitted by an element and the atomic number of the element. Every atomic number between 1 and 92 was accounted for, which means that there are no more "undiscovered" elements except possibly artificial elements with very high atomic numbers yet to be synthesized.

Atomic numbers and atomic masses are usually included in the boxes with the chemical symbols in the periodic table. The atomic number is the integer. (The mass number, also an integer, is given in parentheses for the most stable isotope of the synthetic elements.)

The periodic table is a tremendous source of information for students who learn to use it well. In Chapter 4, we will learn to use the periodic table to predict the electronic configuration of each of the elements, and in Chapter 5, we will use it to predict outermost electron shell occupancy. The table's numeric data are used in later chapters on formula calculations and stoichiometry, and its information on chemical trends is applied in the chapters on bonding and molecular structure.

Snapshot Review

❏ The periodic table was originally developed using atomic masses and chemical and physical properties of the elements, but it is now known that the atomic number is the real basis of the periodic table.

A. How did Mendeleyev know to leave spaces in his periodic table for gallium and germanium?

Key Terms

Key terms are defined in the Glossary.

atom (3.2)
atomic mass (3.3, 3.4)
atomic mass scale (3.4)
atomic mass unit (3.4)
atomic number (3.3)
atomic weight (3.4)
atomic weight scale (3.4)
Dalton's atomic theory (3.2)
electron (3.3)

isotope (3.3)
law of constant composition (3.1)
law of definite proportions (3.1)
law of multiple proportions (3.1)
mass number (3.3)
molecule (3.2)
neutral (3.3)
neutron (3.3)

nucleus (3.3)
percent (3.1)
postulate (3.2)
proportion (3.1)
proton (3.3)
relative scale (3.4)
subatomic particle (3.3)
weighted average (3.4)

Symbols/Abbreviations

A (mass number) (3.3)

n (number of neutrons) (3.3)

p (number of protons) (3.3)

Z (atomic number) (3.3)

amu (atomic mass unit) (3.4)

Summary

Lavoisier discovered the law of conservation of matter, which states that matter cannot be created or destroyed during chemical reactions or physical changes. This generalization increased chemists' efforts to measure the masses of elements in compounds and resulted in two more laws. The law of definite proportions states that the percentage of each element in any sample of a pure compound is always the same. According to the law of multiple proportions, if the mass of one of the elements in two or more compounds of the same elements is held constant, the masses of each other element form a small, whole-number ratio. (Section 3.1)

Dalton suggested that the elements are composed of indivisible atoms and that the atoms of each element have a characteristic mass, different from the mass of any other element. He stated that the atoms combine to form molecules when the elements combine to form compounds. These postulates explained the laws of chemical combination known at that time, but most of them have been

amended in light of later discoveries. However, the atom is still considered to be the fundamental particle of an element. (Section 3.2)

In the past 200 years, numerous experiments have shown that the atom is not indivisible but is composed of electrons plus a nucleus containing protons and neutrons. The nucleus does not change in any chemical reaction. The characteristics of the subatomic particles (Table 3.1) should be memorized. The number of protons, called the atomic number, governs the number of electrons in the neutral atom. The sum of the numbers of protons and neutrons is called the mass number. All atoms of a given element have the same atomic number, which differs from the atomic numbers of other elements. Different atoms of the same element may have different numbers of neutrons and thus different mass numbers. Such atoms are *isotopes* of each other. An isotope is identified by the symbol of the element, with the mass number as a superscript to the left. (Section 3.3)

Solution

(a) The average of one bottle of each size is

$$\frac{2.00 \text{ L} + 1.00 \text{ L}}{2} = 1.50 \text{ L}$$

(b) The average of all the bottles is

$$\frac{7(2.00 \text{ L}) + 3(1.00 \text{ L})}{10} = 1.70 \text{ L}$$

(c) This weighted average calculated in part (b) takes into account the number of each size bottle.

EXAMPLE 3.9

(a) Calculate the percentage of 2-L bottles in Example 3.8. (b) Calculate the percentage of 1-L bottles in Example 3.8. (c) Determine the weighted average using the percentages rather than the actual numbers of bottles.

Solution

(a) $\dfrac{7 \text{ two-liter bottles}}{10 \text{ bottles total}} = 70\%$

(b) $\dfrac{3 \text{ one-liter bottles}}{10 \text{ bottles total}} = 30\%$

(c) $\dfrac{70\%(2.00 \text{ L}) + 30\%(1.00 \text{ L})}{100\%} = 1.7 \text{ L}$

EXAMPLE 3.10

Naturally occurring copper consists of 69.17% ^{63}Cu, which has a mass of 62.9396 amu, and 30.83% ^{65}Cu, which has a mass of 64.9278 amu. Calculate the atomic mass of copper.

Solution

The weighted average is given by the sum of the fraction of ^{63}Cu times its mass and the fraction of ^{65}Cu times its mass:

$$(0.6917)(62.9396 \text{ amu}) + (0.3083)(64.9278 \text{ amu}) = 63.55 \text{ amu}$$

Practice Problem 3.10 Naturally occurring gallium consists of 60.108% ^{69}Ga, with a mass of 68.9256 amu, and 39.892% ^{71}Ga, with a mass of 70.9247 amu. Calculate the atomic mass of gallium.

Atomic masses of naturally occurring elements are listed in the periodic table. (Because atomic mass is the weighted average of *naturally occurring* isotopes, artificial elements by definition do not have atomic masses. The mass number of the most stable isotope of each artificial element is placed in parentheses in the box for the element in the table.) Naturally occurring samples of an element have almost exactly the same mixture of isotopes, no matter what the source. For example, water from the rain forest of the Amazon, from an iceberg in the Arctic Ocean, or from the combustion of an oak tree in New York contains oxygen that is 99.759% ^{16}O, 0.037% ^{17}O, and 0.204% ^{18}O. Because the relative percentages of the isotopes in any naturally occurring element are remarkably constant, the average of the isotopic masses is also constant (to four, five, or even six significant digits). Thus, Dalton's postulate of a constant mass for the atoms of an element explained the laws of chemical combination because there is a constant *average* mass.

Snapshot Review

❐ Atomic mass is *defined* as the weighted average of the masses of the naturally occurring mixture of isotopes of an element. Be careful to distinguish it from *mass number* and the *mass of a particular atom*.

❐ Historically, atomic mass was determined from mass ratios, such as were used to develop the law of definite proportions. Now, the mass and percentage of each isotope is used.

A. In a compound containing one atom of X for every atom of oxygen, the ratio of masses is 8.58 g X per gram of oxygen. Identify element X.

B. Element X consists of 78.99% of atoms with mass 23.985 amu, 10.00% of atoms with mass 24.986 amu, and the rest of the atoms of mass 25.983 amu. Identify element X.

3.5   Development of the Periodic Table

Figure 3.8   Dmitri Mendeleyev

Many atomic masses were determined as a direct result of Dalton's postulates and the work that they stimulated, and scientists attempted to relate the atomic masses of the elements to the elements' properties. This work culminated in the development of the periodic table by Dmitri Mendeleyev (1834-1907) (Figure 3.8) and independently by Lothar Meyer (1830-1895). Because Mendeleyev did more with his periodic table, he is often given sole credit for its development.

Mendeleyev put the elements known in the 1860s in ascending order according to their atomic masses (atomic numbers had not yet been defined) and noticed that the properties of every seventh known element were similar. He arranged the elements in a table, with elements having similar properties in the same group. At several points where an element did not seem to fit well in the position its atomic mass called for, he postulated that there was an undiscovered element for that position. For example, the next known element after zinc (Zn) by atomic mass was arsenic (As). However, because arsenic's properties were much more similar to those of phosphorus (P) than to those of aluminum (Al) or silicon (Si), Mendeleyev predicted that two elements that fit the positions under aluminum and silicon in the periodic table had not yet been discovered. (Figure 3.9). He described their expected properties from those of the elements above and below them in the table. His predictions helped other chemists discover these elements, now known as gallium (Ga) and germanium (Ge).

Figure 3.7 The Problem with Weighing Atoms

If we try to weigh one grain of rice on a bathroom scale, we get an inkling of the very much more difficult task of weighing atoms. (The ratio of the mass of an atom to that of the smallest mass weighable on any balance is about 10^{-22} g/10^{-6} g, or 10^{-16}. This is much lower than the ratio of the mass of a grain of rice to that of a person, which is about 10^{-3} g/10^{5} g, or 10^{-8}.)

Historic Determination of Atomic Mass

The early pioneers of chemistry, trying to verify Dalton's atomic theory, could not measure the mass of individual atoms. The best they could do was to measure the masses of equal numbers of atoms (or other known ratios of atoms) of two (or more) elements at a time, to determine their relative masses. They established one element as a standard, gave it an arbitrary value of atomic mass, and used that value to establish the atomic mass scale. The last naturally occurring mixture of isotopes that was used as a standard was oxygen, defined as having an atomic mass of exactly 16 **atomic mass units** (amu). That standard has been replaced; see the next subsection. The atomic mass unit is tiny; it takes 6.02×10^{23} amu to make 1.00 g. We can see how **atomic masses,** sometimes called **atomic weights,** were determined historically by using the analogy presented in Example 3.6.

EXAMPLE 3.6

A student buys beverages for a party. He buys an equal number of bottles of two sizes. The total volume of all the bottles of the first size is 27.5 L and the total volume of the second size is 16.5 L. What is the ratio of volumes of the first size of beverage to the second?

Solution

Let x equal the number of bottles of each size. The volume of each bottle of the first size is thus (27.5 L)/x. The volume of a bottle of the second size is (16.5 L)/x. The ratio of the two is thus

$$\frac{(27.5 \text{ L})/x}{(16.5 \text{ L})/x} = 1.67$$

Practice Problem 3.6   A student buys twice the number of bottles of one size of beverage than bottles of a second for a party for his group. The total volume of all the bottles of the first size is 6.50 L, and the total volume of the second size is 13.0 L. What is the ratio of volumes of each bottle of the first size of beverage to that of each bottle of the second?

This method is illustrated for elements in Example 3.7.

EXAMPLE 3.7

A compound contains equal numbers of nickel atoms and oxygen atoms. A sample of this compound contains 8.15 g of nickel and 2.22 g of oxygen. Calculate the atomic mass of nickel from this information.

Solution

Let x = the number of atoms of each element

Then

$$\frac{(8.15\ \text{g})}{x} = \text{the mass of each nickel atom, and}$$

$$\frac{(2.22\ \text{g})}{x} = \text{the mass of each oxygen atom}$$

Thus the ratio of masses is

$$\frac{(8.15\ \text{g})/x}{(2.22\ \text{g})/x} = 3.67$$

Since the atomic mass of oxygen is 16.0 amu, the atomic mass of nickel is $3.67(16.0\ \text{amu}) = 58.7\ \text{amu}$.

After it has been determined as shown, the atomic mass of nickel can be used to determine the atomic masses of other elements.

Practice Problem 3.7   Oxygen and selenium form a compound containing twice as many oxygen atoms as selenium atoms. In a sample of the compound, the ratio of masses of selenium to oxygen is 2.47 to 1.00. Calculate the atomic mass of selenium.

How could the early chemists be sure that their samples of two elements had equal numbers of atoms? They made a compound of the elements in which the atomic ratio was 1 : 1. They did not need to know the exact number of atoms of each element, only that the atoms were present in a 1 : 1 ratio.

Modern Determination of Atomic Mass

The modern method of determining atomic mass uses the ^{12}C isotope as the standard, with a mass defined as exactly 12 amu. (The atomic mass of carbon on this scale is 12.011 amu, and that of oxygen is 15.9994 amu.) The atomic mass of an element is defined as the **weighted average** of the actual masses of its naturally occurring isotopes (not the mass numbers of the isotopes). A weighted average is the average taking into account the relative numbers of atoms of each type of isotope. The concept of weighted average may be understood using an analogy to a situation in everyday life, presented in Examples 3.8 and 3.9.

EXAMPLE 3.8

A supermarket is having a special, selling a package of seven 2.00-L bottles of soda at regular price and including three 1.00-L bottles free. (a) What is the average volume of two bottles—one bottle of each size? (b) What is the average volume of all 10 bottles together? (c) Explain the meaning of the term *weighted average*.

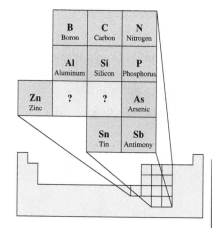

Figure 3.9 A Portion of Mendeleyev's Periodic Table

The periodic table is based on the atomic numbers of the elements, not the atomic masses.

Several other elements seemed out of order. For example, their atomic masses placed iodine (I) before tellurium (Te), but their chemical properties required the opposite order. Mendeleyev concluded that the atomic masses must have been determined incorrectly and put these two elements in positions reflecting their properties. We now know that the periodic properties of the elements are based on their atomic numbers, not their atomic masses, which explains Mendeleyev's difficulty with the placement of certain elements.

EXAMPLE 3.11

In the periodic table, locate two pairs of elements besides iodine and tellurium that are out of order, based on their atomic masses.

Solution

The elements argon and potassium and the elements cobalt and nickel are in reverse order with respect to their atomic masses.

Practice Problem 3.11   Are any elements in the periodic table out of order according to their atomic numbers?

An entire group of elements—the noble gases—was discovered after the periodic table was first formulated. These elements are colorless, odorless gases and almost totally inert. Their lack of combining capacity means that they are not found in any naturally occurring compound. If some compound had had a percentage of its mass unaccounted for, chemists would have known to look for the missing elements, but because the noble gases do not combine spontaneously with substances that they come into contact with in nature, there was no clue to their existence.

That each element fits properly into place in a vertical column proves the fundamental correctness of arranging the elements according to their atomic numbers and chemical properties. Henry Moseley (1887-1915) discovered a quantitative relationship between the wavelength of X-rays emitted by an element and the atomic number of the element. Every atomic number between 1 and 92 was accounted for, which means that there are no more "undiscovered" elements except possibly artificial elements with very high atomic numbers yet to be synthesized.

Atomic numbers and atomic masses are usually included in the boxes with the chemical symbols in the periodic table. The atomic number is the integer. (The mass number, also an integer, is given in parentheses for the most stable isotope of the synthetic elements.)

The periodic table is a tremendous source of information for students who learn to use it well. In Chapter 4, we will learn to use the periodic table to predict the electronic configuration of each of the elements, and in Chapter 5, we will use it to predict outermost electron shell occupancy. The table's numeric data are used in later chapters on formula calculations and stoichiometry, and its information on chemical trends is applied in the chapters on bonding and molecular structure.

Snapshot Review

❏ The periodic table was originally developed using atomic masses and chemical and physical properties of the elements, but it is now known that the atomic number is the real basis of the periodic table.

A. How did Mendeleyev know to leave spaces in his periodic table for gallium and germanium?

Key Terms

Key terms are defined in the Glossary.

atom (3.2)
atomic mass (3.3, 3.4)
atomic mass scale (3.4)
atomic mass unit (3.4)
atomic number (3.3)
atomic weight (3.4)
atomic weight scale (3.4)
Dalton's atomic theory (3.2)
electron (3.3)

isotope (3.3)
law of constant composition (3.1)
law of definite proportions (3.1)
law of multiple proportions (3.1)
mass number (3.3)
molecule (3.2)
neutral (3.3)
neutron (3.3)

nucleus (3.3)
percent (3.1)
postulate (3.2)
proportion (3.1)
proton (3.3)
relative scale (3.4)
subatomic particle (3.3)
weighted average (3.4)

Symbols/Abbreviations

A (mass number) (3.3)

n (number of neutrons) (3.3)

p (number of protons) (3.3)

Z (atomic number) (3.3)

amu (atomic mass unit) (3.4)

Summary

Lavoisier discovered the law of conservation of matter, which states that matter cannot be created or destroyed during chemical reactions or physical changes. This generalization increased chemists' efforts to measure the masses of elements in compounds and resulted in two more laws. The law of definite proportions states that the percentage of each element in any sample of a pure compound is always the same. According to the law of multiple proportions, if the mass of one of the elements in two or more compounds of the same elements is held constant, the masses of each other element form a small, whole-number ratio. (Section 3.1)

Dalton suggested that the elements are composed of indivisible atoms and that the atoms of each element have a characteristic mass, different from the mass of any other element. He stated that the atoms combine to form molecules when the elements combine to form compounds. These postulates explained the laws of chemical combination known at that time, but most of them have been amended in light of later discoveries. However, the atom is still considered to be the fundamental particle of an element. (Section 3.2)

In the past 200 years, numerous experiments have shown that the atom is not indivisible but is composed of electrons plus a nucleus containing protons and neutrons. The nucleus does not change in any chemical reaction. The characteristics of the subatomic particles (Table 3.1) should be memorized. The number of protons, called the atomic number, governs the number of electrons in the neutral atom. The sum of the numbers of protons and neutrons is called the mass number. All atoms of a given element have the same atomic number, which differs from the atomic numbers of other elements. Different atoms of the same element may have different numbers of neutrons and thus different mass numbers. Such atoms are *isotopes* of each other. An isotope is identified by the symbol of the element, with the mass number as a superscript to the left. (Section 3.3)

92

The naturally occurring mixture of isotopes in any sample of a given element has almost exactly the same percentage of each isotope as any other sample. Therefore, the average mass of all the atoms in any sample of the element is constant (to four or more significant digits). That weighted average is called the atomic mass (which is not the same as the mass number or the mass of an atom). Atomic masses are reported on a relative scale, with an atom of the ^{12}C isotope being defined as having a mass of exactly 12 amu. (Section 3.4)

When arranged in order of increasing atomic mass, the various elements, with a few exceptions, have periodically recurring properties. Mendeleyev produced a periodic table based on this ordering. Later, it was learned that the atomic number is the basis for the chemical properties of an element, so the modern periodic table arranges the elements in order of increasing atomic number, with elements having similar properties arranged in vertical groups. The periodic table has many uses in the study of chemistry. (Section 3.5)

Items for Special Attention

■ Atomic mass and mass number are not the same. Atomic mass refers to the naturally occurring mixture of isotopes; mass number refers to an individual isotope. Atomic mass is an average and is never an exact integer; mass number is a sum (of the number of protons plus the number of neutrons) and is always an integer. Except for the artificial elements, mass numbers are not given in the periodic table.

■ Atoms have masses between 1 and 250 atomic mass units, nowhere near as large as 1 g. Be careful to use the correct units for the masses of individual atoms and for the masses of weighable samples.

■ In the periodic table, the elements are arranged so that their atomic numbers are in increasing order and grouped vertically so that elements with similar chemical properties are in the same group (vertical column).

Answers to Snapshot Reviews

3.1 A. 25.0 g (from the law of conservation of mass)
    B. In the given sample:

$$\frac{70.90 \text{ g Cl}}{208.2 \text{ g total}} \times 100\% = 34.05\% \text{ Cl}$$

Therefore 34.05% in each of the others. (Percent composition is intensive; it does not depend on the sample size.)

C. $\dfrac{1.269 \text{ g Fe}}{1.000 \text{ g Cl}}$ means $\dfrac{1.000 \text{ g Cl}}{1.269 \text{ g Fe}} = \dfrac{0.7880 \text{ g Cl}}{1.000 \text{ g Fe}}$

$\dfrac{1.907 \text{ g Fe}}{1.000 \text{ g Cl}}$ means $\dfrac{1.000 \text{ g Cl}}{1.907 \text{ g Fe}} = \dfrac{0.5244 \text{ g Cl}}{1.000 \text{ g Fe}}$

$\dfrac{0.7880 \text{ g Cl}}{0.5244 \text{ g Cl}} = \dfrac{1.50}{1} = \dfrac{3}{2}$ ratio

3.2 A. The first compound has 4 atoms of B for every 2 atoms of A, the second has 3 atoms of B for every 2 atoms of A. Per 2 atoms of A, the ratio of B is 4 atoms in the first

compound to 3 atoms in the second, and therefore 4 g to 3 g. The mass of B in the second compound is

$$4.80 \text{ g in compound 1} \left(\frac{3 \text{ g in compound 2}}{4 \text{ g in compound 1}} \right)$$

$$= 3.60 \text{ g in compound 2}$$

3.3 A. 16 protons
    B. Atomic number 16, mass number 34
    C. ^1H
3.4 A. The atomic mass of oxygen is 16.0 amu, so the atomic mass of X is

$$(16.0 \text{ amu})(8.58) = 137 \text{ amu}$$

The element is barium.
    B. $(0.7899)(23.985 \text{ amu}) + (0.1000)(24.986 \text{ amu}) +$
        $(0.1101)(25.983 \text{ amu}) = 24.31 \text{ amu}$
        The element is magnesium.
3.5 A. He knew that arsenic, the next known element, was similar to phosphorus and not to aluminum or silicon.

Self-Tutorial Problems

3.1 At a racetrack, the winning horse paid "5 to 2." How much does a gambler win for each dollar bet on that horse? Is that ratio an integral ratio?

3.2 Two compounds are each composed of elements X and Z. The first contains 6.10 g of Z for every gram of X. Of

the following possibilities, which ones could be the correct number of grams of Z per gram of X in the second compound?

(a) 6.10 g   (b) 3.05 g

(c) 12.2 g   (d) 6.05 g

3.3   On what standard are all atomic masses presently based?

3.4   Which of the following are synonyms?

atomic mass   mass number   mass of an atom
atomic number   atomic weight

3.5   (a) How many protons are in a potassium atom?

(b) What is the atomic number of potassium?

(c) What is the number of positive charges on a potassium nucleus?

3.6   Which of the three following numbers, each of which appears on the periodic table inside the front cover, is an atomic number, which is an atomic mass, and which is a mass number?

(a) 65   (b) 101.07   (c) (242)

3.7   (a) What is the unit of electric charge used at the atomic level?

(b) What is the unit of atomic mass?

3.8   What is the weighted average of three masses of 4.21 g, seven masses of 5.55 g, and two masses of 6.42 g?

3.9   What characteristic of an atom did Dalton think was the most important?

3.10 What is the difference between the symbol for an element and the symbol for an isotope of that element?

3.11 Of atomic number, atomic mass, and mass number, which two appear with most of the symbols for the elements in the periodic table?

3.12 What is the difference between the mass of an atom and the mass number of the atom?

3.13 Potassium and iodine react to form one compound only. In a certain reaction, 20.0 g of potassium reacts completely with 64.9 g of iodine to produce potassium iodide.

(a) How much potassium iodide is produced?

(b) How much iodine would react with 4.00 g of potassium?

(c) How much iodine would react with 7.29 g of potassium?

(d) What law allows you to answer each prior part of this problem?

3.14 A 29.7-g sample of a certain compound contains 85.63% carbon and 14.37% hydrogen.

(a) How much carbon is in a 9.08-g portion of this sample?

(b) How much carbon is in 9.08 g of a different sample of this compound?

3.15 A 4.73-g sample of element A combines completely with a 12.11-g sample of element B. What is the total mass of the product?

3.16 A 4.22-g sample of magnesium was burned, yielding 7.00 g of magnesium oxide. How many grams of oxygen was taken up in the reaction?

3.17 A 6.73-g sample of an element combines completely with another element to make 12.14 g of a compound. What mass of the second element reacted?

3.18 Which two types of subatomic particles must be present in equal numbers for an atom to be neutral?

3.19 (a) Which element has atomic number 23?

(b) Which element has an atomic mass of 23.0 amu (to three significant figures)?

(c) Locate the elements of part (a) and part (b) on the periodic table.

3.20 (a) What is the average of a 30.0-g mass and a 46.0-g mass?

(b) What is the weighted average of eight 30.0-g masses and twelve 46.0-g masses?

(c) What is the weighted average mass of three chlorine atoms with mass 35.0 amu each and one chlorine atom with mass 37.0 amu?

3.21 Why did Mendeleyev not use atomic numbers instead of atomic masses as the basis for his periodic table?

3.22 In the periodic table (inside front cover), locate five elements for which mass numbers rather than atomic masses are given.

Problems

3.1 Laws of Chemical Combination

3.23 If 31.9 mg of a compound containing only carbon and hydrogen is burned completely in oxygen and yields 87.7 mg of carbon dioxide and 71.8 mg of water, how much oxygen is used up?

3.24 When 7.80 mg of a compound containing only carbon and hydrogen was burned completely in 28.3 mg of oxygen, 23.3 mg of carbon dioxide and some water were formed. Calculate the mass of the water.

3.25 A 7.33-g sample of mercury(I) oxide was decomposed into mercury and oxygen, yielding 7.05 g of mercury.

(a) What mass of oxygen was obtained?

(b) What fraction of the compound was oxygen?

(c) What percentage of the compound was oxygen?

3.26 A 18.6-g sample of a compound contains 39.35% sodium and 60.65% chlorine.

(a) Calculate the mass of chlorine present.

(b) Calculate the mass of chlorine present in a 30.0-g sample of the same compound.

3.27 Sodium and chlorine react to form one compound only. In a certain reaction, 2.241 g of sodium reacts completely with 3.454 g of chlorine to produce sodium chloride.

(a) How much chlorine would react with 15.44 g of sodium?

(b) How much sodium would react with 0.7206 g of chlorine?

3.28 Sodium and chlorine react to form one compound only. In a certain reaction, 20.0 g of sodium and 30.8 g of chlorine react completely. How much chlorine would remain unreacted if 20.0 g of sodium and 50.0 g of chlorine were allowed to react?

3.29 A compound is formed between elements A and B in which two atoms of B combine with each atom of A. Each atom of B has a mass of 127 amu, and each atom of A has a mass of 24.3 amu.

(a) Calculate the mass ratio.

(b) Which ratio is integral, the ratio of atoms or masses or both?

3.30 The ratio of masses of sulfur and oxygen in sulfur dioxide is 1.0 g to 1.0 g. Is this fact a proof of the law of multiple proportions?

3.31 The ratio of the mass of carbon to the mass of oxygen in carbon monoxide is about 3 g to 4 g. Does this fact confirm the law of multiple proportions?

3.32 Solve Example 3.3 (p. 79) again, this time using 1 g of oxygen in each compound. Is the law of multiple proportions still valid?

3.33 A sample of a compound composed of only carbon and hydrogen contains 79.89% carbon. Show that this compound and the one in Problem 3.14 obey the law of multiple proportions.

3.34 Show that each of the following sets of data obeys the law of multiple proportions:

(a)

	First Compound	Second Compound
Element 1	92.26%	85.63%
Element 2	7.74%	14.37%

(b)

	Element 1	Element 2
First compound	92.26%	7.74%
Second compound	85.63%	14.37%

3.35 Show that the following data obey the law of multiple proportions:

	Compound 1	Compound 2
Element X	103.1 g	96.23 g
Element Y	7.96 g	14.87 g

3.36 Two compounds are each composed of elements A and B. The first contains 2.468 g of B for every gram of A. Of the following possibilities, which ones could be the

correct number of grams of B per gram of A in the second compound?

(a) 1.234 g   (b) 4.936 g

(c) 2.512 g   (d) 2.468 g

3.2 Dalton's Atomic Theory

3.37 (a) What happens to a scientific hypothesis if experiments show it to be incorrect?

(b) To which of Dalton's postulates did this first happen?

3.38 The formula for water is H_2O, signifying that there are two atoms of hydrogen for every atom of oxygen. If Dalton's fifth postulate had been true, what would the formula for water have been?

3.39 According to Dalton's atomic theory, all atoms of the same element have the same mass. If an atom of zinc has a mass of 65.4 amu and an atom of sulfur has a mass of 32.1 amu:

(a) What is the mass ratio of one atom of zinc to one atom of sulfur?

(b) What is the total mass of 100 atoms of zinc? What is the total mass of 100 atoms of sulfur?

(c) What is the ratio of masses of 100 atoms of zinc to 100 atoms of sulfur?

(d) Choose an arbitrary, large number of atoms of zinc. Then calculate the mass of that number and the mass of an equal number of sulfur atoms. Calculate the ratio of the total masses.

(e) What can you conclude about the ratio of masses of equal numbers of zinc and sulfur atoms?

3.40 Would it make any difference in the prior problem if average masses had been used? Explain.

3.41 Draw a figure like that of Figure 3.4 for potassium oxide, K_2O, and potassium peroxide, K_2O_2. For a given number of oxygen atoms, what is the ratio of potassium atoms in the two compounds?

3.42 All naturally occurring samples of boron trifluoride, when purified, contain the same percentage of boron and the same percentage of fluorine. Naturally occurring fluorine consists of only one isotope. What do the constant percentages say about the two naturally occurring isotopes of boron?

3.43 The atoms of element Z each have about 12 times the mass of a ^9Be atom. Another element, X, has atoms whose mass is about one-fourth the mass of Z atoms. A third element, Q, has atoms with $1\frac{1}{3}$ the mass of X atoms.

(a) Make a table of relative atomic masses based on ^9Be as 9 amu.

(b) Identify the elements Z, X, and Q.

3.44 Sulfur dioxide (SO_2) has two atoms of oxygen per atom of sulfur, and sulfur trioxide (SO_3) has three atoms of oxygen per atom of sulfur. The mass ratio of sulfur to oxygen in SO_2 is 1.0 : 1.0. What is the mass ratio of sulfur to oxygen in SO_3?

3.45 Naturally occurring silicon consists of 92.21% ^{28}Si, which has a mass of 27.97693 amu, 4.70% ^{29}Si, which has a mass of 28.97649 amu, and 3.09% of ^{30}Si, which has a mass of 29.97376 amu. Calculate the atomic mass of silicon.

3.46 A compound is formed between elements A, B, and C in which two atoms of A combine with each atom of B and four atoms of C. Each atom of A has a mass of 39.1 units, each atom of B has a mass of 32.0 units, and each atom of C has a mass of 16.0 units.

 (a) Is there a definite ratio of masses of one element to the other?

 (b) Calculate the mass ratio of A to B and of C to B.

3.47 Plot the mass number versus the atomic number for the last seven actinide elements. Is there any relationship between the mass numbers and atomic numbers (for these elements that have very similar atomic numbers)?

3.3 Subatomic Particles

3.48 Identify the only stable isotope that contains no neutrons.

3.49 Restate Dalton's first three postulates in amended form, based on modern information.

3.50 Isotopes of which element have:

 (a) The smallest mass number

 (b) The smallest atomic number

 (c) The largest number of protons

3.51 Which transition metal isotopes whose mass numbers are given in the periodic table on the inside front cover of the text have the greatest number of neutrons?

3.52 Identify the elements in the periodic table that are *not* naturally occurring.

3.53 Complete the following table for neutral atoms of specific isotopes:

Isotopic Symbol	Atomic Number	Mass Number	No. of Protons	No. of Neutrons	No. of Electrons
(a) ^{112}Cd	——	——	——	——	——
(b) ——	49	115	——	——	——
(c) ——	81	——	——	122	——
(d) ——	——	80	34	——	——
(e) $^{128}_{52}$——	——	——	——	——	——
(f) ——	——	——	——	54	42
(g) ——	——	——	45	58	——

3.54 Write the symbol for an isotope:

 (a) Containing one proton and two neutrons

 (b) For which the atomic number is 1 and there is one neutron

 (c) For which the atomic number is 1 and the mass number is 1

 (d) With a mass number of 3 and containing one neutron

 (e) With a mass number of 3 and containing two neutrons

3.55 In the table in Problem 3.53, two pieces of quantitative information are given in each part.

 (a) What two pieces of information are given in part (a)?

 (b) Why would the atomic number and the number of electrons not be sufficient to complete any part?

 (c) Why would the number of protons and the number of electrons not be sufficient to complete any part?

3.56 Complete the following table, concerning uncombined atoms:

Isotopic Symbol	Atomic Number	Mass Number	No. of Protons	No. of Electrons	No. of Neutrons
——	——	——	50	——	66
——	44	——	——	——	56
——	——	174	70	——	——
——	56	138	——	——	——

3.57 Complete the following table for neutral atoms of specific isotopes:

Isotopic Symbol	Atomic Number	Mass Number	No. of Protons	No. of Neutrons	No. of Electrons
(a) ^{134}Xe	——	——	——	——	——
(b) ——	27	60	——	——	——
(c) ——	——	144	——	84	——
(d) ——	22	——	——	26	——
(e) ——	——	——	——	106	72
(f) ——	——	126	52	——	——
(g) ——	——	——	16	18	——

3.58 Deuterium (symbol: ^2D) is a special name for the isotope that contains one proton and one neutron.

 (a) Of what element is deuterium a part?

 (b) Write the more familiar symbol for this isotope.

3.59 Which isotope whose mass number is given in the periodic table on the inside front cover of the text has the

 (a) Largest mass number

 (b) Largest number of neutrons

 (c) Smallest mass number

 (d) Smallest number of neutrons

3.4 Atomic Mass

3.60 Which element has atoms with average mass about 10 times those of the fluorine atom?

3.61 Which element has atoms with average mass about 35 times those of the average helium atom?

3.62 (a) If 37.4% of the people in a Weight Watchers graduating class weigh 185.0 pounds each and the rest weigh 187.0 pounds each, what is the average weight of the class?

(b) If 37.40% of naturally occurring rhenium atoms have an atomic mass of 184.953 amu and the rest have an atomic mass of 186.956 amu, what is the atomic mass of rhenium?

3.63 After a calculation, a student reported the atomic mass of an element as 2.2×10^{-3} amu. The student later changed the value to $2.2 \times 10^{+3}$ amu. Which value, if either, is more probably correct?

3.64 One can guess the mass number of the predominant isotope for many elements from the atomic mass of the element, but not in all cases. The mass numbers of the isotopes of selenium are 74, 76, 77, 78, 80, and 82. Explain why the atomic mass is so close to 79 amu.

3.65 ^{80}Br does not occur naturally. Explain how bromine gets its atomic mass of 79.909 amu.

3.66 ^{108}Ag does not occur naturally. Explain how silver gets its atomic mass of 107.87 amu.

3.67 Calculate the atomic mass of rubidium if 72.17% of naturally occurring rubidium atoms have a mass of 84.9118 and 27.83% have a mass of 86.9092 amu.

3.68 Which of the following represent(s) the mass of one atom (to three significant figures)?

(a) 0.500 amu   (b) 12.0 g

(c) 6.02×10^{23} amu   (d) 2.11×10^3 amu

(e) 74.9 amu

3.69 A compound contains almost equal masses of fluorine and selenium. Using their atomic masses, determine the formula of the compound.

3.70 The mass of iodine in a certain compound is almost exactly twice that of the only other element—copper. Using their atomic masses, determine the formula of the compound.

3.71 Round off the atomic masses of the first 18 elements to two decimal places each.

3.5 Development of the Periodic Table

3.72 How important was it to the work of Mendeleyev that atomic mass and atomic number rise somewhat proportionally? Explain.

3.73 The following are the formulas for some oxides of seven fourth-period elements:

K_2O CaO Ga_2O_3 GeO_2 As_2O_3 SeO_2 Br_2O

     Predict the formula for an oxide of each of the elements directly above these in the periodic table.

3.74 The following are the formulas for certain fluorides of fourth-period elements:

KF CaF_2 GaF_3 GeF_4 AsF_3 SeF_2 BrF

     Predict the formula for a fluoride of each of the elements directly above these in the periodic table.

3.75 From the following properties of chlorine and iodine, predict the corresponding properties of bromine:

Chlorine	Iodine	Bromine
Gas under normal conditions	Solid under normal conditions	_____
Light yellow	Deep violet	_____
Reacts with metals	Reacts with metals	_____
Reacts with oxygen	Reacts with oxygen	_____
Does not conduct electricity	Does not conduct electricity	_____

General Problems

3.76 Could you use the average number of neutrons, instead of atomic number, to build a periodic table as good as that of Mendeleyev?

3.77 At a racetrack, the winning horse paid $1.75 for each dollar bet. What odds were posted?

3.78 What factors limit the number of significant digits in the atomic mass of an element with two naturally occurring isotopes?

3.79 Two compounds of carbon, hydrogen, and oxygen have the following percent compositions. Show that these compounds obey the law of multiple proportions.

(a) 62.1% C, 10.3% H, 27.6% O

(b) 52.2% C, 13.0% H, 34.8% O

3.80 The radius of an average nucleus is one ten-thousandth of the radius of the atom as a whole.

(a) What is the ratio of the *volume* of the atom as a whole to the volume of the nucleus? ($V = \frac{4}{3}\pi r^3$)

(b) Does the result justify the assertion that the volume of the atom is mostly empty space (with some electrons in it)?

3.81 Is there any possibility that the sulfur in the head of a match can combine with *all* the oxygen in the atmosphere of the Earth to form a compound? Explain, using a law studied in this chapter.

3.82 In a certain compound, 8.761 g of element B is combined with 15.55 g of element A. In another compound of A and B, 15.55 g of A could possibly be combined with which ones of the following masses of B?

(a) 4.381 g (b) 2.920 g (c) 17.52 g

(d) 5.841 g (e) 8.761 g

3.83 The law of multiple proportions applies to two or more compounds of the same two or more elements. Show that the following data support the law:

	% H	% S	% O
Compound 1	2.44	39.02	58.54
Compound 2	5.88	94.12	
Compound 3	2.04	32.65	65.31

3.84 The law of multiple proportions applies to two or more compounds of the same two or more elements. Show that the following data support the law:

	% C	% H	% O
Compound 1	52.2	13.0	34.8
Compound 2	74.9	25.1	

3.85 A 14.9-g sample of element A reacts incompletely with a 7.11-g sample of element B. What is the total mass of the product plus the portion of A that did not react?

3.86 Explain why Mendeleyev could predict the existence of germanium but missed the entire group of noble gases.

3.87 A typical atom has a radius of about 10^{-10} m. Estimate the radius of a typical nucleus.

3.88 Naturally occurring sulfur consists of 95.0% ^{32}S, which has a mass of 31.97207 amu, 0.76% ^{33}S, which has a mass of 32.97146 amu, and 4.22% ^{34}S, which has a mass of 33.96786 amu. Calculate the atomic mass of sulfur. How many significant digits are there in the final value?

3.89 Calculate the atomic mass of selenium from the following data:

Isotope	Natural Abundance (%)	Relative Mass (amu)
^{74}Se	0.87	73.9205
^{76}Se	9.02	75.9192
^{77}Se	7.58	76.9199
^{78}Se	23.52	77.9173
^{80}Se	49.82	79.9165
^{82}Se	9.19	81.9167

3.90 (a) Calculate the mass of oxygen in a 4.75-g sample of nitrogen monoxide, using the answer to Example 3.2.

(b) How much oxygen should be combined with the same mass of nitrogen as in Example 3.2 to form the compound nitrogen dioxide, assuming that there is twice the mass of oxygen per gram of nitrogen in nitrogen dioxide as there is in nitrogen monoxide?

(c) What is the percent composition of nitrogen dioxide?

3.91 The atomic mass of chlorine is 35.453 amu. Does any atom of any isotope of chlorine have a mass of 35.453 amu? Explain.

3.92 The atomic mass of fluorine is 18.9984 amu. Explain why the answer to the prior problem would not be correct for this problem.

3.93 (a) Plot mass number versus atomic number for ^{1}H, ^{16}O, ^{56}Fe, ^{96}Mo, ^{138}Ba, ^{197}Au, and ^{238}U.

(b) Are atomic number and mass number directly proportional?

(c) What can you say about the relationship of these two quantities?

3.94 The masses of the atoms of the only two stable isotopes of boron are 10.013 amu and 11.009 amu, and its atomic mass is 10.811 amu. Calculate the percentage of each isotope. [*Hint:* Let x equal the fraction of one of the isotopes, and $(1 - x)$ equal the fraction of the other.]

3.95 Calculate the atomic mass of lithium from the following data:

Isotope	Natural Abundance (%)	Relative Mass (amu)
^{6}Li	7.5	6.0151
^{7}Li	92.5	7.0160

3.96 Sodium and iodine react to form one compound only. In a certain reaction, 10.00 g of sodium and 55.17 g of iodine react completely.

(a) How much sodium iodide is produced?

(b) How much iodine would react if 10.00 g of sodium and 75.00 g of iodine were allowed to react?

(c) How much sodium iodide would be produced?

(d) What law allowed you to answer each of the prior parts of this problem?

3.97 Naturally occurring silicon consists of 92.2% ^{28}Si, which has a mass of 27.9769 amu, 4.67% ^{29}Si, which has a mass of 28.9765 amu, and 3.18% ^{30}Si, which has a mass of 29.9738 amu. Calculate the atomic mass of silicon.

4

Electronic Configuration of the Atom

Fireworks. Energy, input from a chemical reaction, is emitted as light

Review Clues

Objectives

4.1 To understand the dual nature of light and the relationships among its energy, frequency, and wavelength

4.2 To use the Bohr theory of energy levels in atoms to explain light emission and absorption by gaseous atoms

4.3 To use quantum numbers to write the electronic structures of the atoms in their most stable states

4.4 To write detailed electronic configurations for the elements, using the permitted values for the individual quantum numbers, the $n + \ell$ rule, and the Pauli exclusion principle

4.5 To write electronic configurations in a shorter notation, using the concepts of shells, subshells, and orbitals

4.6 To understand the spatial orientation of the most common orbitals and the uncertain nature of locating the electron in the atom

4.7 To represent pictorially the energies of the subshells in atoms and of the electrons that occupy those subshells

4.8 To relate each element's position in the periodic table to the electronic configuration of its atoms, and to deduce electronic structures using the periodic table

In Chapter 3, we learned that atoms owe their characteristics to their subatomic particles—protons, neutrons, and electrons. Electrons occur in regions of space outside the nucleus, and the electronic structure is responsible for all of the atom's chemical properties and many of its physical properties. The number of electrons in a neutral atom is equal to the number of protons in the nucleus. That simple description enables us to deduce much about atoms, especially concerning their interactions with one another (Chapter 5). However, a more detailed model of the atom enables even fuller explanations, including the reason for the differences between main group elements and elements of the transition and inner transition series.

Many details presented in this chapter are based on mathematics beyond the scope of this course, so some postulates must be accepted as "rules of the game." When the rules are followed, the explanations that result match the actual properties of the elements, which is assurance that the postulates are valid.

Section 4.1 briefly describes some of the physical properties of light, especially the relationship of its wavelength to the energy of its particles. Section 4.2 describes how Niels Bohr deduced that electrons occur in shells having distinct energies. His theory was a milestone, but it does not explain the properties of atoms other than hydrogen. Section 4.3 introduces the quantum numbers, which provide a more satisfactory picture of electronic structure for atoms with more than one electron. The dependence of the energy of an electron on its quantum numbers is discussed in Section 4.4, and shells, subshells, and orbitals are covered in Section 4.5. The shapes of orbitals are described in Section 4.6, and diagrams depicting the energy levels of subshells are presented in Section 4.7. The electronic configuration of the atom is responsible for the chemical and physical properties of an element. The relationship between electronic configuration and position on the periodic table is developed in Section 4.8.

4.1   A Brief Exploration of Light

We saw in Chapter 3 that light from the Sun was broken into a spectrum and that a new element—helium—was discovered, identified by the dark lines in that spectrum. It is essential to learn at least a little about the physical nature of light in order to understand how the lines in the spectrum can tell us about energy levels in the atoms.

Visible light is a tiny fraction of the **electromagnetic spectrum,** which includes gamma rays, X-rays, ultraviolet light, visible light, infrared light, microwaves, and radio waves (Figure 4.1). The word **light** is sometimes used to mean only visible light (the portion of the electromagnetic spectrum detectable by the human eye) and sometimes to mean the entire electromagnetic spectrum. In this text, light will be used to mean the entire electromagnetic spectrum, and when visible light is meant, the word *visible* will be included.

Light can be described as a wave motion because it can be refracted by a prism (see Figure 3.5) and diffracted by a grating. These phenomena can be explained only by light possessing wave properties. The **wavelength** (λ) is the distance between two successive crests (Figure 4.2). The amplitude (A) is the maximum displacement from the mean position. The **frequency** (ν) is the number of crests that pass any point, such as point X, per second.

> Be sure to distinguish between the words *photon* and *proton*.

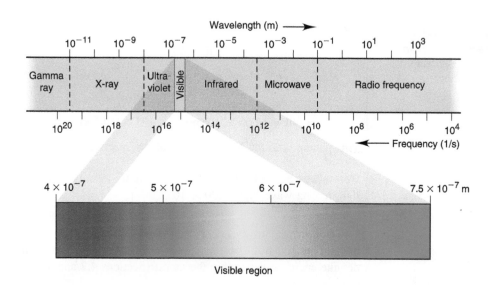

Figure 4.1 The Electromagnetic Spectrum

Light also has a particle nature—it can best be described as a stream of particles called **photons.** The properties of light emitted by glowing (red hot) objects and the photoelectric effect can be explained only with light as a stream of particles. The energy of the photons (E) is related to the frequency of the waves (represented by ν, Greek *nu*):

$$E = h\nu$$

where h is a constant known as Planck's constant with a value of 6.63×10^{-34} J·s. The frequency of any wave is inversely proportional to its wavelength (λ). In the case of light, the proportionality constant is the velocity of light (c), equal to 3.00×10^8 m/s. (That value is equal to 186,000 *miles per second!*)

$$\nu = \frac{c}{\lambda}$$

Note that E and ν are directly proportional, and both are inversely proportional to λ. Once any of these values is known for light, the other two can be calculated.

> The main point to understand is that a precisely known wavelength ensures a precisely known energy of light particles. The fact that the light from gaseous atoms of the elements have precise wavelengths, and therefore precise energies, led Niels Bohr to the conclusion that atoms have precisely defined energy levels (Section 4.2).

EXAMPLE 4.1

The energy of a photon is 7.50×10^{-16} J. Calculate the frequency and the wavelength of the light.

Figure 4.2 Properties of Wave Motion

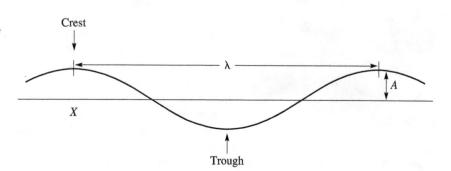

> Notice the units of *h* and *ν*:
> joules times seconds for *h* and
> the reciprocal of seconds for *ν*.

Solution

$$E = h\nu$$

$$7.50 \times 10^{-16} \text{ J} = (6.63 \times 10^{-34} \text{ J·s})\nu$$

$$\nu = 1.131 \times 10^{18}/\text{s} = 1.13 \times 10^{18}/\text{s}$$

$$\lambda = c/\nu = (3.00 \times 10^8 \text{ m/s})/(1.131 \times 10^{18}/\text{s}) = 2.65 \times 10^{-18} \text{ m}.$$

This photon is in the X-ray portion of the spectrum.

Practice Problem 4.1   Calculate the energy of the photons in green light having wavelength 5.00×10^{-7} m.

A most important concept that we will learn is that distinct wavelengths of light emitted from gaseous atoms result from electronic transitions between definite energy states within the atoms (Sections 4.2 and 4.4).

Snapshot Review

ChemSkill Builder 9.2

❏ Light has both wave and particle properties. Its wavelength (λ) is inversely proportional to its frequency (ν) and also to the energy of its photons: $E = h\nu = hc/\lambda$.

A. Calculate the energy of a photon of light if $\lambda = 1.73 \times 10^{-8}$ m.

B. If the frequency of light decreases from violet light to red light, what happens to the (a) energy of the photons? (b) wavelength?

4.2 Bohr Theory

Figure 4.3 Niels Bohr

When gaseous atoms of a given element are heated, they emit light of only specific energies. When gaseous atoms of that same element absorb light, they absorb those same energies (see Figure 3.6). To explain these phenomena of **light emission** and **light absorption,** Niels Bohr (1885–1962) (Figure 4.3) postulated that the electrons in atoms are arranged in **orbits,** each with a definite energy. The **Bohr theory** was the first to include the explanation that electrons in atoms have **discrete energy levels;** that is, electrons may be found only in orbits with specific energies.

When an atom absorbs energy, an electron is "promoted" to a higher energy level. Because each orbit has a discrete energy level, the *difference* in energy between the orbits is also definite. After an electron has been promoted to a higher energy level, it falls back to a lower energy level (Figure 4.4). When it falls back, light of energy equal to the difference in energy between the orbits is emitted from the atom. In a different experiment, when light is absorbed by the atom, the electron is raised from one orbit to another one. Because there is the same energy difference between the orbits, the same energy of light is absorbed. An example of these effects is shown in Figure 4.5. Some of the possible electron transitions in a hydrogen atom are diagrammed in Figure 4.6.

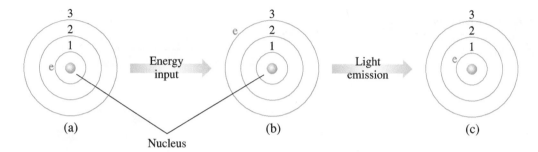

Figure 4.4 *Schematic Diagram of Light Emission from an Excited Hydrogen Atom*

The first three Bohr orbits, or energy levels, are labeled 1–3. The electron in part (a) is in the lowest energy orbit, so the atom is in the ground state. Energy is put into the atom, most often as heat, electrical energy, or light, and the electron is promoted to a higher energy level, as shown in part (b) where the electron happens to be in the third orbit. This is an excited state of the hydrogen atom, and is unstable. The electron falls spontaneously to the first orbit (either directly or through the second orbit), giving off light energy corresponding to the energy difference between the orbits between which it falls.

EXAMPLE 4.2

How many photons of light will be emitted when the electron in Figure 4.4(b) falls (1) directly to the first orbit? (2) to the second and then to the first orbit as shown in the transition from part (b) of the figure to part (c)?

Solution

(1) One

(2) Two, one for each transition

Practice Problem 4.2   Compare the energy of the one photon of Example 4.2(a) to the sum of the energies of the two photons of part (b).

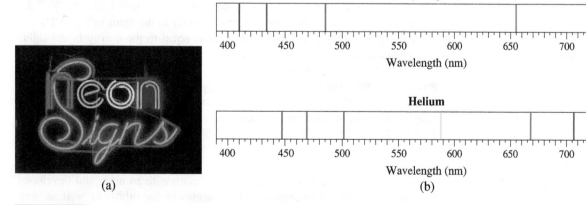

(a)   (b)

Figure 4.5   *Emission of Light by Gaseous Atoms*

(a) When neon atoms are excited by electrical energy, electron transitions between their energy levels yield wavelengths of light that produce the familiar red color of a neon sign. Wavelengths corresponding to a large number of different transitions combine to yield that color. Other gases are used to produce other colors, although we refer to all such signs in everyday conversation as "neon" signs. (b) When hydrogen and helium, with fewer electrons than neon, are similarly excited, fewer transitions occur. These emission spectra are relatively simple. Hydrogen and helium are the major components in our Sun.

Figure 4.6 Energy Levels and Some Possible Electron Transitions in the Hydrogen Atom

(not drawn to scale)

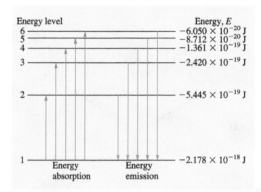

EXAMPLE 4.3

The energy of the first orbit of the hydrogen atom is -2.178×10^{-18} J, and that of the second orbit is -5.445×10^{-19} J. (A negative value means that the electron in the atom has a lower energy than a free electron has.)

(a) What energy change takes place when an electron in a hydrogen atom moves from the first to the second orbit?

(b) What energy change takes place when an electron moves from the second to the first orbit?

Solution

(a) The difference in energy between the orbits is 1.634×10^{-18} J. That much energy must be *absorbed* (for example, in the form of light, heat, or electricity) to get the electron promoted to the second orbit. If light is absorbed, light of that particular energy and no other energy is involved.

(b) The difference in energy between the two orbits is still 1.634×10^{-18} J. In this case, the energy is *emitted* (given off) in the form of light. The energy of the light emitted in this case is equal to the energy of the light absorbed in part (a).

Practice Problem 4.3   The energy of the third orbit of the hydrogen atom is -2.420×10^{-19} J. How much energy is emitted when an electron moves from (a) the third to the first orbit and (b) the third to the second orbit?

Bohr postulated circular orbits for the electrons in an atom and developed a mathematical model to represent the energies of the orbits, as well as their distances from the atom's nucleus. His model worked very well for the hydrogen atom. It could be used to calculate the energy of the emitted and absorbed light, as well as the radius of the atom. However, the intensity of the various wavelengths of light involved was not explained well. Moreover, no other atom was explained well at all. Bohr's theory has since been replaced by a quantum mechanical model, but it was a milestone because Bohr was the first to postulate energy levels in atoms.

Snapshot Review

❏ Bohr postulated that the electrons in an atom revolved about the nucleus in circular orbits and absorbed or emitted light only when they changed from one orbit to another.

❏ Bohr's postulate that electrons have distinct energy levels in atoms was a milestone in the understanding of the nature of the atom.

A. If Bohr's theory applies only to the hydrogen atom and it doesn't explain the intensities of its spectral lines well, why is it important enough for us to study?

B. How many different paths can the electron use to go from the fourth orbit to the first?

4.3 Quantum Numbers

Each electron in an atom is associated with a set of four **quantum numbers.** The names of the quantum numbers, along with their symbols and permitted values, are given in Table 4.1.

The **principal quantum number** (n) can have any positive integral value, but the electrons in atoms in their most stable states have principal quantum numbers with values from 1 through 7 only. The most stable electronic state of an atom is called its **ground state.** Any higher energy state is called an **excited state.** (Unless "excited state" is specified in later discussions, ground state is implied.) The principal quantum number has the largest role in determining the energy of the electron, and it is also the main factor in determining how far the electron is, on average, from the nucleus. Thus, it is the most important quantum number.

For each value of n, the **angular momentum quantum number** (ℓ) for an electron can have integral values from zero to ($n - 1$); it cannot be as large as n. The angular momentum quantum number has a small role in determining the energy of the electron, and it determines the shape of the volume of space that the electron can occupy (see Section 4.6).

EXAMPLE 4.4

What values for ℓ are permitted for an electron with (a) $n = 4$ and (b) $n = 2$?

Table 4.1 The Quantum Numbers

Name	Symbol	Permitted Values	Examples
Principal quantum number	n	Any positive integer	$1, 2, 3, \ldots$
Angular momentum quantum number	ℓ	Any integer from zero to ($n - 1$)	$0, \ldots, (n - 1)$
Magnetic quantum number	m_ℓ	Any integer from $-\ell$ to $+\ell$	$-\ell, \ldots, 0, \ldots, +\ell$
Spin quantum number	m_s	$-\frac{1}{2}$ or $+\frac{1}{2}$	$-\frac{1}{2}, +\frac{1}{2}$

Solution

(a) ℓ = 0, 1, 2, or 3, but no higher   (b) ℓ = 0 or 1 (ℓ cannot be as high as n)

Note that the value of ℓ is not necessarily equal to $(n - 1)$ but can vary from zero up to $(n - 1)$.

Practice Problem 4.4 *How many* different values of ℓ are permitted for an electron with (a) n = 4 and (b) n = 2?

For each value of the angular momentum quantum number (ℓ), the **magnetic quantum number** (m_ℓ) has values ranging from $-\ell$ through zero to $+\ell$ in integral steps. The value of m_ℓ does not ordinarily affect the energy of an electron, but it does determine the orientation in space of the volume that can contain the electron (Section 4.6).

EXAMPLE 4.5

What values of m_ℓ are permitted for an electron with (a) ℓ = 2 and (b) ℓ = 0?

Solution

(a) m_ℓ = $-2, -1, 0, 1,$ or 2 (b) m_ℓ = 0

Practice Problem 4.5 *How many* different values of m_ℓ are permitted for an electron with (a) ℓ = 2 and (b) ℓ = 0?

EXAMPLE 4.6

Can we tell what values of m_ℓ are permitted for an electron with n = 3?

Solution

The permitted values of m_ℓ depend on the value of ℓ, not on the value of n. The most we can say in this case is that ℓ is limited to 0, 1, or 2, so m_ℓ must be 0 if ℓ = 0, it may be $-1, 0,$ or $+1$ if ℓ = 1, and it may be $-2, -1, 0, 1,$ or 2 if ℓ = 2.

Practice Problem 4.6 What is the lowest value of m_ℓ permitted for any electron with n = 4?

Section   Row   Seat
RFLD   109A   12

Rock Concert

Date
SATURDAY
APRIL 22, 2006
1:15PM

TICKET
Z25511123421

PRICE (TAX INCLUDED) **$14.00**
ADMIT ONE SUBJECT TO CONDITIONS ON BACK

APRIL 22, 2006

PRICE (TAX INCLUDED) **$14.00**

Section   Row   Seat
RFLD   109A   12

Figure 4.7 Ticket to Rock Concert

No two tickets from the same concert hall can have the same set of section designation, row number, seat number, and date.

The **spin quantum number** (m_s) may have values of $-\frac{1}{2}$ or $+\frac{1}{2}$ only. The value of m_s does not depend on the value of any other quantum number. The spin value gives the orientation of the magnetic field associated with the electron.

Another important limitation on the quantum numbers of electrons in atoms, in addition to those listed in Table 4.1, is the **Pauli exclusion principle.** This principle states that no two electrons in an atom can have the same set of four quantum numbers. This is like the business law that states that no two tickets to a rock concert can have the same set of date and section, row, and seat numbers (Figure 4.7). The row number may depend on the section number, and the seat number may depend on the row number, but the date does not depend on any of the other three. Similarly, the spin quantum number is independent of the other three quantum numbers.

Together with the $n + \ell$ rule, discussed in the next section, the Pauli exclusion principle determines the number of electrons in each of the shells in an atom.

Snapshot Review

ChemSkill Builder 9.6

❑ Each electron in an atom has four quantum numbers, which govern its energy and average distance from the nucleus, among other things. The permitted values for the quantum numbers are critical.

A. What are the permitted values for the principal quantum number, n?
B. What are the permitted values of m_s for an electron with $n = 2$ and $\ell = 0$?
C. How many different values of m_ℓ are permitted for an electron with an ℓ value of 3?

4.4   Relative Energies of Electrons

The energies of the electrons in an atom are of paramount importance to the atom's properties. Electrons increase in energy as the sum $n + \ell$ increases. We call this the **$n + \ell$ rule**. Thus, we can make a list of sets of quantum numbers in order of their increasing energies by ordering the electrons according to increasing values of $n + \ell$. As a corollary, if two electrons have the same value of $n + \ell$, then the one with the lower n value is lower in energy. If the two n values are the same and the two ℓ values are the same, then the electrons are equal in energy. In an atom, electrons with the same energy are said to be **degenerate**.

EXAMPLE 4.7

Suppose that we must choose two integers with the lowest sum in the following ranges: For the first, we may choose any integer between 1 and 7. For the second, we may choose any nonnegative integer below the first. What integers must we select?

Solution

The lowest sum will come from the lowest possible first integer (1) and the lowest possible (and only possible) second integer (0).

Let's determine sets of four quantum numbers for the electrons of the ground states of the atoms of the first 10 elements. Hydrogen has only one electron. For that electron to be in its lowest energy state, it needs the lowest possible sum of n and ℓ, so we will choose the lowest value of n: $n = 1$.

Then, referring to Table 4.1, we determine values for the other three quantum numbers:

With $n = 1$, the only permitted value of ℓ is 0.

With $\ell = 0$, the only permitted value of m_ℓ is 0.

The value of m_s can be either $-\frac{1}{2}$ or $+\frac{1}{2}$.

The set of quantum numbers for hydrogen in its ground state can therefore be either of these:

$$
\begin{array}{ccc}
n = & 1 & \qquad \text{or} \qquad & n = & 1 \\
\ell = & 0 & & \ell = & 0 \\
m_\ell = & 0 & & m_\ell = & 0 \\
m_s = & -\tfrac{1}{2} & & m_s = & +\tfrac{1}{2}
\end{array}
$$

Since the n values and the ℓ values are the same in these two sets of quantum numbers, these possible configurations represent the same energy. Thus, either set of quantum numbers could represent the electron of hydrogen.

A helium atom has two electrons, so we need two sets of quantum numbers. To represent the atom in its lowest energy state, we want each electron to have the lowest energy possible. If we let the first electron have the value of 1 for its principal quantum number, its set of quantum numbers will be the same as one of those given previously for the one electron of hydrogen. The other electron of helium can then have the other set of quantum numbers.

$$
\begin{array}{cc}
\textit{One electron} & \textit{The other electron} \\
\textit{of helium} & \textit{of helium} \\
n = \;\; 1 & n = \;\; 1 \\
\ell = \;\; 0 & \ell = \;\; 0 \\
m_\ell = \;\; 0 & m_\ell = \;\; 0 \\
m_s = -\tfrac{1}{2} & m_s = +\tfrac{1}{2}
\end{array}
$$

Both of these electrons have the same energy because they have the same n value and the same ℓ value. Thus, either one could have been chosen as the first electron.

EXAMPLE 4.8

Could both electrons of helium have the value $m_s = +\frac{1}{2}$ with $n = 1$?

Solution

No. If n is 1, then ℓ and m_ℓ must both have values of 0 (see Table 4.1). If m_s were $+\frac{1}{2}$ for both electrons, they would have the same set of four quantum numbers, which is a violation of the Pauli principle.

Practice Problem 4.8   What is the maximum number of electrons an atom could have if the maximum value of n is 2 and each electron has a value of ℓ equal to 0?

A lithium atom has three electrons. The first two of these can have the same sets of quantum numbers as the two electrons of helium. What should the set of quantum numbers for the third electron be? We cannot choose the lowest permitted value for n, which is 1, because ℓ and m would then both be 0. If we choose $-\frac{1}{2}$ as the value of m_s, the third electron would have a set of quantum numbers exactly the same as that of one of the first two electrons, and if we choose the value $m_s = +\frac{1}{2}$, the third electron would have the same set of quantum numbers as the other. Because neither of these situations is permitted by the Pauli principle, n cannot be 1 for the third electron. We must choose the next higher value, $n = 2$. With $n = 2$, the permitted values of ℓ are 0 and 1. Because $\ell = 0$ will give a lower value for the sum $n + \ell$, we choose that value for ℓ. With $\ell = 0$, m_ℓ must be 0, and we can choose either $-\frac{1}{2}$ or $+\frac{1}{2}$ for m_s. The quantum numbers for the three electrons of the lithium atom can thus be as follows:

First electron of lithium	Second electron of lithium	Third electron of lithium
$n = 1$	$n = 1$	$n = 2$
$\ell = 0$	$\ell = 0$	$\ell = 0$
$m_\ell = 0$	$m_\ell = 0$	$m_\ell = 0$
$m_s = -\frac{1}{2}$	$m_s = +\frac{1}{2}$	$m_s = -\frac{1}{2}$ (or $+\frac{1}{2}$)

We continue deducing quantum numbers for the additional electrons of the first 10 elements. Beryllium (Be) has four electrons. With $m_s = -\frac{1}{2}$ for its third electron, the fourth electron of beryllium will have $n = 2$, $\ell = 0$, $m_\ell = 0$, and $m_s = +\frac{1}{2}$. For the fifth electron of boron (B), we cannot use the combination $n = 2$ and $\ell = 0$ because of the Pauli principle, so we use $n = 2$ and $\ell = 1$. There are three possible values for m_ℓ with $\ell = 1$, and together with the two possible values for m_s, they yield six combinations of quantum numbers with $n = 2$ and $\ell = 1$. The configurations of the first 10 electrons in a multielectron atom are shown in Table 4.2. It must be emphasized that the value of m_ℓ and the sign of the m_s value are arbitrary in some cases but not in others (see Problem 4.10 at the end of the chapter).

We can continue in this manner, building up the configuration of each element by adding a set of quantum numbers for one "last" electron to the configuration of the element before it. This process of adding one electron to those of the preceding element is called the **build-up principle.**

EXAMPLE 4.9

Write the sets of quantum numbers for the last eight electrons of argon, along with the sets given in Table 4.2 for the first 10 electrons.

Table 4.2 Possible Sets of Quantum Numbers for the Ten Electrons of Neon

Quantum Number	First Electron	Second Electron	Third Electron	Fourth Electron	Fifth Electron	Sixth Electron	Seventh Electron	Eighth Electron	Ninth Electron	Tenth Electron
n	1	1	2	2	2	2	2	2	2	2
ℓ	0	0	0	0	1	1	1	1	1	1
m_ℓ	0	0	0	0	-1	0	$+1$	-1	0	$+1$
m_s	$-\frac{1}{2}$	$+\frac{1}{2}$	$-\frac{1}{2}$	$+\frac{1}{2}$	$-\frac{1}{2}$	$-\frac{1}{2}$	$-\frac{1}{2}$	$+\frac{1}{2}$	$+\frac{1}{2}$	$+\frac{1}{2}$

Table 4.3 Possible Sets of Quantum Numbers for the Last Eight Electrons of Argon

Quantum Number	Eleventh Electron	Twelfth Electron	Thirteenth Electron	Fourteenth Electron	Fifteenth Electron	Sixteenth Electron	Seventeenth Electron	Eighteenth Electron
n	3	3	3	3	3	3	3	3
ℓ	0	0	1	1	1	1	1	1
m_ℓ	0	0	-1	0	$+1$	-1	0	$+1$
m_s	$-\frac{1}{2}$	$+\frac{1}{2}$	$-\frac{1}{2}$	$-\frac{1}{2}$	$-\frac{1}{2}$	$+\frac{1}{2}$	$+\frac{1}{2}$	$+\frac{1}{2}$

Solution

The sets are shown in Table 4.3. Note that the combination $n = 3$, $\ell = 1$ has the same sum of n and ℓ as $n = 4$, $\ell = 0$. Because the sum is the same, the combination with the lower n value is used for each of the thirteenth through eighteenth electrons because it is lower in energy.

When we try to add the nineteenth electron to write the configuration for potassium (K), we encounter a new situation. The combination with the next lowest sum of n and ℓ is $n = 4$, $\ell = 0$. The combination $n = 3$, $\ell = 2$ is higher in energy. The nineteenth through twenty-first electrons can have the following sets of quantum numbers:

Quantum number	Nineteenth electron	Twentieth electron	Twenty-first electron
n	4	4	3
ℓ	0	0	2
m_ℓ	0	0	-2
m_s	$-\frac{1}{2}$	$+\frac{1}{2}$	$-\frac{1}{2}$
$n + \ell$	4	4	5

The fact that electrons having quantum number values $n = 4$ and $\ell = 0$ are lower in energy than electrons with $n = 3$ and $\ell = 2$ is of extreme importance; it explains the existence and position on the periodic table of the transition metals. This point will be explained later.

EXAMPLE 4.10

Arrange the following electrons, identified only by their n and ℓ quantum numbers, in order of increasing energy from lowest to highest.

(a) $n = 3, \ell = 2$ (b) $n = 5, \ell = 0$

(c) $n = 4, \ell = 2$ (d) $n = 4, \ell = 1$

(e) $n = 5, \ell = 1$

Solution

Calculate the sum $n + \ell$ for each electron:

(a) $n = 3, \ell = 2$, so $n + \ell = 5$ (b) $n = 5, \ell = 0$, so $n + \ell = 5$

(c) $n = 4, \ell = 2$, so $n + \ell = 6$ (d) $n = 4, \ell = 1$, so $n + \ell = 5$

(e) $n = 5, \ell = 1$, so $n + \ell = 6$

The ones with lower values of $n + \ell$ are lower in energy, so electrons (a), (b), and (d) are lower in energy than (c) and (e). The sum $n + \ell$ is the same for (a), (b), and (d), so (a), the one with the lowest n value, is lowest in energy and (d) is next. The sum $n + \ell$ is the same for (c) and (e), so (c), the one with the lower n value, is lower in energy. Thus, the order of increasing energy is (a) $<$ (d) $<$ (b) $<$ (c) $<$ (e).

Practice Problem 4.10   Arrange the following electrons, identified only by their n and ℓ quantum numbers, in order of increasing energy from lowest to highest.

(a) $n = 4, \ell = 1$ (b) $n = 5, \ell = 2$ (c) $n = 5, \ell = 0$

(d) $n = 6, \ell = 0$ (e) $n = 5, \ell = 1$

Snapshot Review

❑ The $n + \ell$ rule, the Pauli exclusion principle, and the permitted values of the quantum numbers enable us to determine the order of the electrons in an atom in increasing energy.

❑ Atoms in their ground states have all their electrons with the lowest possible values of $n + \ell$.

❑ If two electrons have the same sum $n + \ell$ but have different n values, the one with the lower n value is lower in energy.

A. In each part, determine which electron, labeled X or Y, has the lower energy:

(a) X: $n = 4, \ell = 0$ Y: $n = 3, \ell = 2$

(b) X: $n = 3, \ell = 1$ Y: $n = 4, \ell = 0$

(c) X: $n = 5, \ell = 2$ Y: $n = 5, \ell = 1$

4.5   Shells, Subshells, and Orbitals

A **shell** is defined as a group of electrons in an atom all having the same principal quantum number. A **subshell** is defined as a group of electrons in an atom all having the same principal quantum number and also the same angular momentum quantum number. If two electrons in an atom have the same principal quantum number, the same angular momentum quantum number, and the same magnetic quantum number, the electrons are said to be in the same **orbital.**

EXAMPLE 4.11

Show that a maximum of two electrons can occupy a given orbital.

Solution

By definition, the electrons in a given orbital have the same n value, the same ℓ value, and the same m_ℓ value. According to the Pauli exclusion principle, they must therefore have different values for their spin quantum numbers (m_s).

Because only two m_s values ($-\frac{1}{2}$ and $+\frac{1}{2}$) are permitted, the maximum number of electrons in a given orbital is two.

Practice Problem 4.11   What is the maximum number of electrons that will fit into the first subshell of the second shell of an atom?

Even though the m_ℓ and m_s values do not affect the energy of the electron, it is still important to learn about them. The number of combinations of permitted values of these quantum numbers determines the maximum number of electrons in a given type of subshell. For example, in a subshell for which $\ell = 2$, m_ℓ can have five different values ($-2, -1, 0, +1$, and $+2$), and m_s can have two different values ($-\frac{1}{2}$ and $+\frac{1}{2}$). The ten different combinations of m_ℓ and m_s allow a maximum of ten electrons in any subshell for which $\ell = 2$.

EXAMPLE 4.12

How many electrons are permitted in a subshell for which (a) $\ell = 0$? (b) for $\ell = 3$?

Solution

(a) When $\ell = 0$, $m_\ell = 0$. Because m_ℓ has only one permitted value and m_s has two, there are two different combinations of m_ℓ and m_s for this subshell. Thus, it can be occupied by a maximum of two electrons.

(b) Seven permitted m_ℓ values ($-3, -2, -1, 0, +1, +2$, and $+3$) times two permitted m_s values ($-\frac{1}{2}$ and $+\frac{1}{2}$) makes 14 combinations. A maximum of 14 electrons can occupy this subshell.

Writing out each quantum number value for every electron in an atom is very time-consuming. A more efficient method is to group all the electrons in a given subshell. In this method, the following four lowercase letters represent the possible ℓ values:

Value of ℓ	Letter
0	s
1	p
2	d
3	f

Because only n and ℓ values affect the energies of electrons, the electrons with the same n value and the same ℓ value all have the same energy. In other words, all the electrons in a given subshell are degenerate. Each subshell is denoted by its principal quantum number and the letter designation for ℓ. For example, for neon, with atomic number 10, the sets of quantum numbers for the 10 electrons are listed in Table 4.2. We can group them as follows:

Value of n	Value of ℓ	Number of electrons	Subshell designation
1	0	2	1s
2	0	2	2s
2	1	6	2p

We write the **electronic configuration** by listing each subshell in order of increasing energy, with a superscript giving the number of electrons in that subshell. That is, the detailed electronic configuration for a neon atom is

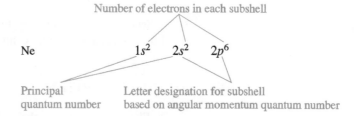

This configuration is read aloud as follows: "one ess two, two ess two, two pee six." (The superscripts are not exponents, so words such as *square* are not used.) The sum of the superscripts is the total number of electrons in the atom.

EXAMPLE 4.13

Using sets of quantum numbers from Table 4.2, write the detailed electronic configuration of fluorine.

Solution

Fluorine, with atomic number 9, has 9 electrons. The first 9 electrons shown in the table will fit into three subshells, as follows:

$$1s^2 \, 2s^2 \, 2p^5$$

Note that the $2p$ subshell can hold a maximum of 6 electrons, but in fluorine, only 5 electrons are left for that subshell.

Practice Problem 4.13 What element has the following electronic configuration?

$$1s^2 \, 2s^2 \, 2p^3$$

EXAMPLE 4.14

Write the detailed electronic structure of vanadium (V). Comment on the relative energies of the "last" 5 electrons.

Solution

$$1s^2 \, 2s^2 \, 2p^6 \, 3s^2 \, 3p^6 \, 4s^2 \, 3d^3$$

Because the "last" 3 electrons are added to an inner shell (following the $n + \ell$ rule) instead of the outermost shell, the $3d$ subshell of a vanadium atom must be higher in energy than the $4s$ subshell.

Practice Problem 4.14 What element has the following electronic configuration?

$$1s^2\, 2s^2\, 2p^6\, 3s^2\, 3p^6\, 4s^2\, 3d^6$$

In Section 4.8, we will learn to use the periodic table as a memory device to aid us in writing electronic configurations.

 ## *Snapshot Review*

❒ Electrons in a given shell all have the same n value; electrons in a given subshell all have the same n value and the same ℓ value; electrons in a given orbital all have the same n value, the same ℓ value, and the same m_ℓ value.

❒ Detailed electronic configurations of elements give the subshells in increasing order of energies with the number of electrons occupying each subshell as a right superscript.

A. Give the detailed electronic configuration of (a) O, (b) S.
B. Give the detailed electronic configuration of Mn.

4.6 Shapes of Orbitals

An orbital is an allowed energy state in an atom. Each orbital is designated by the three quantum numbers n, ℓ, and m_ℓ. Because m_s is not specified, either value of m_s can be used, and a maximum of two electrons can occupy any given orbital in an atom.

Knowing exactly both the location and the momentum of an electron in an atom at the same time is impossible. This fact is known as the **Heisenberg uncertainty principle.** Therefore, scientists describe the *probable* locations of electrons. These locations describe the **orbital shapes,** which are important when the atom forms bonds with other atoms, because the orbital shapes are the basis of the geometry of the resulting molecule.

It is equally probable that s orbital electrons will be located in any direction about the nucleus. We say that an s orbital is spherically symmetrical. The 1s orbital is pictured in Figure 4.8(a). Because an electron with $\ell = 1$ has three possible m_ℓ values, any p subshell has three orbitals. Each one lies along one of the coordinate axes—x, y, or z—as shown in Figure 4.8(b). Each p orbital consists of two 3-dimensional **lobes** centered on one of the axes. An atom has five 3d orbitals, corresponding to the five possible m_ℓ values ($-2, -1, 0, +1,$ and $+2$) for a subshell with $\ell = 2$. Their orientations are shown in Figure 4.8(c).

Snapshot Review

❒ The s orbitals are spherically symmetrical, and the p and d orbitals are oriented as shown in Figure 4.8. Do not mistake the individual lobes of the p and d orbitals as separate orbitals.

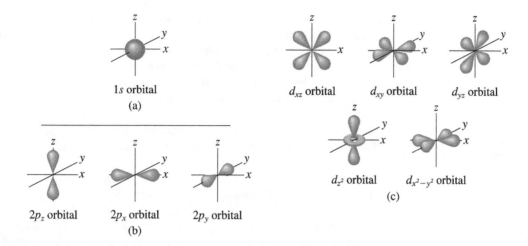

1s orbital
(a)

d_{xz} orbital d_{xy} orbital d_{yz} orbital

d_{z^2} orbital $d_{x^2-y^2}$ orbital

(c)

2p_z orbital   2p_x orbital   2p_y orbital
(b)

Figure 4.8 *Shapes of Orbitals*

(a) The 1s orbital.
(b) The three 2p orbitals.
(c) The five 3d orbitals.

A. (a) Along what axis does the p_y orbital lie? (b) Along what axis does the d_{z^2} orbital lie? (c) Along what axes does the $d_{x^2-y^2}$ orbital lie?

4.7 Energy Level Diagrams

Energy level diagrams are models for portraying electrons' occupancy of an atom's orbitals. They help chemists predict how many electrons occupy each orbital of a subshell. Electron occupancy of the individual orbitals is important in determining an atom's magnetic properties. A line or a box or a circle is used to represent each orbital. An energy level diagram that could hold the electrons of any known atom is shown in Figure 4.9. The energy level diagram is like a graph in one dimension: The higher a subshell is placed, the higher the energy of that subshell. The lines are spaced horizontally from left to right only to prevent crowding so that the diagram is easier to read.

The lowest line on the energy level diagram represents the orbital in the 1s subshell of the atom. Much higher in the diagram, indicating a much higher

Figure 4.9 Energy level Diagram

(not drawn to scale)

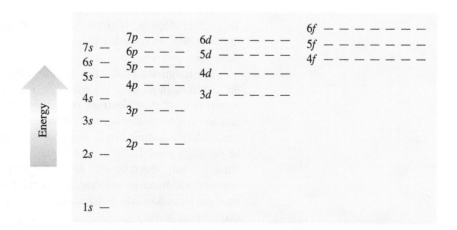

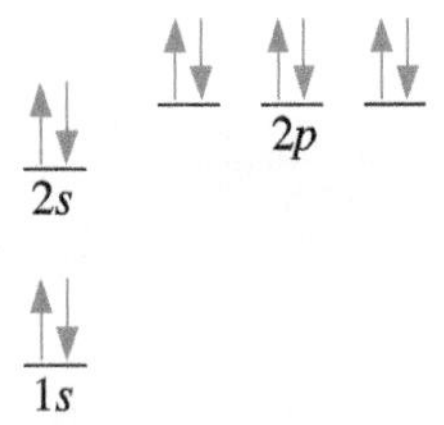

Figure 4.10 Electron Occupancy of the Neon Atom

energy, lies the line for the $2s$ orbital. Somewhat higher than that are the three lines for the orbitals of the $2p$ subshell. The third shell lies at even higher energies and consists of an s subshell, a p subshell, and a d subshell. Note that the $3d$ subshell lies at a slightly higher energy than the $4s$ subshell. The order of energy in the diagram is the same as that given by the $n + \ell$ rule.

We will most often focus our attention on the portion of the energy level diagram containing the last electron added, in which we are most interested. The orbitals that lie above that portion are assumed to be empty, and any orbitals that lie below those pictured are almost always completely filled when the atom is in its ground state.

We represent each electron with an arrow. Different electron spins (m_s value of $-\frac{1}{2}$ or $+\frac{1}{2}$) are indicated by arrows pointing downward or upward. Because each line represents one orbital, each line may hold a maximum of two arrows. If two arrows are present, they must be pointing in opposite directions. The energy level diagram representing the neon atom is shown in Figure 4.10.

Hund's rule states that the electrons *within a given subshell* remain as *unpaired as possible*. Moreover, if there are two or more unpaired electrons in a given subshell, they all must occupy different orbitals and have the same electron spin (all arrows representing unpaired electrons in a subshell point up or all point down). The energy level diagrams for the carbon, nitrogen, and oxygen atoms illustrate these rules:

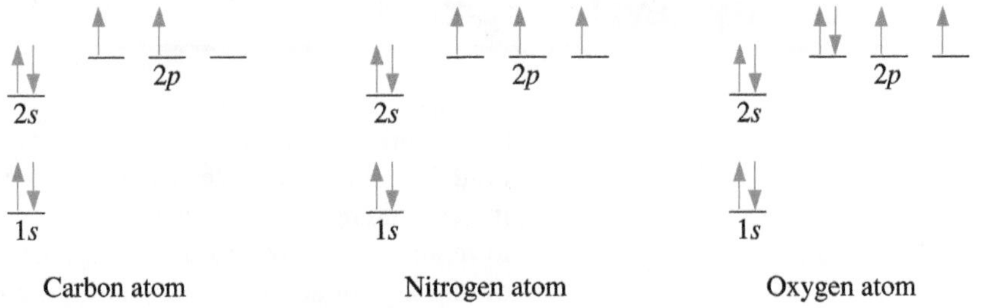

Carbon atom   Nitrogen atom   Oxygen atom

In the carbon atom, the lowest two subshells are filled; all electrons are paired in filled subshells. The $2p$ subshell has two electrons in the three orbitals, so each electron occupies a separate orbital. Moreover, both electrons have the same spin—both arrows point upward (alternatively, both could point downward). They are said to have parallel spin. In the nitrogen atom, the $2p$ subshell is half filled. Each electron occupies a different orbital, and all arrows point in the same direction. In the oxygen atom, the $2p$ subshell is again partially filled. To get four electrons into the three orbitals requires the pairing of two electrons in one orbital. In the other two orbitals, the electrons are unpaired and have the same spin.

The **magnetic properties** of atoms enable us to tell experimentally if all the electrons in an atom are paired or, if not, how many electrons are unpaired. Atoms with all their electrons paired are repelled slightly from a magnetic field, and are said to be *diamagnetic*. If at least one electron per atom in a sample is unpaired, the sample tends to be drawn into a magnetic field, and is said to be *paramagnetic*. The greater the number of unpaired electrons, the greater the attraction into the magnetic field. (In elemental iron, cobalt, and nickel, the unpaired electrons in adjacent atoms reinforce one another, and a very much stronger attraction into a magnetic field results. These are the metals of which magnets are made.)

EXAMPLE 4.15

How many unpaired electrons are in (a) a fluorine atom, (b) an oxygen atom, and (c) a boron atom?

Solution

Fluorine atom   Oxygen atom   Boron atom

The energy level diagrams show one unpaired electron in a fluorine atom, two in an oxygen atom, and one in a boron atom.

Practice Problem 4.15   How many unpaired electrons are in (a) an argon atom and (b) a carbon atom?

Snapshot Review

ChemSkill Builder 9.3

❑ An energy level diagram shows the individual orbitals graphically with increasing energy toward the top. Because only two electrons fit into any orbital (thus on any line), the electronic configuration of the atom can be deduced using such a diagram.

❑ Electrons *in a given subshell* occupy the orbitals singly with their spins aligned until the subshell is half full, after which they start to pair up.

A. How many unpaired electrons are present in the ground state of (a) a phosphorus atom? (b) a selenium atom?

4.8 Periodic Variation of Electronic Configuration

The outermost part of the electronic configuration is the main factor that determines the chemical properties of the elements.

The elements display a **periodicity of electronic configuration.** For example, if we examine the detailed electronic configurations of the alkali metals, we find that the outermost shell (specifically, the *s* subshell) of electrons contains only a single electron in each case. The alkaline earth metals have two outermost *s* electrons. The elements within each other group of the periodic table also have similarities in their outermost electronic configurations. We deduce that the outermost part of the electronic configuration is the main factor that determines the chemical properties of the elements because the periodic table was constructed from data about the properties of the elements.

EXAMPLE 4.16

Write the electronic configurations of O, S, Se, Te. What feature makes them have similar chemical properties?

Solution

O	$1s^2\, 2s^2\, 2p^4$
S	$1s^2\, 2s^2\, 2p^6\, 3s^2\, 3p^4$
Se	$1s^2\, 2s^2\, 2p^6\, 3s^2\, 3p^6\, 4s^2\, 3d^{10}\, 4p^4$
Te	$1s^2\, 2s^2\, 2p^6\, 3s^2\, 3p^6\, 4s^2\, 3d^{10}\, 4p^6\, 5s^2\, 4d^{10}\, 5p^4$

The $ns^2\, np^4$ configuration of the outermost (nth) shell is common to all the group VIA elements and different from the outermost configuration of the other elements. It is the cause of their similar chemical properties.

Practice Problem 4.16   Write the electronic configurations of N, P, As, and Sb. State the feature that makes them have similar chemical properties.

> We can use the periodic table to help us write electronic configurations of the atoms of the elements.

We can use the periodic table to help us write electronic configurations of the atoms of the elements. The periodic table can be divided into blocks corresponding to the type of subshell occupied by the last electron added (Figure 4.11). The two groups at the left of the periodic table—the alkali metals and the alkaline earth metals—constitute the s block because their last electrons occupy s subshells. Hydrogen and helium also are in this block, and we must mentally shift helium to a place beside hydrogen for this purpose. The six periodic groups at the right of the table constitute the p block; their last electrons go into p subshells. The transition metals belong to the d block, and the f block consists of the inner transition metals.

Note the similarity between the number of elements in a particular block in each period and the maximum number of electrons permitted in the corresponding type subshell:

ChemSkill Builder
9.4, 9.5

Type of subshell or block	Maximum number of electrons in subshell	Number of elements in a particular block in each period
s	2	2
p	6	6
d	10	10
f	14	14

> The electronic structure of atoms is the basis for the periodic behavior of the elements.

After each noble gas, a new shell of electrons is started, as is a new period of the periodic table. It turns out that electronic structure is the basis for the periodic behavior of the elements.

The four transition metal series arise because, for each of these elements, an electron has been added to the next-to-outermost shell. Addition of 10 electrons to the $3d$ subshell *after the completion of the $4s$ subshell* causes 10 elements to occur after calcium to be the first elements in their periodic groups. The second, third, and fourth transition series occur because the $4d$, $5d$, and $6d$ subshells add electrons after the start of the fifth, sixth, and seventh shells,

Figure 4.11 Using the Periodic Table to Write Electronic Configurations

For the s and p blocks, the principal quantum number is equal to the period number. For the d block, the principal quantum number is equal to the period number minus 1. For the f block, the principal quantum number is equal to the period number minus 2.

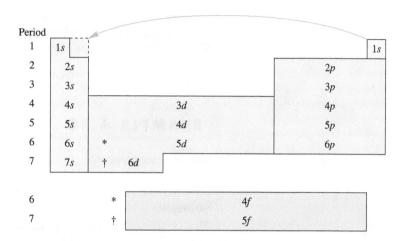

respectively. The inner transition elements stem from the addition of electrons to f subshells two shells lower than the outermost shell of their atoms.

Because the periodic table reflects the electronic structures of the atoms, we can use it to deduce the configuration of any atom. We use the periodic table with its s, p, d, and f blocks, as shown in Figure 4.11. We imagine helium to be next to hydrogen in the $1s$ block. To determine the electronic configuration of an element, we start at hydrogen—element 1—and continue *in order of atomic numbers* until we get to the element in question. The subshells come from the blocks in the periodic table, and the numbers of electrons (the superscripts in the configuration) are the numbers of elements in the blocks up to the element in question. Thus, we determine the electronic configuration of phosphorus to be

$$1s^2 \, 2s^2 \, 2p^6 \, 3s^2 \, 3p^3$$

EXAMPLE 4.17

Using the periodic table as an aid, write the detailed electronic configuration for each of the following elements:

(a) S   (b) Fe   (c) Lu

Solution

(a) $1s^2 \, 2s^2 \, 2p^6 \, 3s^2 \, 3p^4$

(b) $1s^2 \, 2s^2 \, 2p^6 \, 3s^2 \, 3p^6 \, 4s^2 \, 3d^6$

(c) $1s^2 \, 2s^2 \, 2p^6 \, 3s^2 \, 3p^6 \, 4s^2 \, 3d^{10} \, 4p^6 \, 5s^2 \, 4d^{10} \, 5p^6 \, 6s^2 \, 5d^1 \, 4f^{14}$

Practice Problem 4.17   Using the periodic table as an aid, write the detailed electronic configuration for each of the following elements:

(a) V   (b) Br   (c) Ge

A more compact notation can sometimes be used to reduce the effort of writing long electronic configurations while retaining almost as much information. We are most interested in the outermost shell and the inner subshells having nearly the same energies. We can therefore write the detailed electronic configuration for just that shell and those subshells of the atom, and we use the symbol of the preceding noble gas in square brackets to represent all the other electrons. For example, the electronic configuration of Ac (element 89) is denoted

$$\text{Ac: } [\text{Rn}] \, 7s^2 \, 6d^1$$

EXAMPLE 4.18

Write the electronic configuration for thallium (element 81), using the shortened notation.

Solution

$$\text{Tl: } [\text{Xe}] \, 6s^2 \, 4f^{14} \, 5d^{10} \, 6p^1$$

The symbol for the preceding noble gas, Xe, is written in square brackets. Then, starting at Cs, the alkali metal in the same period as thallium, we write $6s^2$ for Cs and Ba, $4f^{14}$ for the lanthanide elements, $5d^{10}$ for the elements from La to Hg, and $6p^1$ for Tl. We must be especially careful to follow the atomic numbers after elements 57 (La) and 89 (Ac), where the two inner transition series start. Note that the superscripts in the previous configuration plus the atomic number of Xe (54) add up to the atomic number of Tl (81).

Practice Problem 4.18   Write the electronic configuration for uranium using the shortened notation.

Using the periodic table as a mnemonic device has several advantages over relying on the $n + \ell$ rule and other rules:

1. The periodic table is generally available for reference during examinations.
2. The order of subshells is given "automatically."
3. The maximum number of electrons in each subshell matches the number of elements in each block.
4. To write a shortened notation for an element, we can start at the alkali metal in the same period.

No matter which "rule" or memory device we use to write configurations, some transition metals and inner transition metals have configurations different from our expected configurations. Some of these occur because of the added stability associated with half-filled or fully filled subshells. For example, chromium and copper have actual configurations with two such outermost subshells instead of only the fully filled $4s$ subshell and $3d$ subshell neither half nor fully filled, as expected:

> Some transition metals and inner transition metals have configurations different from our expected configurations.

	Actual configuration	*Expected configuration*
Cr:	$1s^2 \, 2s^2 \, 2p^6 \, 3s^2 \, 3p^6 \, 4s^1 \, 3d^5$	$1s^2 \, 2s^2 \, 2p^6 \, 3s^2 \, 3p^6 \, 4s^2 \, 3d^4$
Cu:	$1s^2 \, 2s^2 \, 2p^6 \, 3s^2 \, 3p^6 \, 4s^1 \, 3d^{10}$	$1s^2 \, 2s^2 \, 2p^6 \, 3s^2 \, 3p^6 \, 4s^2 \, 3d^9$

Most, but not all, cations formed from atoms of these elements have the same configuration predicted by our "rules" or predicted from their actual configurations, and the compounds containing these cations are of more interest to chemists than the uncombined atoms of these elements anyway. (Section 5.2)

Snapshot Review

❏ Atoms in a given periodic group have similar outermost electronic configurations.

❏ The periodic table results from the electronic configurations of the atoms, and so it can be used as a memory device to deduce these configurations.

A. Deduce the outermost electronic configuration of Lr without bothering to assign the inner 86 electrons to subshells.

Key Terms

Key terms are defined in the Glossary.

angular momentum quantum number (4.3)
Bohr theory (4.2)
build-up principle (4.4)
degenerate (4.4)
discrete energy levels (4.2)
electromagnetic spectrum (4.1)
electronic configuration (4.5)
energy level diagram (4.7)
excited state (4.3)
frequency (4.1)
ground state (4.3)

Heisenberg uncertainty principle (4.6)
Hund's rule (4.7)
light (4.1)
light absorption (4.2)
light emission (4.2)
lobe (4.6)
magnetic properties (4.7)
magnetic quantum number (4.3)
$n + \ell$ rule (4.4)
orbit (4.2)
orbital (4.5)
orbital shape (4.6)

Pauli exclusion principle (4.3)
periodicity of electronic configuration (4.8)
photon (4.1)
principal quantum number (4.3)
quantum numbers (4.3)
shell (4.5)
spin quantum number (4.3)
subshell (4.5)
wavelength (4.1)

Symbols/Abbreviations

c (velocity of light) (4.1)

d (a subshell) (4.5)

f (a subshell) (4.5)

ℓ (angular momentum quantum number) (4.3)

λ (*lambda*, wavelength) (4.1)

m_ℓ (magnetic quantum number) (4.3)

m_s (spin quantum number) (4.3)

n (principal quantum number) (4.3)

v (*nu*, frequency) (4.1)

p (a subshell) (4.5)

s (a subshell) (4.5)

Summary

The chemical properties of atoms depend on their electronic structures. The number of electrons in a neutral atom is equal to the number of protons in the nucleus—the atomic number of the element.

Light is electromagnetic radiation that has properties of both wave motion and a stream of particles (photons). The wavelength of light (as a wave) is inversely proportional to the energy of its photons (particles). (Section 4.1)

Bohr first proposed the concept that electrons are arranged in discrete energy levels in the atom, which explained the emission of specific energies of light when gaseous atoms are heated. Although Bohr's theory could

not explain many other details of the behavior of atoms, it was a milestone in relating electronic structure and properties of atoms. (Section 4.2)

The modern theory of electronic structure is based on the assignment of four quantum numbers to each electron in an atom. The principal quantum number, n, governs the energy of the electron and also its probable distance from the nucleus. The angular momentum quantum number, ℓ, also has an effect on the energy and determines the shape of the volume of space that the electron can occupy. The magnetic quantum number, m_ℓ, determines the orientation in space of the volume occupied by the electron, and the spin quantum number, m_s, indicates the spin of the electron on its axis. The limits on the quantum numbers (Table 4.1) must be memorized. The Pauli exclusion principle states that no two electrons in an atom can have the same set of four quantum numbers. (Section 4.3)

The $n + \ell$ rule governs the order of increasing energy of the electrons in the atom. Subshells are filled with electrons in the order of increasing $n + \ell$, with due regard for the limitations on the quantum numbers and for the Pauli exclusion principle. In each case, the "last" electron can be added to the configuration of the element before, using a procedure known as the build-up principle. (Section 4.4)

Electrons in a given shell of an atom all have the same n value. Electrons in a given subshell of an atom all have the same n value and the same ℓ value. Electrons in a given orbital of an atom all have the same n value, the same ℓ value, and the same m_ℓ value. By convention, subshells are designated using lowercase letters that correspond to the various ℓ values, and the electronic configuration of an atom is written using superscripts for the numbers of electrons occupying the subshells (for example, $1s^2$ indicates that two electrons occupy the $1s$ subshell). (Section 4.5)

Electrons in the various orbitals occupy portions of space having specified shapes (see Figure 4.8). (These are important when the shapes of molecules are considered in Section 13.4.) (Section 4.6)

Energy level diagrams portray electrons' occupation of the orbitals in an atom. Such diagrams are useful for understanding Hund's rule and atoms' magnetic properties. Hund's rule states that in partially filled subshells, the electrons occupy orbitals singly and have the same spins as far as possible. If all the electrons in a substance are paired (two electrons in each occupied orbital), the substance will be repelled slightly from a magnetic field. However, if at least one electron in each formula unit is unpaired, the substance will be drawn into a magnetic field. (Section 4.7)

The properties of the elements stem from their electronic configurations, and the properties place them in their locations in the periodic table. In each group, the elements have a characteristic outermost electronic configuration. The existence of the transition and inner transition elements stems from adding electrons to inner shells after outer shells have been started. Because the periodic table reflects the electronic structures of the atoms, it can be used as a memory device when writing electronic configurations. The ability to write and understand such configurations is a very important skill. (Section 4.8)

Items for Special Attention

■ The frequency of light is a number per second, so its unit is the reciprocal of seconds: $1/s$ or s^{-1}. The units of h are joules *times* seconds.

■ When electrons undergo transitions to higher shells, energy is *absorbed* by the atom; when electrons undergo transitions to lower shells, energy is *emitted* by the atom.

■ There is a difference between the questions "How many m_ℓ values are possible?" and "What are the possible m_ℓ values?" The number of m_ℓ values is the number of orbitals in the subshell.

■ We can think of electrons in shells as being similar to small children on a ladder: They can never be between levels and are most stable at the lowest energy level possible.

■ The p, d, and f orbitals have more than one lobe each. Do not mistake each lobe for a separate orbital.

Answers to Snapshot Reviews

4.1 A. $E = \dfrac{hc}{\lambda} = \dfrac{(6.63 \times 10^{-34}\ \text{J·s})(3.00 \times 10^8\ \text{m/s})}{1.73 \times 10^{-8}\ \text{m}}$
$= 1.15 \times 10^{-17}\ \text{J}$

B. (a) The energy decreases.
(b) The wavelength increases.

4.2 A. It was the first postulate of discrete energy levels in atoms, a critical breakthrough.

B. Four. $(4 \rightarrow 3 \rightarrow 2 \rightarrow 1; 4 \rightarrow 3 \rightarrow 1; 4 \rightarrow 2 \rightarrow 1; 4 \rightarrow 1)$

4.3 A. Any positive integer. (The integers 1 through 7 are the most important.)

B. $-\frac{1}{2}$ or $+\frac{1}{2}$. (m_s does not depend on the value of any other quantum number.)

C. Seven $(-3, -2, -1, 0, 1, 2, 3)$

4.4 A. (a) X (lower $n + \ell$), (b) X (equal $n + \ell$, lower n), and
(c) Y (lower $n + \ell$)

4.5 A. (a) O: $1s^2\,2s^2\,2p^4$; (b) S: $1s^2\,2s^2\,2p^6\,3s^2\,3p^4$

B. Mn: $1s^2\,2s^2\,2p^6\,3s^2\,3p^6\,4s^2\,3d^5$

4.6 A. (a) The y-axis, (b) the z-axis, and (c) the x- and y-axes

4.7 A. (a) Three, (b) Two

4.8 A. [Rn] $7s^2\,6d^1\,5f^{14}$

Self-Tutorial Problems

4.1 If an athlete runs around a track 12 times in an hour, what is her frequency (including the unit)?

4.2 Multiply the wavelength and frequency values at any point in Figure 4.1. What value results? Repeat the procedure for a second point. Does the same or different value result? Explain these results.

4.3 What difference is there, if any, when the instructor states "The first line in the visible spectrum of hydrogen has a definite (a) wavelength." (b) frequency." (c) energy of its photons."

4.4 For what element is the Bohr theory most useful?

4.5 What values are possible for the principal quantum number n for electrons in the ground state of an atom of Ac, element 89?

4.6 (a) What is the difference, if any, between an s subshell and an s orbital?

(b) What is the difference, if any, between a p subshell and a p orbital?

4.7 (a) If 10 marbles are placed in an empty ice cream cone, how many will have the lowest position?

(b) If the cone is held steady, how many will have the lowest position possible under the circumstances?

(c) Do the 10 electrons in a neon atom in its ground state all have the same energy?

(d) Will all 10 have the lowest energy possible under the circumstances?

4.8 What principles or rules affect the energies of electrons in an atom?

4.9 (a) Can two tickets to a concert have the same section, the same row, the same seat, and the same date?

(b) How many of these must be different to avoid seating problems?

(c) Can two electrons in the same atom have the same n value, the same ℓ value, the same m_ℓ value, and the same m_s value?

(d) How many of these must be different to have a permissible situation?

4.10 For the electrons of Table 4.2, is the sign of the m_s value arbitrary for (a) the first electron, (b) the second electron, (c) the fifth electron, (d) the tenth electron?

4.11 Explain why helium, with two outermost electrons, has the same inertness characteristic of neon and argon, each with eight outermost electrons.

4.12 Add the energies for the change of the electron in the hydrogen atom from the third orbit to the second plus that from the second orbit to the first (see Example 4.3 and Practice Problem 4.3 for data). Compare your answer to the energy for the change from the third orbit to the first, and explain your result.

Problems

4.1 A Brief Exploration of Light

4.13 Calculate the frequency of a photon of light of wavelength 6.563×10^{-7} m, corresponding to a line in the visible spectrum of hydrogen.

4.14 Use the equation $E = hc/\lambda$ with E in joules, c in meters per second, and λ in meters to determine the units of h.

4.15 Calculate the wavelength of a photon of light of energy 4.09×10^{-19} J, corresponding to a line in the visible spectrum of hydrogen.

4.16 Label Figure 4.1 with an axis having units of energy.

4.17 Calculate the frequency and wavelength of a 4.85×10^{-19} J photon, corresponding to a line in the visible spectrum of hydrogen.

4.18 Calculate the energy of a photon of light of wavelength 4.340×10^{-7} m, corresponding to a line in the visible spectrum of hydrogen.

4.19 The frequency of a certain beam of light is 7.00×10^{11}/s. Calculate the wavelength and the energy of its photons. Determine in what portion of the electromagnetic spectrum the beam lies.

4.2 Bohr Theory

4.20 Describe qualitatively the relationship between energy and the electron transitions occurring in the neon gas in a neon sign.

4.21 List the possible series of electron transitions for an electron descending from the sixth shell to the third in a hydrogen atom.

4.22 How many different wavelengths of light would be emitted if many identical atoms underwent the changes described in the prior problem?

4.3 Quantum Numbers

4.23 What values of ℓ are permitted for an electron with $n = 4$?

4.24 What values of m_ℓ are permitted for an electron with $\ell = 3$?

4.25 What values of m_s are permitted for an electron with $n = 5$, $\ell = 3$, and $m_\ell = +2$?

■ Problems

4.26 Which of the following sets of quantum numbers is (are) *not* permitted?

(a) $n = 3, \ell = 0, m_\ell = +1, m_s = -\frac{1}{2}$

(b) $n = 3, \ell = 2, m_\ell = -1, m_s = -1$

(c) $n = 3, \ell = -2, m_\ell = 0, m_s = -\frac{1}{2}$

(d) $n = 3, \ell = 3, m_\ell = -2, m_s = +\frac{1}{2}$

4.27 Make a chart showing all possible values of ℓ, m_ℓ, and m_s for an electron with $n = 2$ and another with $n = 3$.

4.4 Relative Energies of Electrons

4.28 (a) What values of m_ℓ are permitted for an electron with $\ell = 5$?

(b) How many different values of m_ℓ are permitted for an electron with $\ell = 5$?

4.29 Arrange the following electrons, identified only by their n and ℓ quantum numbers, in order of increasing energy from lowest to highest.

(a) $n = 6, \ell = 3$ (b) $n = 6, \ell = 2$

(c) $n = 5, \ell = 3$ (d) $n = 5, \ell = 2$

4.30 Arrange the following electrons in order of increasing energy:

(a) $n = 5, \ell = 1$ (b) $n = 4, \ell = 2$

(c) $n = 4, \ell = 3$ (d) $n = 6, \ell = 0$

4.31 Arrange the following electrons in order of increasing energy:

(a) $n = 5, \ell = 1, m_\ell = -1, m_s = +\frac{1}{2}$

(b) $n = 5, \ell = 1, m_\ell = 0, m_s = -\frac{1}{2}$

(c) $n = 5, \ell = 1, m_\ell = 1, m_s = -\frac{1}{2}$

(d) $n = 5, \ell = 1, m_\ell = 0, m_s = +\frac{1}{2}$

4.32 Compare the energies of the following electrons, identified by their quantum numbers only:

(a) $n = 3, \ell = 2, m_\ell = 1, m_s = +\frac{1}{2}$

(b) $n = 3, \ell = 2, m_\ell = -1, m_s = -\frac{1}{2}$

(c) $n = 3, \ell = 2, m_\ell = 0, m_s = +\frac{1}{2}$

4.33 Arrange the following four electrons in order of increasing energy:

(a) $n = 4, \ell = 0, m_\ell = 0, m_s = -\frac{1}{2}$

(b) $n = 3, \ell = 1, m_\ell = -1, m_s = +\frac{1}{2}$

(c) $n = 3, \ell = 2, m_\ell = 0, m_s = -\frac{1}{2}$

(d) $n = 4, \ell = 1, m_\ell = +1, m_s = -\frac{1}{2}$

4.5 Shells, Subshells, and Orbitals

4.34 What does the number of ℓ values permitted for a given n value have to do with the number of subshells in a shell?

4.35 What does the number of m_ℓ values permitted for a given ℓ value have to do with the number of orbitals in a subshell?

4.36 Explain why the helium atom is stable with only two electrons in its outermost shell, but beryllium is not.

4.37 How many electrons are present in each of the following atoms? Assuming that each is a neutral atom, identify the element.

(a) $1s^2 2s^2 2p^6 3s^2 3p^1$

(b) $1s^2 2s^2 2p^6 3s^2 3p^6 4s^2 3d^1$

(c) $1s^2 2s^2 2p^6 3s^2 3p^6 4s^2 3d^{10} 4p^6$

4.38 How many electrons are permitted (a) in a d orbital and (b) in a d subshell?

4.39 Write detailed electronic configurations for Li, C, and Mg.

4.40 (a) How many orbitals are in the $2p$ subshell?

(b) How many orbitals are in the $3p$ subshell?

(c) How many orbitals are in the $4p$ subshell?

(d) What is the maximum number of electrons permitted in a $5p$ subshell?

4.41 In a given atom, what is the maximum number of electrons that can have the following quantum numbers?

(a) $n = 5, \ell = 2$

(b) $n = 4, \ell = 3$

(c) $n = 3, \ell = 0$

(d) $n = 4, \ell = 1$, and $m_\ell = -1$

4.42 (a) What is the letter designation for $\ell = 3$?

(b) How many different m_ℓ values are possible for an electron in a subshell for which $\ell = 3$?

(c) How many different orbitals are in an $\ell = 3$ subshell?

(d) What is the maximum number of electrons in an $\ell = 3$ subshell?

4.43 (a) How many $2p$ orbitals are present in any atom?

(b) What is the maximum number of electrons in the $2p$ subshell?

(c) How many electrons are present in the $2p$ subshell of a fluorine atom?

(d) Explain why the subshell is not full in the fluorine atom.

4.6 Shapes of Orbitals

4.44 According to Figure 4.8(c), which two $3d$ orbitals cannot have an electron in the xz-plane?

4.45 According to Figure 4.8(b), which $2p$ orbital cannot have an electron in the xz-plane?

4.46 How many d orbitals are pictured in Figure 4.8?

4.47 (a) How many of the p orbitals pictured in Figure 4.8(b) are oriented along an axis? (b) How many of the d orbitals pictured in Figure 4.8(c) are oriented along axes?

4.7 Energy Level Diagrams

4.48 What is the maximum number of *unpaired* electrons in (a) an *s* subshell, (b) a *p* subshell, (c) a *d* subshell, and (d) an *f* subshell?

4.49 How many unpaired electrons are present in the ground state of an atom if six electrons are present in each of the following subshells? There are no other unpaired electrons.

(a) 4*p* subshell   (b) 4*d* subshell

(c) 5*f* subshell

4.50 Draw an energy level diagram, and determine the number of unpaired electrons in an atom of each of the following:

(a) B   (b) O   (c) Ne   (d) Si

4.51 Which of the following configurations represents the outermost shell of the ground state of phosphorus?

4.52 How many unpaired electrons are in an atom in the ground state, assuming that all other subshells are either completely full or empty, if its outermost *p* subshell contains (a) three electrons, (b) five electrons, (c) four electrons?

4.53 Draw an energy level diagram for the cobalt atom.

4.54 How many unpaired electrons are in an atom in the ground state, assuming that all other subshells are either completely full or empty, if its outermost *d* subshell contains (a) four electrons, (b) six electrons, (c) seven electrons?

4.8 Periodic Variation of Electronic Configuration

4.55 Use the periodic table to deduce how many electrons can fit into any (a) *s* subshell, (b) *p* subshell, (c) *d* subshell, and (d) *f* subshell.

4.56 (a) How many electrons are added to an atom in the build-up process before the start of the second shell? How many elements are in the periodic table before the start of the second period?

(b) How many electrons are added to an atom in the build-up process before the start of the third shell? How many elements are in the periodic table before the start of the third period?

(c) How many electrons are added to an atom in the build-up process before the start of the fourth shell? How many elements are in the periodic table before the start of the fourth period?

4.57 Locate in the periodic table (a) the element that has the first 3*d* electron and (b) the element that is the first to complete its 2*s* subshell.

4.58 Write detailed electronic configurations for (a) Be, (b) Mg, (c) Ca, and (d) Sr.

4.59 Write detailed electronic configurations for the following:

(a) As   (b) Ar   (c) Al

(d) V   (e) Ni

4.60 Write detailed electronic configurations of the following:

(a) Ge   (b) Mn   (c) N   (d) Br   (e) Fe

4.61 Write detailed electronic configurations for O, S, Se, and Te, and deduce the outermost configuration for Po.

4.62 Use the periodic table to write the outer electronic configuration for each of the following elements:

(a) Tl   (b) La   (c) Gd

4.63 Use the periodic table to write outer electronic configurations for the following elements:

(a) Pb   (b) Fr   (c) Lu   (d) Pt

4.64 Use the periodic table to write outer electronic configurations for the following elements:

(a) Rf (element 104)   (b) U   (c) Ba

4.65 Write outer electronic configurations for the following:

(a) Os   (b) Hf   (c) Ce

General Problems

4.66 The Bohr theory has been essentially replaced. Explain why *any* theory is ever rejected.

4.67 Identify the element from each of the following *partial* configurations of neutral atoms:

(a) $\ldots 4s^2\, 3d^5$ (b) $\ldots 5s^2\, 4d^{10}\, 5p^4$

(c) $\ldots 6p^3$ (d) $\ldots 5s^1$

(e) $\ldots 3d^{10}\, 4p^5$ (f) $\ldots 7s^2\, 6d^1\, 5f^{14}$

4.68 The energy of each of the first six shells of hydrogen given in Figure 4.6. Calculate the energies emitted w⁄ the electrons in many hydrogen atoms descend from fifth shell to the second. (*Hint:* See Problem 4.21.)

4.69 What type (*s*, *p*, *d*, *f*) electron was the last electr⁄ in the buildup process to

(a) A nonmetal

(b) A transition element

(c) An inner transition element

(d) A main group metal (two answers)

4.70 The orange line in the hydrogen spectrum (see Figure 4.5) is the change of the electron from the third orbit to the second; the green line is the change from the fourth orbit to the second; the two violet lines are the changes from the fifth and sixth orbits to the second, respectively. Without looking at any figures, deduce which color represents the most energy, and which represents the least. Is wavelength directly proportional to energy?

4.71 Can you identify the following element from its inner electronic configuration? $1s^2\, 2s^2$ . . . Explain.

4.72 In answering the question, "What is the maximum value for ℓ for any electron in the ground state of Lr, element 103?" several students gave the following answers and reasoning. Which one is correct?

(a) The maximum $\ell = 6$ because the outermost shell has $n = 7$, and ℓ cannot be more than $n - 1$.

(b) The maximum $\ell = 3$ because the f subshell has an ℓ value of 3, and there is no subshell with a bigger ℓ value in Lr.

(c) The maximum $\ell = 1$ because the outermost shell cannot have more than 8 electrons, and $\ell = 1$ is the maximum ℓ for a filled octet.

4.73 Does an electron gain or lose energy in each of the following transitions?

(a) From a $5f$ subshell to a $4d$ subshell

(b) From a $5s$ subshell to a $4p$ subshell

(c) From a $6p$ subshell to a $5d$ subshell

4.74 What is the maximum number of *unpaired* electrons in (a) the $3d$ subshell of an atom and (b) the $4f$ subshell of an atom?

4.75 What is wrong with each of the following ground state configurations?

(a) $1s^2\, 1p^6\, 2s^2\, 2p^3$ (b) $1s^1\, 2s^2\, 2p^4$

(c) $1s^2\, 2p^6\, 3d^{10}\, 4f^{14}$ (d) $1s^2\, 2s^2\, 2p^4\, 3s^2\, 3p^6$

(e) $[Xe]\, 6s^2\, 5d^{10}\, 4f^{15}$ (f) $1s^2\, 2s^2\, 2p^6\, 3s^2\, 3p^6\, 4s^2\, 3d^{14}$

(g) $1s^2\, 2s^4\, 2p^6\, 3s^2$ (h) $1s^2\, 2s^2\, 2p^6\, 2d^{10}$

(i) $1s^2\, 2s^2\, 2p^6\, 3s^2\, 3p^6\, 4s^2\, 4d^{10}\, 4p^3$

4.76 Which one(s) of the following configurations are *not* permitted for an atom in its ground state?

(a) $1s^2\, 2s^2\, 2p^2$ (b) $1s^2\, 2s^2$ (c) $1s^6\, 2s^6\, 2p^6$

(d) $1s^1\, 2s^1$

4.77 How many unpaired electrons are present in the ground state of an atom if there are five electrons in each of the following subshells? There are no other unpaired electrons.

(a) $3p$ subshell   (b) $3d$ subshell   (c) $4f$ subshell

4.78 Is the Bohr theory or the quantum mechanical theory better to describe the electronic arrangement of

(a) Argon   (b) Aluminum   (c) Antimony

4.79 Deduce the expected electronic configuration of (a) Cr, (b) Cu, and (c) Ce.

4.80 Calculate the energy of the first line of the hydrogen spectrum. Its wavelength (λ) is 410 nm.

4.81 Figure 4.11 shows that the periodic table is based on the electronic structure of the atoms. Explain how Mendeleyev was able to create the periodic table without knowing about the electron at all.

4.82 What is the maximum number of unpaired electrons in the ground state of an atom in which only the $1s$, $2s$, $2p$, $3s$, and $3p$ subshells have any electrons?

4.83 Which one(s) of the following sets of quantum numbers is (are) *not* permitted?

(a) $n = 4, \ell = 3, m_\ell = 2, m_s = -\frac{1}{2}$

(b) $n = 4, \ell = 2, m_\ell = -3, m_s = +\frac{1}{2}$

(c) $n = 2, \ell = 1, m_\ell = 1, m_s = -\frac{1}{2}$

(d) $n = 2, \ell = 2, m_\ell = 1, m_s = +\frac{1}{2}$

(e) $n = 3, \ell = 1, m_\ell = 1, m_s = -1$

4.84 Which metal in each of the following sets will be drawn into a magnetic field the most?

(a) Zn   Mn   V

(b) Ca   Cu   Cd

(c) Sc   Cu   V

(d) Ti   Tl   Ga

4.85 (a) Draw an energy level diagram for iodine.

(b) Can you use this diagram for the electronic structure of sodium?

(c) Explain why one large energy level diagram is sufficient for all the elements.

4.86 Would the actual configuration of the chromium atom (see p. 119) or the configuration expected by the $n + \ell$ rule be drawn more into a magnetic field.

5

Chemical Bonding

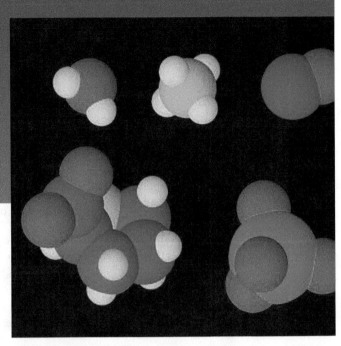

Models of simple molecules

Review Clues

Objectives

5.1	To interpret and write chemical formulas
5.2	To write octet rule electronic structures for the formation of ionic compounds and to deduce the formulas of compounds of main group metals with nonmetals
5.3	To write electron dot diagrams for keeping track of the valence electrons in compounds, especially those of main group elements
5.4	To learn how to deduce the formulas of compounds of main group metals with nonmetals, and the formulas of compounds of any combination of metal ion and nonmetal ion if we know the charges on the ions
5.5	To write electron dot diagrams for the compounds of two or more nonmetals bonded with shared electron pairs, and also for polyatomic ions

The electronic structure of an uncombined atom, first discussed in Chapter 4, determines the ability of that atom to combine with other atoms to produce molecules or ionic compounds. In this chapter, the fundamentals of chemical bonding are covered. To discuss compounds, chemical formulas are required. Moreover, when symbols for atoms are combined in a chemical formula, some type of bonding is implied. Therefore, chemical formulas are introduced first, in Section 5.1. (More information about chemical formulas will be presented in Chapter 7.) Ionic bonding, which occurs when electrons are transferred from one atom to another, is treated in Section 5.2. A convenient way to picture atoms with their outermost electrons—the electron dot diagram—is presented in Section 5.3. The number of electrons transferred from one atom to another, or the charges on the resulting ions, enable us to deduce the formulas for binary ionic compounds (Section 5.4). Atoms held together solely by covalent bonds form units called molecules (or much larger units called macromolecules). Covalent bonding, in which the sharing of electrons is the primary method of bonding, is introduced in Section 5.5, which also discusses compounds with both ionic and covalent bonding.

> Writing a chemical formula implies bonding of some type.

> Ionic bonding involves transfer of electrons. Covalent bonding involves electron sharing. In many ternary compounds, both ionic and covalent bonding occur.

5.1   Chemical Formulas

Just as a symbol identifies an element, a **formula** is a combination of symbols that identifies a compound, an ion, or a molecule of an element. However, chemical formulas do much more. A formula also indicates the relative quantities of the elements contained in the compound or ion and implies some kind of chemical bonding between the atoms.

Molecules of Elements

Formulas are used to identify molecules of free elements. A **molecule** contains two or more nonmetallic atoms bonded together. Many free (uncombined) nonmetallic elements exist as molecules, such as H_2, N_2, O_2, F_2, Cl_2, Br_2, and I_2, as well as P_4 and S_8 (Figure 5.1). The formula P_4 indicates four phosphorus atoms bonded together. This formula does not represent a compound, because only one kind of atom is present. **Elemental** phosphorus in its lowest energy form occurs in such molecules.

Seven elements occur as **diatomic molecules** (molecules with two atoms) *when they are not combined with other elements*. Fortunately, these elements are easy to remember because, except for hydrogen, they form a shape like a seven in the periodic table, starting at the element with atomic number 7 (Figure 5.2).

Hydrogen molecules (H_2) are so much more stable than separated hydrogen atoms that the reaction of the atoms to form molecules produces a lot of heat:

$$2\,H \rightarrow H_2 + heat$$

Production of a given number of H_2 molecules from hydrogen atoms produces more heat than the production of the same number of CO_2 molecules from burning carbon (charcoal) in oxygen. Construction workers take advantage of the reaction of atomic hydrogen to weld steel pieces together in the absence of oxygen. That condition is desirable because oxygen might make the steel rust.

> Seven elements occur as diatomic molecules *when they are not combined with other elements*.

128   CHAPTER 5 ■ Chemical Bonding

Figure 5.1 *Some Elements That Occur as Molecules*

(a) Cl_2, chlorine
(b) P_4, white phosphorus (the most stable form of elemental phosphorus)
(c) S_8, rhombic sulfur (the most stable form of elemental sulfur)

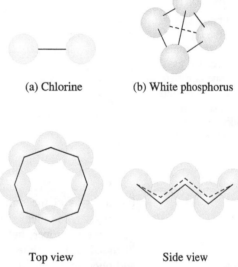

(a) Chlorine   (b) White phosphorus

Top view   Side view
(c) Rhombic sulfur

Where do the hydrogen atoms come from? They are produced by electrical discharge in a welding torch, such as is diagrammed in Figure 5.3.

In addition to its stable elementary form, O_2, oxygen can also exist as O_3 molecules, a form called **ozone.** Ozone can be formed when an electrical discharge passes through oxygen gas, and it is also formed in the upper atmosphere—the ozone layer—when high-energy rays from outer space bombard O_2 molecules. The ozone molecules in the upper atmosphere are important because they absorb harmful ultraviolet light from the Sun. This prevents some of that light from reaching the Earth's surface, where it could injure humans and other animals. The O_3 molecule is more reactive than O_2 and decomposes spontaneously but slowly:

$$2\,O_3 \rightarrow 3\,O_2$$

Ozone is a powerful oxidizing agent. In the atmosphere near the surface of the Earth, it is irritating and injurious in concentrations greater than two parts per million. It can be used as a disinfectant and a bleach.

Figure 5.2 *The Seven Elements That Form Diatomic Molecules*

Note that the shape formed by six of these elements in the periodic table looks like the number 7, starting at atomic number 7.

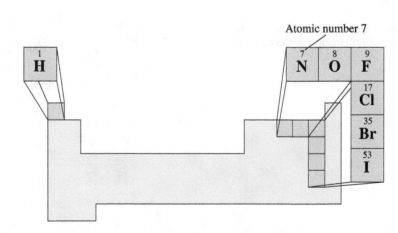

Figure 5.3 Welding Torch

Hydrogen gas is piped into a special tube in which many of the H_2 molecules are separated into atoms by an electrical discharge. The gas flow is adjusted to the rate at which most of the H atoms recombine into molecules just as they exit from the torch. The heat produced at that point is intense enough to weld pieces of steel together.

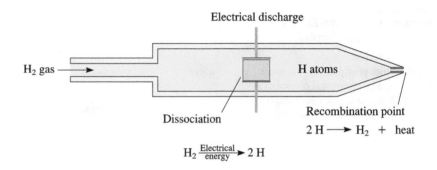

Some other free (uncombined) elements also occur in different forms. Different forms of the same element are called **allotropes** of each other. Except for oxygen, the elements that form diatomic molecules when uncombined do not form allotropes, but many other nonmetals do. The allotropes of carbon—diamond and graphite—are perhaps best known to the general public. Sulfur and phosphorus are also notable for forming allotropes.

Binary Compounds

Atoms of two or more different nonmetals can bond together to form molecules of a compound. H_2O, CH_4, and CH_4O are examples.

In the formula for a **binary compound** (a compound containing only two elements), the element that attracts electrons less is usually written first. The elements are assigned an **electronegativity** that reflects their affinity for electrons in chemical bonds. The elements that attract electrons most are said to have the highest electronegativities or to be the most **electronegative.** Fluorine, the most electronegative element, is assigned an electronegativity of 4.0, and the other elements have values relative to that of fluorine. The elements that attract electrons least are said to have the lowest electronegativities or to be the most **electropositive.**

Values for the electronegativities of the main group elements are presented in Figure 5.4. Except for those of the noble gases, the electronegativities of the

Figure 5.4 Electronegativities of the Main Group Elements

H 2.1								He
Li 1.0	Be 1.5		B 2.0	C 2.5	N 3.0	O 3.5	F 4.0	Ne
Na 0.9	Mg 1.2		Al 1.5	Si 1.8	P 2.1	S 2.5	Cl 3.0	Ar
K 0.8	Ca 1.0		Ga 1.6	Ge 1.8	As 2.0	Se 2.4	Br 2.8	Kr 3.0
Rb 0.8	Sr 1.0		In 1.7	Sn 1.8	Sb 1.9	Te 2.1	I 2.5	Xe 2.6
Cs 0.7	Ba 0.9		Tl 1.8	Pb 1.9	Bi 1.9	Po 2.0	At 2.2	Rn
Fr 0.7	Ra 0.9							

Figure 5.5 Periodic Variation
of Electronegativity

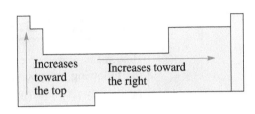

elements increase toward the right and toward the top of the periodic table
(Figure 5.5). Fluorine has the highest electronegativity of any element, and oxygen has the second highest value. The most electropositive element is francium
(Fr). The metals are more electropositive than the nonmetals. Thus, in the formula of a binary compound, the metal, if one is present, is written first. If no
metal is present, the nonmetal closer to the metal portion of the periodic table
is written first. Some examples of binary compounds of nonmetals are CO, H_2O,
SO_2, and SiO_2.

Formulas for binary compounds of hydrogen do not follow the rule just discussed. Hydrogen is written first in the formula if the compound is an acid
(Chapter 8) and written later if the compound is not an acid. For example, HCl
is hydrochloric acid, and NH_3 is ammonia. The position of the H in these formulas indicates that HCl is an acid and NH_3 is not. H_2O and H_2O_2 are exceptions to this rule; neither is an acid.

Formula Units

> A subscript multiplies the
> number of atoms of the
> *preceding* element (or the
> number of preceding groups if
> the subscript follows a closing
> parenthesis).

The collection of atoms represented by a formula is called a **formula unit.** A
chemical formula consists of symbols of element(s), often with **subscripts** that
tell how many atoms of each element are present per formula unit. The subscript *follows* the symbol of the element it multiplies. If no subscript is present,
one atom of the element is indicated. Parentheses may be used in a formula to
group bonded atoms together, and a subscript after the closing parenthesis tells
how many of that group are present per formula unit. The following formulas
illustrate the meanings of subscripts in formulas:

CO	One carbon atom and one oxygen atom are bonded in one formula unit.
SO_2	One sulfur atom and two oxygen atoms are bonded in one formula unit.
$Ba_3(PO_4)_2$	Three barium atoms and two PO_4 groups, each containing one phosphorus atom and four oxygen atoms, are present in one formula unit. The atoms in the PO_4 groups are bonded to each other in some way, as is the compound as a whole (Section 5.5).
H_2	Two atoms of hydrogen are bonded in one formula unit.
H_2O	Two atoms of hydrogen and one atom of oxygen are bonded in one formula unit. This formula unit represents one molecule of water.

Figure 5.6 Blue Hydrate CuSO$_4$·5H$_2$O (left), and White, Anhydrous CuSO$_4$ (right)

EXAMPLE 5.1

How many atoms of each element are present in one formula unit of each of the following compounds?

(a) Mg(ClO$_3$)$_2$ (b) (NH$_4$)$_2$SO$_3$ (c) CH$_3$CH$_2$OH   (d) S$_8$

Solution

(a) 1 Mg, 2 Cl, 6 O   (b) 2 N, 8 H, 1 S, 3 O

(c) 2 C, 6 H, 1 O   (d) 8 S

Practice Problem 5.1   How many atoms of each element are present in one formula unit of each of the following compounds?

(a) Hg$_2$Cl$_2$ (b) NH$_4$H$_2$PO$_4$

A few compounds have formulas that are written with a **centered dot,** as in CuSO$_4$·5H$_2$O. In general, the dots connect the formulas of two or more compounds that could exist independently but are bonded in some way in a single compound. The coefficient (5) after the centered dot multiplies everything after it until the end of the formula. Thus, 10 hydrogen atoms and 9 oxygen atoms are in one formula unit of CuSO$_4$·5H$_2$O. This particular formula could have been written CuSO$_4$(H$_2$O)$_5$. When water is one of the compounds in a formula with a centered dot, the combination is called a **hydrate.** The compound *without* the attached water is said to be **anhydrous,** meaning "without water." Anhydrous CuSO$_4$ and its hydrate are pictured in Figure 5.6.

EXAMPLE 5.2

What is the difference between the formulas (NH$_4$)$_3$PO$_3$ and N$_3$H$_{12}$PO$_3$?

Solution

Although both formulas have the same ratios of atoms of each element to atoms of all the others and to formula units of the compound, the first formula states that the atoms of nitrogen and hydrogen are bonded together in some way in each of three NH$_4$ groups.

Practice Problem 5.2

(a) Write a formula that implies that a CH$_3$ group is connected to a CO$_2$H group by two CH$_2$ groups.

(b) Write a formula showing just the numbers of atoms of each element in this compound.

In reading formulas aloud, the number is simply stated for any subscript following a symbol, as in H$_2$O: "H two O." To express parentheses followed by a subscript 2, the words "taken twice" are used; for a subscript 3, the words "taken three times" are used, and so on. The centered dot is read "dot." Here are some examples to illustrate these conventions:

Hg_2Br_2	"H g two B r two"
$Ba_3(PO_4)_2$	"B a three P O four taken twice"
$CH_3(CH_2)_4CH_3$	"C H three, C H two taken four times, C H three"
$CuSO_4 \cdot 5H_2O$	"C u S O four dot five H two O"

Snapshot Review

❑ The chemical formula for a substance tells us (a) the relative numbers of atoms of each element and (b) that the elements in it are all bonded in some way.

A. How many atoms of hydrogen are present per atom of phosphorus in $(NH_4)_2HPO_4$?
B. Which element in $SeCl_2$ is more electronegative?
C. What is the formula for elemental oxygen?

5.2 Ionic Bonding

The electrons in atoms are arranged in groups, those in each group having nearly the same energies. These energy levels are often referred to as shells. The first shell of any atom can hold a maximum of 2 electrons; the second shell can hold a maximum of 8 electrons; and the other shells can hold a maximum of 8 electrons when they are the outermost shell, but a greater number when they are not (Table 5.1). The **outermost shell** is the last shell that contains electrons. Before the next-to-outermost shell starts to expand past 8 electrons, the (new) outermost shell must hold 2 electrons.

Electrons can be transferred from metal atoms to nonmetal atoms to achieve a more stable, lower energy state. The noble gases are composed of stable atoms; no reactions of the first three (He, Ne, Ar) have been discovered, and the others (Kr, Xe, Rn) are almost completely unreactive. The stability of the

Table 5.1 Maximum Electron Occupancy of Shells

Shell Number	Maximum Occupancy as the Outermost Shell	Maximum Occupancy as an Inner Shell
1	2	2
2	8	8
3	8	18
4	8	32
5	8	50*
6	8	72*
7	8*	98*

*More than the number of electrons available in any atom

Atoms tend to accept, donate, or share electrons to achieve the electronic structure of the nearest noble gas.

noble gases is due to the 8 electrons in the outermost shell of each atom (2 electrons in the case of helium). In fact, 8 electrons in the outermost shell is a stable configuration for most main group atoms. Atoms other than those of the noble gases tend to form ionic or covalent bonds (or both) with other atoms to achieve this electronic configuration. The 8 electrons in the outermost shell are called an **octet.** The tendency of atoms to be stable with 8 electrons in the outermost shell is called the **octet rule.** In some compounds, one (or more) of the atoms does not obey the octet rule. Some exceptions to the octet rule will be mentioned briefly in Section 5.5.

Because the maximum number of electrons in the first shell of an atom is 2, helium is stable with 2 electrons in its only occupied shell. The other very light elements—hydrogen, lithium, and beryllium—tend to form stable states by achieving the 2-electron configuration of helium. Having 2 electrons in the first shell, *when that is the only shell and therefore the outermost shell,* is a stable state, and the 2 electrons are sometimes called a **duet.** When there is only one shell, 2 electrons in that shell act like 8 electrons in any other outermost shell. Therefore, an atom with 2 electrons in its outermost first shell is often said to obey the octet rule, although "duet rule" would be more precise.

The **valence shell** is the shell of highest principal quantum number.

The **valence shell** of electrons in an atom is the outermost shell of electrons of the *uncombined* atom. The electrons in that shell are called **valence electrons.** If all the electrons are removed from that shell, the next inner shell becomes the new outermost shell. For example, the sodium atom has 2 electrons in its first shell, 8 electrons in its second shell (the maximum), and its last electron in its third shell. The valence shell is the third shell. If the 1 electron is removed from the third shell, the second shell becomes the outermost shell, containing 8 electrons. The valence shell is still the (now empty) third shell. The number of electrons in the valence shell of an uncombined main group atom is equal to the classical periodic group number of the element (Figure 5.7). The exceptions to this rule are that helium has 2 valence electrons and the other noble gases have 8 valence electrons.

Na: $1s^2\ 2s^2\ 2p^6\ 3s^1$

Na$^+$: $1s^2\ 2s^2\ 2p^6\ 3s^0$

The number of electrons in the valence shell of an uncombined main group atom is equal to the classical periodic group number of the element.

All metals react with nonmetals to form ionic compounds. Main group metals tend to transfer their valence electrons to nonmetals, and nonmetals tend to accept enough electrons from these metals to achieve their octets. For example, a sodium atom has 1 electron in its valence shell, and a chlorine atom has 7 electrons in its valence shell. When they react, the sodium atom transfers that 1 electron to the chlorine atom, forming two charged species called **ions.** Both of these ions have 8 electrons in their outermost shells. (The sodium ion has 8 electrons in its second shell, now its outermost shell.) *The electronic configurations of both ions are those of noble gas atoms* (the sodium ion has that of a neon atom, and the chlorine ion that of argon). The atoms have not been changed into noble gas atoms, however, because their nuclei have not changed.

Figure 5.7 Numbers of Valence Electrons for Atoms of Main Group Elements

Classical group number:	IA	IIA		IIIA	IVA	VA	VIA	VIIA	0
Modern group number:	1	2		13	14	15	16	17	18
Period 1	1								2
All other periods	1	2		3	4	5	6	7	8

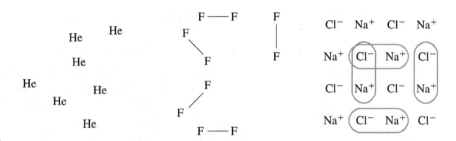

Figure 5.8 *Formula Units of Atoms, Molecules, and Ionic Compounds*

The formula units He and F_2 represent single atoms and diatomic molecules, respectively. Unlike the F_2 molecule, in which one fluorine atom is bonded to a specific other fluorine atom, in the ionic compound NaCl, one Na^+ ion is bonded to six Cl^- ions that are adjacent to it. Each of the Cl^- ions is bonded to six Na^+ ions that are adjacent to it. (The fifth and sixth ions are in layers in front of and behind the layer shown here; see Figure 5.9.) The ratio of Na^+ ions to Cl^- ions is therefore 1 : 1. Any pair of Na^+ and Cl^- ions, such as those circled in red or the one circled in green, is a formula unit.

The sodium ion has a single positive charge because the neutral atom has donated one negatively charged electron. The sodium ion is written as Na^+. The ion formed from the chlorine atom has a single negative charge, resulting from the gain of the electron by the neutral chlorine atom. This ion is written as Cl^-. Oppositely charged bodies attract each other, so Na^+ ions and Cl^- ions attract each other. This kind of attraction is called an *electrostatic attraction*. In general, the transfer of electrons from one atom to another produces oppositely charged ions, which attract each other. The formula for the compound of sodium and chlorine is NaCl, which shows that one Na^+ ion is present for each Cl^- ion (Figure 5.8).

All ionic compounds have an overall net charge of zero because the electrons are transferred but do not disappear. The electrons that some atoms accept to form negative ions are donated by other atoms, which become positive ions. Positively charged ions are called **cations** (pronounced "cat′-ions"), and negatively charged ions are called **anions** (pronounced "an′-ions"). The sodium ion is positive; it is a cation. The ion produced by the chlorine atom accepting an extra electron is negative; it is an anion. If an anion is a **monatomic ion** (having only one atom), its name ends in *-ide,* so Cl^- is called the chloride ion.

Metallic and nonmetallic elements can react with each other to form compounds by transferring electrons from the metal atoms to the nonmetal atoms. The ions formed attract each other because of their opposite charges, and these attractions are called **ionic bonds.** However, in a solid ionic compound, a single pair of ions does not bond together; instead, an almost inconceivably huge number of both types of ions forms a lattice that extends in three dimensions. The three-dimensional nature of the **sodium chloride structure** (Figure 5.9) is typical of ionic solids.

The ionic nature of these compounds (the fact that charged particles are present) can be shown by experiments in which the ions are made to carry an electric current. Pure water does not conduct electricity well. However, if a compound that consists of ions is dissolved in water and the solution is placed between **electrodes** in an apparatus like that shown in Figure 5.10, the solution will conduct electricity when the electrodes are connected to the terminals of a battery. Each type of ion moves toward the electrode that has the *opposite* charge of that of the ion. That is, cations migrate to the negative electrode, called the **cathode,** and anions migrate to the positive electrode, called the **anode.** (The names *cation* and *anion* were derived from the words *cathode* and *anode.*) For electricity to be conducted, the ions must be free to move. In the solid state, an ionic compound will not conduct because the ions are trapped in the lattice. However, if the compound is heated until it melts or if it is dissolved in water, the liquid compound or solution will conduct electricity because the ions are free to move.

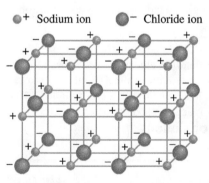

● + Sodium ion   ● − Chloride ion

Figure 5.9 *Sodium Chloride Structure*

Each sodium ion is surrounded by six chloride ions, and each chloride ion is surrounded by six sodium ions. The ratio of sodium ions to chloride ions is 1 : 1, and the formula for sodium chloride is written NaCl. This figure shows only a small portion of the structure, which extends over thousands of ions or more in each direction.

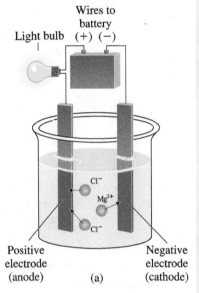

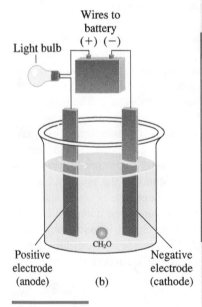

Figure 5.10 Conduction of Electricity by Ions

(a) When an ionic compound such as magnesium chloride, $MgCl_2$, is dissolved in water and a voltage is applied, the positive and negative ions carry the current (the light turns on). (b) When a compound such as CH_2O (formaldehyde), which is not ionic, is used, there are no charged particles to carry the current, and no flow of electricity is observed (the light is off).

Detailed Electronic Configurations of Anions (Optional)

The detailed electronic structures of monatomic ions may be deduced starting from the structures of the corresponding neutral atoms (presented in Chapter 4). Monatomic anions have simply added sufficient electrons to the outermost p subshell to complete that subshell. The $n + \ell$ rule can be used to deduce the structure of the ion as well as that of the neutral atom. For example, the electronic configuration of the nitride ion (the anion of nitrogen) is deduced, starting with the configuration of nitrogen:

$$\text{N atom:} \quad 1s^2\, 2s^2\, 2p^3$$

The nitride ion has a triple negative charge, obtained by gaining three extra electrons. These electrons go into the $2p$ subshell:

$$\text{N}^{3-} \text{ ion:} \quad 1s^2\, 2s^2\, 2p^6$$

This electronic configuration is the same as that of neon. An ion with a configuration like that of a noble gas is said to have a **noble gas configuration.**

EXAMPLE 5.3

Write the electronic configuration for the fluoride ion, F^-.

Solution

$$\text{F atom:} \quad 1s^2\, 2s^2\, 2p^5$$

Adding an electron corresponding to the single negative charge yields the ion:

$$\text{F}^- \text{ ion:} \quad 1s^2\, 2s^2\, 2p^6$$

Practice Problem 5.3   Write the detailed electronic configuration of the oxide ion, O^{2-}.

Detailed Electronic Configurations of Cations (Optional)

To form monatomic cations, metals lose electrons *from the valence shell first.* Some main group metals have more than one subshell of the valence shell occupied by electrons, in which case the electrons in the highest subshell of the valence shell are lost first. For example, the lead atom loses its $6p^2$ electrons to form Pb^{2+}. The configuration is thus

$$\text{Pb}^{2+} \text{ ion:} \quad [\text{Xe}]\, 6s^2\, 5d^{10}\, 4f^{14}$$

EXAMPLE 5.4

Write the outermost electronic configuration for (a) the Tl^+ ion and (b) the Tl^{3+} ion.

Solution

$$\text{Tl atom:} \quad [Xe]\ 6s^2\ 5d^{10}\ 4f^{14}\ 6p^1$$

(a) The outermost shell of the thallium atom has $n = 6$, and the Tl^+ ion is formed by loss of the $6p^1$ electron from that sixth shell:

$$Tl^+ \text{ ion:} \quad [Xe]\ 6s^2\ 5d^{10}\ 4f^{14}\ 6p^0 \quad \text{or} \quad [Xe]\ 6s^2\ 5d^{10}\ 4f^{14}$$

(b) The Tl^{3+} ion loses the $6p^1$ electron plus two others—the $6s^2$ electrons. Those are all the electrons in the sixth shell! Note that the $n + \ell$ rule does not apply to this case; the electrons in the outermost shell (that with the highest n value) are lost first.

$$Tl^{3+} \text{ ion:} \quad [Xe]\ 6s^0\ 5d^{10}\ 4f^{14}\ 6p^0 \quad \text{or} \quad [Xe]\ 5d^{10}\ 4f^{14}$$

Practice Problem 5.4 Write the outermost electronic configuration for (a) Bi^{3+} and (b) Pb^{4+}.

The electronic configurations of transition metal ions, like those of main group ions, are determined by removal of the electrons from the shell of *highest n value first*. Next, electrons may be lost from the *d* subshell next to the valence shell. The capability of removing a variable number of electrons makes it possible for most transition metals to have ions of different charges.

> Transition metal atoms form ions by loss of their outermost electrons first (not those governed by the $n + \ell$ rule).

EXAMPLE 5.5

Write detailed electronic configurations for Co^{2+} and Co^{3+}.

Solution

First, write the configuration for the cobalt atom:

$$\text{Co atom:} \quad 1s^2\ 2s^2\ 2p^6\ 3s^2\ 3p^6\ 4s^2\ 3d^7$$

The outermost shell electrons of the cobalt atom are lost to form the 2+ ion:

$$Co^{2+} \text{ ion:} \quad 1s^2\ 2s^2\ 2p^6\ 3s^2\ 3p^6\ 4s^0\ 3d^7 \quad \text{or} \quad 1s^2\ 2s^2\ 2p^6\ 3s^2\ 3p^6\ 3d^7$$

Then a $3d$ electron is lost to form the 3+ ion:

$$Co^{3+} \text{ ion:} \quad 1s^2\ 2s^2\ 2p^6\ 3s^2\ 3p^6\ 4s^0\ 3d^6 \quad \text{or} \quad 1s^2\ 2s^2\ 2p^6\ 3s^2\ 3p^6\ 3d^6$$

Practice Problem 5.5 Write the electronic configurations of Fe^{2+} and Fe^{3+}.

Inner transition metals lose electrons from their valence shells first, as do the other metals, but they also may lose electrons from the underlying *d* or *f* subshells. It should be noted that most transition and inner transition metal ions do *not* have noble gas configurations.

Snapshot Review

ChemSkill Builder
3.2, 3.4

❐ The outermost shell of electrons in an uncombined atom of main group I–VII elements contains a number of electrons equal to the group number.

❐ When a metal loses electrons, its valence shell is very often left with no electrons, so the next inner shell becomes the "outermost shell" of the resulting ion.

❐ In Chapter 3, the number of electrons in an atom was equal to the number of protons because the atoms were uncharged. (It does not matter that they were isotopes or a mixture of isotopes of the same element.) However, in an ion, the number of electrons is not equal to the number of protons, so ions have charges.

A. How many electrons are in the valence shell and in the outermost shell of (a) Ca? (b) Ca^{2+}?

B. Compare the number of protons and electrons in each of the following: (a) ^{79}Br, (b) Br, and (c) Br^-.

5.3 Lewis Electron Dot Diagrams

The discussion in Section 5.2 showed that the transfer of valence electrons is very important in ionic bonding. Section 5.5 will show that their sharing is very important in covalent bonding. The **Lewis electron dot diagram** is a way to picture the transfer or sharing of valence electrons that aids in understanding both processes. Keep in mind, however, that electron dot diagrams are simplified representations of atoms and not true pictures.

In an electron dot diagram, the symbol of the element represents the nucleus of the atom plus its inner shells of electrons, and dots around the symbol stand for the valence electrons. The dots are placed arbitrarily to the left or right or above or below the symbol. In unbonded atoms, two dots, at most, are located in each position. For example, atoms of the second period elements may be represented as follows:

> These four positions represent the four outermost *s* and *p* orbitals (Chapter 4).

> Atomic orbitals hold a maximum of two electrons each.

$$Li \cdot \quad Be : \quad \overset{\cdot}{B} : \quad \cdot \overset{\cdot}{C} : \quad \cdot \overset{\cdot}{N} : \quad : \overset{\cdot}{O} : \quad : \overset{\cdot}{F} : \quad : \overset{\cdot \cdot}{Ne} :$$

Snapshot Review

ChemSkill Builder
12.2

❐ Electron dot diagrams for uncombined atoms have the valence electrons in four possible, equivalent positions (top, bottom, both sides) with *at most* two electrons in each position.

A. Draw an electron dot diagram for the phosphorus atom.

5.4 Formulas for Ionic Compounds

Let's consider the ionic compound formed by the reaction of sodium and sulfur. The sodium atom has 1 electron in its valence shell. (Sodium is in periodic group IA [1].) When the atom donates this electron to a nonmetal atom, the positive ion formed has an octet like that of neon. However, the sulfur atom, with 6 valence electrons, needs 2 additional electrons. Therefore, it takes *two* sodium atoms to provide the 2 electrons for *one* sulfur atom; so the formula for sodium sulfide is Na_2S.

The reaction of sodium and sulfur to form Na_2S can be visualized easily with electron dot diagrams:

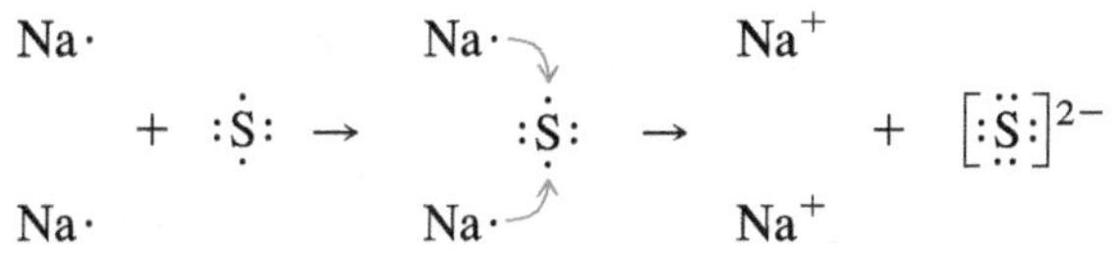

$$Na\cdot \quad\quad\quad Na\cdot\searrow \quad\quad\quad Na^+$$
$$+\; :\dot{\underset{\cdot}{S}}: \;\rightarrow\quad :\dot{\underset{\cdot}{S}}: \;\rightarrow\quad\quad +\; \left[:\ddot{\underset{\cdot\cdot}{S}}:\right]^{2-}$$
$$Na\cdot \quad\quad\quad Na\cdot\nearrow \quad\quad\quad Na^+$$

Electrons from two sodium atoms are needed to allow one sulfur atom to attain its octet. We can write the reaction more simply as follows:

$$2\,Na\cdot + :\dot{\underset{\cdot}{S}}: \rightarrow 2\,Na^+ + \left[:\ddot{\underset{\cdot\cdot}{S}}:\right]^{2-}$$

$$\text{or}\quad\quad 2\,Na + S \rightarrow Na_2S$$

Similarly, the formula of aluminium chloride is $AlCl_3$ because the aluminum atom has 3 valence electrons that it can donate to form the 3+ ion. Charges on the most common monatomic ions are presented in Figure 5.11.

EXAMPLE 5.6

Use electron dot diagrams to picture the combination of aluminum and oxygen atoms.

Figure 5.11 Charges on Common Monatomic Ions

I	II											III	IV	V	VI	VII	
H 1+ 1–																	
Li 1+	Be 2+													N 3–	O 2–	F 1–	
Na 1+	Mg 2+											Al 3+		P 3–	S 2–	Cl 1–	
K 1+	Ca 2+	Sc 3+	Ti 2+ 3+	V 2+ 3+	Cr 2+ 3+	Mn 2+ 3+	Fe 2+ 3+	Co 2+ 3+	Ni 2+ 3+ 4+	Cu 1+ 2+	Zn 2+				Se 2–	Br 1–	
Rb 1+	Sr 2+								Pd 2+ 4+	Ag 1+	Cd 2+		Sn 2+ 4+			I 1–	
Cs 1+	Ba 2+								Pt 2+ 4+	Au 1+ 3+	Hg 2+ *		Pb 2+ 4+				
Fr 1+	Ra 2+																

*Mercury also forms a diatomic ion, Hg_2^{2+}.

Solution

The 6 valence electrons of the two aluminum atoms are transferred to three oxygen atoms, yielding two Al^{3+} ions and three O^{2-} ions. The reaction can be written more simply as follows:

$$2 \cdot Al: + 3 \, :\overset{..}{\underset{.}{O}}: \rightarrow 2 \, Al^{3+} + 3 \left[:\overset{..}{\underset{..}{O}}: \right]^{2-}$$

$$\text{or} \qquad 2 \, Al + 3 \, O \rightarrow Al_2O_3$$

Practice Problem 5.6   Use electron dot diagrams to picture the combination of magnesium and nitrogen atoms.

Al atom: $1s^2 \, 2s^2 \, 2p^6 \, 3s^2 \, 3p^1$
Al^{3+} ion: $1s^2 \, 2s^2 \, 2p^6$

In compounds, the metals of periodic groups IA, IIA, and IIIB (1, 2, and 3), as well as zinc, cadmium, aluminum, and silver, always form ions with positive charges equal to the element's classical periodic group number.

The charge on every monatomic anion (except H^-) is equal to the classical group number of the element minus 8. The number of added electrons is the absolute value of that difference.

We can predict the charges on the ions of some elements but not others. In their compounds, the metals of periodic groups IA, IIA, and IIIB (1, 2, and 3), as well as zinc, cadmium, aluminum, and silver, always form ions with positive charges equal to the element's classical periodic group number. These elements are indicated with a blue background in Figure 5.11. The charge on every monatomic anion except H^- is equal to the classical group number of the element minus 8. These elements are presented with a red background in Figure 5.11. The number of added electrons is the absolute value of that difference. (Not all nonmetals form monatomic anions, however.) Hydrogen can react with very active metals to form the hydride ion, H^-, which has the 2-electron configuration of helium. The maximum positive charge on a monatomic cation is $4+$; the maximum negative charge on a monatomic anion is $3-$. In addition to the generalities just presented, note that each of the elements of the first transition series except scandium forms an ion with a $2+$ charge, and the eight middle ones also form an ion having another charge. (The transition metals form ions having different charges by donating varying numbers—0, 1, or 2—of their inner electrons to nonmetals.)

Because the overall charge on any ionic compound is zero, we can determine the formula of an ionic compound by balancing the charges on the cations and anions. That is,

Number of positive charges = Number of negative charges

The compound of Pb^{4+} and O^{2-} is thus PbO_2 because there are four negative charges on two O^{2-} ions to balance the four positive charges on one Pb^{4+} ion.

We can even write formulas for compounds whose ions are totally unfamiliar to us, as long as we know their charges. For example, the compound of AB_4^{2+} and XY_3^{2-} is AB_4XY_3 and that for AB_4^{2+} and XZ_2^{3-} is $(AB_4)_3(XZ_2)_2$.

EXAMPLE 5.7

Determine the formula of the compound of calcium and oxygen.

Solution

Ca: $1s^2\ 2s^2\ 2p^6\ 3s^2\ 3p^6\ 4s^2$
O: $1s^2\ 2s^2\ 2p^4$

Ca^{2+}: $1s^2\ 2s^2\ 2p^6\ 3s^2\ 3p^6$
O^{2-}: $1s^2\ 2s^2\ 2p^6$

Calcium, in group IIA, has 2 valence electrons, and oxygen, in group VIA, has 6. Each oxygen atom needs 2 additional electrons to form O^{2-}, which has an octet in its valence shell, and each calcium atom can supply these 2 electrons to form Ca^{2+}. Therefore, it takes one calcium atom to supply the electrons for one oxygen atom, and the formula for calcium oxide is CaO. Alternatively, we can say that it takes one dipositive calcium ion to balance the charge on one dinegative oxide ion.

Practice Problem 5.7 Determine the formula of the compound of magnesium and nitrogen.

EXAMPLE 5.8

Determine the formula of (a) the compound containing Cr^{2+} and S^{2-} and (b) the compound containing Cr^{3+} and O^{2-}.

Solution

The relative numbers of cations and anions in a compound depend only on their charges and not on the identities of the ions.

(a) One Cr^{2+} ion can balance the charge on one S^{2-} ion. Therefore, the ions bond in a 1:1 ratio to form CrS.

(b) It takes three O^{2-} ions to balance the charge on two Cr^{3+} ions, so the formula is Cr_2O_3.

Practice Problem 5.8 Determine the formula of (a) the compound containing Cu^{2+} and F^- and (b) the compound containing Cr^{2+} and P^{3-}.

EXAMPLE 5.9

Write the formula for each type of ion in the following compounds:

(a) RbI   (b) BaS   (c) Li_2S (d) Al_2O_3

Solution

(a) Rb^+ I^- (b) Ba^{2+} S^{2-} (c) Li^+ S^{2-} (d) Al^{3+} O^{2-}

The charges on the cations are equal to the numbers of valence electrons originally in the atoms, and the charges on the anions are equal to 8 minus the number of valence electrons. The numbers of valence electrons for these elements are easily determined from their periodic group numbers. The two lithium ions in the compound of part (c) are not bonded to each other because they are both positive and repel each other. They should not be written with a subscript (except in the formula for the compound, Li_2S, in which they are both bonded to the sulfide ion). If we want to show that two lithium ions are present, we must write $2\,Li^+$.

Practice Problem 5.9 Write formulas for the ions in Mg_3P_2.

Because all compounds have overall charges of zero, we can deduce the charges on some metals' cations from the total charge on the anions bonded to them. For example, in $CuCl$ and $CuCl_2$, the charges on the copper ions are 1+ and 2+, respectively. The 1+ charge on the copper ion in $CuCl$ is required to balance the 1− charge on one Cl^- ion. The 2+ charge on the copper in $CuCl_2$ is required to balance the 1− charge on each of *two* Cl^- ions.

EXAMPLE 5.10

What is the charge on each cation in (a) Cu_2O and (b) CuO?

Solution

(a) The charge on each cation must be 1+ because two cations are required to balance the charge on one O^{2-} ion.

(b) The charge on the cation must be 2+, to balance the 2− charge on one O^{2-} ion.

Practice Problem 5.10   What is the charge on each cation in (a) $AgCl$ and (b) PbO_2?

Snapshot Review

ChemSkill Builder
3.2, 3.4

❑ The charge on the formula of a complete compound must be zero, so the total of the positive and of the negative charges must be equal. The smallest integral numbers of cations and anions are used to achieve charge neutrality.

❑ Most main group cations and all monatomic anions have characteristic charges that are easy to learn, so in their compounds with other ions, the charges on the other ions are easy to deduce.

A. Write the formula for the compound of La^{3+} and S^{2-}.

B. Write the formulas of the ions in each of the following compounds:
   (a) VCl_2 (b) PbO_2 (c) Ti_2O_3.

5.5 Covalent Bonding

Metal atoms can donate electrons to nonmetal atoms, but nonmetal atoms do not form monatomic positive ions because they would have to donate too many valence electrons to form octets. (Single nonmetal atoms do not donate electrons at all, but some groups of nonmetal atoms can. This will be discussed later in this section.)

Nonmetal atoms can accept electrons from metal atoms if such atoms are present; otherwise, they can attain an octet by **electron sharing.** A **covalent bond** consists of shared electrons. One pair of electrons shared between two atoms constitutes a *single* covalent bond, generally referred to as a **single bond.** An **unshared pair** of valence electrons is called a **lone pair.** Elements or compounds bonded only by covalent bonds form molecules.

> The formula unit of a covalently bonded group of atoms is called a molecule.

Consider the hydrogen molecule, H_2. Each atom of hydrogen has one electron and would be more stable with two electrons (the helium configuration). There is no reason why one hydrogen atom would donate its electron and the other accept it. Instead, the two hydrogen atoms can *share* their electrons:

$$H\cdot + \cdot H \rightarrow H\!:\!H$$

Electrons shared between hydrogen atoms are counted toward the duets of *both* atoms. In the hydrogen molecule, each hydrogen atom has a total of two electrons in its first shell and, thus, a stable configuration. Electrons shared between other nonmetal atoms are counted toward the *octets* of both.

EXAMPLE 5.11

Draw an electron dot diagram for HCl. Label the single bond and the lone pairs.

Solution

Practice Problem 5.11 Draw an electron dot diagram for Cl_2. Label the single bond and the lone pairs.

In electron dot diagrams for uncombined atoms, the four areas around the symbol can hold a maximum of two electrons each. However, be aware that up to three pairs of electrons can sometimes be placed between covalently bonded atoms.

Another representation of molecules is the **structural formula,** in which each electron pair being shared by two atoms is represented by a line or dash. Electrons not being shared may be shown as dots in such a representation. Structural formulas for H_2 and HCl are

$$H — H \qquad H — \ddot{\underset{\cdot\cdot}{C}}l\!:$$

Two atoms can share more than one pair of electrons to make an octet for each atom. Consider the nitrogen molecule:

$$:N:::N: \quad \text{or} \quad :N\equiv N:$$

In this case, three electron pairs are shared, and each nitrogen atom has an octet of electrons. There is one lone pair of electrons on each nitrogen atom. Three pairs of electrons shared between the same two atoms constitute a **triple bond.** If two pairs of electrons are shared, a **double bond** results. Consider the carbon dioxide molecule:

$$:\ddot{O}::C::\ddot{O}: \quad \text{or} \quad :\ddot{O}=C=\ddot{O}:$$

Double bonds

The term **multiple bond** refers to either a double or triple bond.

With a few simple rules, recognizing compounds that consist of molecules is fairly easy. All compounds that are gases or liquids at room temperature are molecular. (Solid compounds may be molecular.) Most compounds that do not have a metal atom or an ammonium ion (NH_4^+) in them are molecular. When not combined with other elements, most nonmetallic elements form molecules. (The noble gases have monatomic molecules; their atoms are uncombined.)

EXAMPLE 5.12

Which of the following formula units consist of uncombined atoms, which consist of molecules, and which consist of ions?

(a) O_2 (b) Ne   (c) NO_2 (d) NH_4Cl (e) Na_2O

Solution

(a) O_2 consists of molecules.

(b) Ne consists of uncombined atoms.

(c) NO_2 consists of molecules.

(d) NH_4Cl is ionic, even though it contains no metal atoms.

(e) Na_2O consists of ions.

Practice Problem 5.12 Which of the following formula units consist of uncombined atoms, which consist of molecules, and which consist of ions?

(a) H_2 (b) He   (c) HCl   (d) HgO

Very large molecules, containing billions and billions of atoms, are called **macromolecules.** Diamond, graphite, and silica (sand) are examples (Figure 5.12). Formulas for macromolecules cannot state the number of atoms of each element

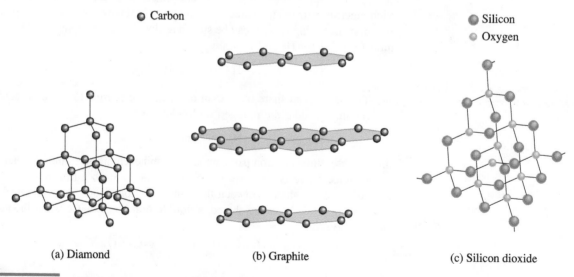

(a) Diamond   (b) Graphite   (c) Silicon dioxide

Figure 5.12 Macromolecules of diamond, graphite, and silica

All of the atoms pictured in each case, plus millions more, make up one giant molecule. (a) In diamond, carbon atoms are connected in a three-dimensional structure. (b) In graphite, carbon atoms are connected in sheets or layers. (c) Silica (silicon dioxide) has a structure somewhat like that of diamond, except that it contains silicon and oxygen atoms instead of carbon atoms, and an oxygen atom bridges each pair of silicon atoms.

in each molecule because there are too many. Therefore, these formulas give only the simplest ratio of atoms of one element to any others present. For example, the formula for both diamond and graphite is C and that for silica is SiO_2.

Systematic Method for Drawing Electron Dot Diagrams

Drawing electron dot diagrams for some compounds or ions can get complicated. If a diagram in which each nonmetal atom except hydrogen has an octet cannot be made by using only single bonds, move pairs of unshared electrons to positions between atoms, forming double or triple bonds. However, for compounds or ions that obey the octet rule, a more systematic approach may be used. We will use $PSCl_3$, in which the phosphorus atom is the central atom, as an example.

Steps	**Example**
	S Cl P Cl Cl
Step 1: Determine the arrangement of the atoms.	
Step 2: Determine the total number of valence electrons *available* from all the atoms in the formula unit.	1 P $1 \times 5 =$ 5 valence electrons 1 S $1 \times 6 =$ 6 valence electrons 3 Cl $3 \times 7 = 21$ valence electrons total 32 valence electrons
Step 3: Determine the total number of electrons *required* to get 8 electrons around each nonmetal atom except hydrogen and 2 electrons around each hydrogen atom.	1 P 8 electrons 1 S 8 electrons 3 Cl 24 electrons total 40 electrons
Hydrogen atoms need only 2 electrons in their outermost shells, and most main group metal ions need none.	
Step 4: Subtract the number of electrons available from the number required to determine the number of shared electrons. (The shared electrons are counted for each atom; that is, they are counted twice to obtain the total number of electrons needed.)	$40 - 32 = 8$ electrons to be shared
Step 5: Distribute the shared pairs *between* adjacent atoms.	S Cl:P:Cl Cl
Step 6: Distribute the rest of the electrons to positions other than between atoms, making sure that the number of electrons required for each atom (step 3) is now present.	Each atom now has 8 electrons: :S: :Cl:P:Cl: :Cl:

EXAMPLE 5.13

Draw an electron dot diagram for CO_2, in which the oxygen atoms are both bonded to the carbon atom.

Solution

Atoms	Valence electrons available	Valence electrons required
C	$1 \times 4 = 4$	$1 \times 8 = 8$
2 O	$2 \times 6 = \underline{12}$	$2 \times 8 = \underline{16}$
Total	16	24

The number of electrons to be shared is $24 - 16 = 8$. Put two pairs of electrons between each pair of adjacent atoms:

$$O::C::O \qquad \text{(Incomplete)}$$

Adding the other available electrons (8) yields the complete electron dot diagram:

$$:\ddot{O}::C::\ddot{O}:$$

Be sure to check that all the atoms have the proper octets (duets for hydrogen atoms) and that all valence electrons and no other electrons are shown.

$$(:\ddot{O}::)(C::)(\ddot{O}:)$$

Practice Problem 5.13   Draw an electron dot diagram for HN_3, hydrazoic acid.

EXAMPLE 5.14

Draw an electron dot diagram for formaldehyde, CH_2O, in which the hydrogen and oxygen atoms are all bonded to the carbon atom.

Solution

Atoms	Valence electrons available	Valence electrons required
2 H	$2 \times 1 = 2$	$2 \times 2 = 4$
C	$1 \times 4 = 4$	$1 \times 8 = 8$
O	$1 \times 6 = \underline{6}$	$1 \times 8 = \underline{8}$
Total	12	20

There are $20 - 12 = 8$ electrons shared. One double bond is needed for 8 electrons to be shared between the three pairs of atoms. The hydrogen atoms cannot be involved in a double bond because their maximum number of valence electrons is 2. Therefore, the double bond must be between the carbon atom and the oxygen atom. The structure showing only the shared electrons is

$$H:C::O \quad \text{(Incomplete)}$$
$$\ddot{H}$$

Then the unshared electrons are added:

$$H:C::\ddot{O}:$$
$$\ddot{H}$$

There are 8 electrons around the carbon atom and 8 electrons around the oxygen atom, as well as 2 electrons around each hydrogen atom:

Practice Problem 5.14 Draw an electron dot diagram for H_2O_2, in which each oxygen atom is bonded to one hydrogen atom.

The first problem in drawing an electron dot diagram for a complicated structure is to determine which atoms are bonded to which other atoms. Many common molecules and ions have one atom of one element and several atoms of another. The single atom of the one element is usually the central atom, with all the other atoms bonded to it.

EXAMPLE 5.15

Draw an electron dot diagram for (a) Cl_2O and (b) NH_3.

Solution

(a) The central atom is the oxygen atom:

$$Cl \quad O \quad Cl$$

The number of shared electrons is $24 - 20 = 4$. The complete diagram is

$$:\ddot{Cl}:\ddot{O}:\ddot{Cl}:$$

(b) The central atom is the nitrogen atom:

$$H$$
$$H \quad N \quad H$$

The number of shared electrons is $14 - 8 = 6$. The complete diagram is

$$H$$
$$H:\ddot{N}:H$$

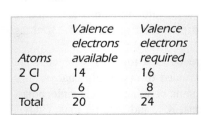

Atoms	Valence electrons available	Valence electrons required
2 Cl	14	16
O	6	8
Total	20	24

Atoms	Valence electrons available	Valence electrons required
N	5	8
3 H	3	6
Total	8	14

Practice Problem 5.15 Draw an electron dot diagram for acetylene, C_2H_2.

EXAMPLE 5.16

Draw an electron dot diagram for hydrazine, N_2H_4, which has two hydrogen atoms bonded to each nitrogen.

Solution

The nitrogen atoms must be bonded to each other, because the hydrogen atoms cannot bond to two atoms. The arrangement of atoms is

$$
\begin{array}{cc}
\text{H} & \text{H} \\
\text{H N} & \text{N H}
\end{array}
$$

The number of shared electrons is $24 - 14 = 10$. The complete diagram is

$$
\begin{array}{cc}
\text{H} & \text{H} \\
\text{H:\ddot{N}:\ddot{N}:H} &
\end{array}
$$

Practice Problem 5.16   Draw an electron dot diagram for NH_2OH.

Atoms	Electrons available	Electrons required
2 N	10	16
4 H	4	8
Total	14	24

Line formulas for more complicated molecules sometimes give clues as to which atoms are bonded to which others. For example, in compounds containing carbon and hydrogen atoms, perhaps along with atoms of others elements, the atoms bonded to each carbon atom are placed after that atom, as in CH_3CH_2OH.

Polyatomic Ions

A great many compounds contain **polyatomic ions** ("many-atom" ions). There are many polyatomic anions but relatively few polyatomic cations. The most important polyatomic cation is the ammonium ion, NH_4^+ (compare with ammonia, NH_3). Some of the most important polyatomic anions are listed in Table 5.2, the first seven of which are also presented in Figure 5.13, along with others.

The atoms *within* a polyatomic ion are bonded together with covalent bonds, but polyatomic ions as a whole are bonded to oppositely charged ions by the attraction of the opposite charges—by ionic bonding. For example, potassium chlorite, $KClO_2$, contains potassium ions, K^+, and chlorite ions, ClO_2^-. The K^+ ions are attracted to the ClO_2^- ions by their opposite charges. The chlorine and oxygen atoms within each ClO_2^- ion are covalently bonded. The electron dot diagram for potassium chlorite is simply a combination of that for the potassium ion and that for the chlorite ion. The representation can be determined by the systematic process described previously. Note that the potassium ion is bonded ionically and that it shares *no* electrons with other atoms. For that reason, no electrons are allotted for its valence shell.

The number of electrons to be shared is $24 - 20 = 4$. The structure, with only the shared electrons:

$$
K^+\left[\,\text{O:Cl:O}\,\right]^- \quad \text{(Incomplete)}
$$

Table 5.2 Some Important Polyatomic Anions

Name	Formula
Nitrate ion	NO_3^-
Sulfate ion	SO_4^{2-}
Carbonate ion	CO_3^{2-}
Phosphate ion	PO_4^{3-}
Chlorate ion	ClO_3^-
Bromate ion	BrO_3^-
Iodate ion	IO_3^-
Hydroxide ion	OH^-
Cyanide ion	CN^-
Acetate ion	$C_2H_3O_2^-$
Chromate ion	CrO_4^{2-}
Dichromate ion	$Cr_2O_7^{2-}$
Permanganate ion	MnO_4^-

Atoms	Valence electrons available	Valence electrons required
K	1	0
Cl	7	8
2 O	12	16
Total	20	24

IV	V	VI	VII
CO_3^{2-}	NO_3^-		
	NO_2^-		
	PO_4^{3-}	SO_4^{2-}	ClO_4^-
	PO_3^{3-}	SO_3^{2-}	ClO_3^-
			ClO_2^-
			ClO^-
	AsO_4^{3-}	SeO_4^{2-}	BrO_4^-
	AsO_3^{3-}	SeO_3^{2-}	BrO_3^-
			BrO_2^-
			BrO^-
			IO_4^-
			IO_3^-
			IO_2^-
			IO^-

Figure 5.13 Formulas of Some Important Polyatomic Main Group Anions

The rest of the electrons are added:

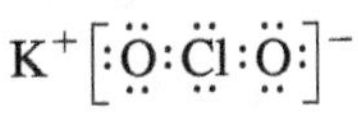

$$K^+\left[:\ddot{O}:\ddot{Cl}:\ddot{O}:\right]^-$$

Be sure to write the charge on each ion because the charge is an integral part of the formula. For example, there is a great difference between ClO_2 and ClO_2^-.

To draw an electron dot diagram for a polyatomic ion alone, we must consider its charge when counting the number of electrons available. One extra electron is present for each negative charge, and 1 fewer electron for each positive charge.

EXAMPLE 5.17

Draw an electron dot diagram for the chlorite ion, ClO_2^-.

Solution

The charge on the ion signifies the presence of an extra valence electron—from some other (unspecified) atom—which must be counted as available:

Atoms	Valence electrons available	Valence electrons required
Cl	7	8
2 O	12	16
Negative charge	1	
Total	20	24

The number of electrons to be shared is $24 - 20 = 4$. The structure, with only the shared electrons:

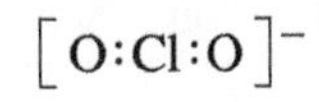

$$\left[O:Cl:O\right]^- \quad \text{(Incomplete)}$$

Adding the other electrons gives

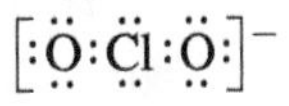

$$\left[:\ddot{O}:\ddot{Cl}:\ddot{O}:\right]^-$$

The structure of the chlorite ion is the same as when the ion was in potassium chlorite. In that case, the potassium atom donated its electron to the chlorite ion. In this case, we do not know where the extra electron came from, but it does not matter. The total number of valence electrons is still 20, and the number of electrons to be shared is still 4. The chlorite ion does not exist in isolation, even though we sometimes write it alone.

Practice Problem 5.17 Draw an electron dot diagram for the phosphate ion, PO_4^{3-}.

EXAMPLE 5.18

Draw an electron dot diagram for the NO_3^- ion.

Solution

The number of shared electrons is $32 - 24 = 8$. Here is the structure with only the shared electrons shown:

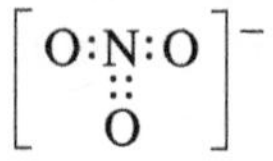

$$\left[\begin{array}{c} O\!:\!N\!:\!O \\ \vdots\vdots \\ O \end{array} \right]^- \quad \text{(Incomplete)}$$

Here is the structure showing all the electrons:

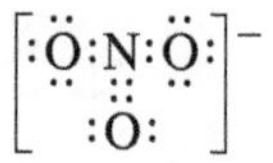

$$\left[\begin{array}{c} \vdots\ddot{O}\!:\!N\!:\!\ddot{O}\!: \\ \vdots\vdots \\ :\ddot{O}: \end{array} \right]^-$$

Atoms	Valence electrons available	Valence electrons required
N	5	8
3 O	18	24
Negative charge	1	
Total	24	32

The double bond was arbitrarily placed between the nitrogen atom and the oxygen atom below it. However, there is no difference between that oxygen and the one to the left of the nitrogen atom or the one to its right. We could draw the double bond between nitrogen and either of those atoms instead. All the following structures are equivalent:

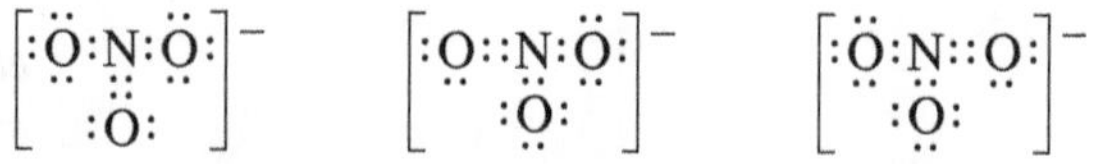

$$\left[\begin{array}{c} :\ddot{O}\!:\!N\!:\!\ddot{O}: \\ \vdots\vdots \\ :\ddot{O}: \end{array} \right]^- \qquad \left[\begin{array}{c} :\ddot{O}\!:\!:\!N\!:\!\ddot{O}: \\ \vdots \\ :\ddot{O}: \end{array} \right]^- \qquad \left[\begin{array}{c} :\ddot{O}\!:\!N\!:\!:\!O: \\ \vdots \\ :\ddot{O}: \end{array} \right]^-$$

In fact, the extra pair of electrons spends some time in each of the three positions, and the structures are said to be **resonance structures** of each other. Note that in each one, all the *atoms* are in the *same positions;* only the electrons have changed positions.

Practice Problem 5.18   Draw all resonance structures for the NO_2^- ion.

Hydrogen atoms very often bond with oxygen atoms but seldom bond with oxygen atoms that are double-bonded to other atoms. Thus, if we have a choice between putting a hydrogen atom on an oxygen atom connected by a single bond to another atom or putting it on one connected by a double bond to another atom, we choose the former.

EXAMPLE 5.19

Draw all resonance structures for HCO_3^-, in which the hydrogen atom is bonded to a single-bonded oxygen atom.

Atoms	Valence electrons available	Valence electrons required
H	1	2
C	4	8
3 O	18	24
Negative charge	1	
Total	24	34

Solution

The number of shared electrons is $34 - 24 = 10$. The structures with the shared electrons are

$$\left[\text{H:O:C::O} \atop \qquad \ddot{\text{O}} \right]^{-} \quad \text{or} \quad \left[\text{H:O:C:O} \atop \qquad \ddot{\text{O}} \right]^{-} \quad \text{(Incomplete)}$$

With all the electrons,

$$\left[\text{H:}\ddot{\text{O}}\text{:C::}\ddot{\text{O}} \atop \qquad :\ddot{\text{O}}: \right]^{-} \quad \text{or} \quad \left[\text{H:}\ddot{\text{O}}\text{:C:}\ddot{\text{O}}: \atop \qquad :\ddot{\text{O}}: \right]^{-}$$

The hydrogen atom can bond equally well to either of the oxygen atoms that are connected to the carbon atom by a single bond, but not to the double-bonded one.

Practice Problem 5.19   Draw an electron dot diagram for HNO_2. ▌

With a little experience, we will all recognize the familiar ions in formulas, which will allow us to deduce the formula of the other ion in the compound, even if it is unfamiliar to us.

EXAMPLE 5.20

Write formulas and electron dot diagrams for the ions in NaH_2AsO_4.

Solution

We recognize that sodium always exists in its compounds as the Na^+ ion. Thus, the other ion must contain all the other atoms and must have a single negative charge. The formulas are Na^+ and $H_2AsO_4^-$. The electron dot diagrams are

$$Na^+ \left[\begin{matrix} :\ddot{\text{O}}: \\ \text{H:}\ddot{\text{O}}\text{:As:}\ddot{\text{O}}\text{:H} \\ :\ddot{\text{O}}: \end{matrix} \right]^{-}$$

Practice Problem 5.20   Write formulas for the ions in $K_4P_2O_7$. ▌

Nonoctet Structures

Not all atoms in molecules or polyatomic ions obey the octet rule; those that do not are said to have **nonoctet structures.** For example, in its compounds boron, which is in the second period of the periodic table, is apt to have fewer than 8 electrons in the valence shell of its atoms. Thus, the boron atom in BF_3 is represented as having only 6 electrons in its valence shell:

$$:\ddot{F}:B:\ddot{F}:$$
$$:\ddot{F}:$$

If the central element in a molecule or polyatomic ion is in the third period or higher and does not obey the octet rule, it is apt to expand its valence shell beyond 8 electrons. The phosphorus atom in PF_5 has 10 electrons around it:

Nonoctet structures are discussed more extensively in more advanced texts.

Snapshot Review

ChemSkill Builder 3.2

❑ Polyatomic ions are discussed in the section on covalent bonding because the bonding *within* these ions is covalent.
❑ Electron dot diagrams for covalently bonded atoms may have four or fewer positions for electrons around an atom, with up to 6 electrons in any one position.
❑ For species that follow the octet rule, the number of electrons around nonmetal atoms other than hydrogen is 8.

A. Draw electron dot diagrams for (a) CH_3CHO and (b) C_3H_6.
B. Draw electron dot diagrams for (a) NCO^- and (b) CH_2O.

Key Terms

Key terms are defined in the Glossary.

allotrope (5.1)
anhydrous (5.1)
anion (5.2)
anode (5.2)
binary compound (5.1)
cathode (5.2)
cation (5.2)
centered dot (5.1)
covalent bond (5.5)
diatomic molecule (5.1)
double bond (5.5)
duet (5.2)
electrode (5.2)
electronegative (5.1)
electronegativity (5.1)

electron sharing (5.5)
electropositive (5.1)
elemental (5.1)
formula (5.1)
formula unit (5.1)
hydrate (5.1)
ion (5.2)
ionic bond (5.2)
Lewis electron dot diagram (5.3)
lone pair (5.5)
macromolecule (5.5)
molecule (5.1)
monatomic ion (5.2)
multiple bond (5.5)
noble gas configuration (5.2)

nonoctet structure (5.5)
octet (5.2)
octet rule (5.2)
outermost shell (5.2)
ozone (5.1)
polyatomic ion (5.5)
resonance structure (5.5)
single bond (5.5)
sodium chloride structure (5.2)
structural formula (5.5)
subscript (5.1)
triple bond (5.5)
unshared pair (5.5)
valence electron (5.2)
valence shell (5.2)

Prefixes/Suffixes

-ide (5.2)

Summary

Chemical formulas identify compounds, ions, or molecules. The formula implies that the atoms are held together by some kind(s) of chemical bond(s). When they are not combined with other elements, hydrogen, nitrogen, oxygen, fluorine, chlorine, bromine, and iodine exist as diatomic molecules (Figure 5.2).

In formulas for binary compounds, the more electropositive element is written first. A formula unit represents the collection of atoms in the formula. Subscripts in a formula indicate the numbers of atoms of the elements in each formula unit. For example, the formula unit H_2O has two hydrogen atoms and one oxygen atom. Formula units of uncombined elements, such as Ne, are atoms. Formula units of covalently bonded atoms are called molecules. Formula units of ionic compounds do not have any special name. In formulas, atoms bonded in special groups may be enclosed in parentheses. A subscript following the closing parenthesis multiplies everything within the parentheses. For example, a formula unit of $Ba(ClO_4)_2$ contains one barium atom, two chlorine atoms, and eight oxygen atoms. Formulas for hydrates have a centered dot preceding a number and the formula for water, such as $CuSO_4 \cdot 5H_2O$. The number multiplies everything following it to the end of the formula (Section 5.1).

Atoms of main group elements tend to accept, donate, or share electrons to achieve the electronic structure of the nearest noble gas. Metal atoms tend to donate electrons and thereby become positive ions. When combining with metals, nonmetal atoms tend to accept electrons and become negative ions. The number of electrons donated or accepted by each atom depends to a great extent on the periodic group number; each atom tends to attain a noble gas configuration. The attraction of oppositely charged ions is called an ionic bond. Transition and inner transition metal atoms donate their valence electrons first but ordinarily do not achieve noble gas configurations. Most of them can also lose electrons from an inner shell and thus can form cations with different charges (Section 5.2).

Electron dot diagrams can be drawn for atoms, ions, and molecules, using a dot to represent each valence electron. These diagrams are most useful for main group elements. The diagrams help in visualizing simple reactions and structures of polyatomic ions and molecules (Section 5.3).

Formulas for ionic compounds may be deduced from the charges on the ions, since all compounds have zero net charge. Given the constituent elements, we can predict the formula for binary compounds of most main group metals. We cannot do so for most transition metals because of their ability to form ions of different charges. (Given the specific ions, we can write a formula for any ionic compound.) Conversely, given the formula of an ionic compound, we can deduce the charges on its ions. Writing correct formulas for compounds and identifying the ions in compounds from their formulas are two absolutely essential skills (Section 5.4).

Nonmetal atoms can share electrons with other nonmetal atoms, forming covalent bonds. In electron dot diagrams, the shared electrons are counted as being in the outermost shell of *each* of the bonded atoms. A single bond consists of one shared electron pair; a double bond consists of two shared electron pairs; a triple bond consists of three shared electron pairs. Macromolecules result from covalent bonding of millions of atoms or more into giant molecules.

Drawing electron dot diagrams for structures containing only atoms that obey the octet rule can be eased by subtracting the number of valence electrons *available* from the number *required* to get an octet (or duet) around each nonmetal atom. The difference is the number of electrons to be shared in the covalent bonds. For an ion, we must subtract 1 available electron for each positive charge on the ion or add 1 available electron for each negative charge. Main group metal ions in general require no outermost electrons; but each hydrogen atom requires 2; and each other nonmetal atom requires 8. Atoms in some compounds do not follow the octet rule (Section 5.5).

Items for Special Attention

■ Because formulas are used to represent unbonded atoms, covalently bonded molecules (Section 5.5), and ionically bonded compounds (Section 5.2), a formula unit can represent an atom, a molecule, or the simplest unit of an ionic compound (Figure 5.8). For example, He represents an uncombined atom; F_2 represents a molecule of an element; CO_2 represents a molecule of a compound;

and NaCl represents one pair of ions in an ionic compound.

■ The seven elements that occur in the form of diatomic molecules (Figure 5.2) form such molecules *only when these elements are uncombined with other elements*. When combined in compounds, they may have one, two, three, four, or more atoms per formula unit, depending on the compound.

■ Learning and using a generalization is easier than memorizing individual facts. For example, once we learn that *in their compounds,* the metals of periodic groups IA, IIA, and IIIB (1, 2, and 3) form ions with charges equal to their group numbers (1+, 2+, and 3+, respectively), we do not have to learn the charges on 16 separate metal ions.

■ An ion is a charged species. A single ion is just *part* of a compound. The charges on ions are integral parts of the formulas of the ions. We must always include the charges when we write formulas for ions alone. For example, it makes quite a difference whether we are referring to SO_3 (sulfur trioxide) or SO_3^{2-} (sulfite ion). Writing the symbol or formula for a single ion does not imply that it can exist alone, but only that the ion of opposite charge is not of immediate interest. We may write the charges on both ions in an ionic compound while we are determining the compound's formula, but we never write the charge on one ion without writing the charge on the other. To finish the formula, we rewrite it without the charges. For example, we write NaCl for Na^+Cl^-.

■ All compounds, whether ionic or covalent, are electrically neutral. The total positive charge on the cations of an ionic compound must therefore be balanced by the total negative charge on the anions.

■ Except for H^-, monatomic anions have charges equal to their classical group number minus 8. (Not all nonmetals form monatomic ions.) Polyatomic anions containing oxygen and one other element are not quite that easy to predict charges for, but generally, the charge is *odd* if the periodic group of the central element is odd and *even* if the periodic group of the central element is even.

■ All the ionic compounds considered in this book are composed of only one type of cation and one type of anion.

■ Electron dot diagrams are most useful for main group elements, and the systematic procedure for drawing electron dot diagrams works only for species in which all atoms obey the octet rule.

■ Nonmetal atoms accept electrons from metal atoms if the metal atoms are available, or else they share electrons; they never donate electrons to form monatomic cations. The largest charge on any monatomic cation is 4+, and on any monatomic anion, it is 3−.

■ The terms *single bond, double bond,* and *triple bond* refer to covalent bonds only.

■ Polyatomic ions are held together by covalent bonds and are attracted to oppositely charged ions by ionic bonds.

■ After a little experience, we will recognize the monatomic and polyatomic ions introduced in this chapter. For example, every time the symbol for an alkali metal or an alkaline earth metal appears *in a compound,* it represents the ion with a charge equal to 1+ or 2+, respectively.

■ Both *chloride ion* and *chloride* can be used to refer to the Cl^- ion. To refer to Na^+, however, we must always include the word *ion* because *sodium* can refer to the element, the atom, or the ion.

■ The alkali metals, the alkaline earth metals, the group IIIB metals, aluminum, zinc, cadmium, and silver have ions with charges equal to their classical group numbers, but *only in their compounds!* When the elements are uncombined, they do not form ions, and the charge on each atom is zero.

Answers to Snapshot Reviews

5.1 A. Nine hydrogen atoms per phosphorus atom
   B. Chlorine is more electronegative; that is why it is written after selenium.
   C. O_2
5.2 A. (a) Two valence and two outermost electrons (the same electrons) and (b) zero valence electrons (fourth shell) and eight outermost electrons (third shell)
   B. (a) Equal, (b) equal, (c) one more electron than proton
5.3 A. $:\overset{\cdot}{\underset{\cdot}{P}}\cdot$

5.4 A. La_2S_3
   B. (a) V^{2+} and Cl^- (b) Pb^{4+} and O^{2-}
      (c) Ti^{3+} and O^{2-}
5.5 A. (a)
```
      H H
   H:C:C::O:
      H
```
   (b)
```
      H H H
   H:C:C::C
      H   H
```
   B. (a) $[:\overset{\cdot\cdot}{N}::C::\overset{\cdot\cdot}{O}:]^-$
   (b)
```
      H
   H:C::O
```

Self-Tutorial Problems

5.1 (a) Distinguish between *valence shell* and *outermost shell*.

   (b) Distinguish between *diatomic* and *binary*.

5.2 Rules for writing diatomic molecules and for deducing the charges on alkali metal ions were introduced in this chapter. Which of these refers only to uncombined elements and which refers only to elements in compounds?

5.3 Explain why hydrogen cannot form

   (a) an H^{2+} ion

   (b) an H^{2-} ion

5.4 Which of the following have ionic bonds, and which have covalent bonds?

   (a) Cl_2 (b) $MgCl_2$ (c) SCl_2

5.5 (a) What is the difference between group IA *metals* and group IA *elements?*

(b) Which of the following statements is correct?

Group IA metals form ions with a $1+$ charge only.

Group IA elements form ions with a $1+$ charge only.

(c) Does the same problem exist for group IIA?

5.6 What is the difference in bonding between $CoCl_2$ and $COCl_2$?

5.7 (a) Write the formula of the compound of Zn^{2+} and Br^-.

(b) Identify the ions present in ZnF_2.

(c) Write the formula of the compound of Sn^{2+} and O^{2-}.

(d) Identify the ions in FeO.

5.8 How many electrons are "available" to draw the electron dot diagram of N^{3-}? Where do they come from?

5.9 What is the charge on zinc in each of the following?

(a) ZnO   (b) $Zn_3(PO_4)_2$ (c) Zn

(d) $ZnCl_2$ (e) $ZnCr_2O_7$

5.10 (a) What is the charge on a calcium atom?

(b) What is the charge on a calcium ion?

(c) What is the charge on a calcium nucleus?

5.11 (a) Which metals form ions of only one charge?

(b) Which metals form ions of $1+$ charge?

5.12 Write the formulas for ammonia and for the ammonium ion.

5.13 Write the formula of the compound of

(a) UO_2^{2+} and AsO_4^{3-}

(b) $(MO_y)^{2+}$ and $(XO_z)^{3-}$, where M and X are some metal and nonmetal and y and z are variables

(c) $(AX_y)^{2+}$ and $(BZ_z)^{3-}$

(d) Does it matter to the subscripts after the parentheses *what* symbols are in the parentheses?

5.14 (a) Is the electron dot diagram of H^- like that of any noble gas?

(b) Is that of H^+?

5.15 What is the difference between ClO_2 and ClO_2^-?

5.16 Determine the formula of each of the following compounds:

(a) The compound of cadmium and sulfur

(b) The compound of Cd^{2+} and S^{2-}

(c) The product of the reaction of cadmium and sulfur

(d) Cadmium sulfide

5.17 In which classical periodic groups are the atoms' valence electrons equal in number to the group number?

5.18 Draw electron dot diagrams for (a) LiH and (b) CaH_2.

5.19 (a) Write the formula of the compound of Ag^+ and O^{2-}.

(b) Identify the ions present in Ag_2S.

5.20 (a) How many valence electrons, if any, are in a magnesium ion?

(b) How many electrons, if any, should a magnesium atom share in its compounds?

5.21 Why was the formula in Practice Problem 5.1(b) not written NH_6PO_4?

5.22 Draw an electron dot diagram for each of the following. Because the species all have the same number of electrons, explain why the diagrams are not all the same.

(a) H^- (b) He   (c) Li^+ (d) Be^{2+}

5.23 What is the charge on (a) the sodium ion, (b) the zinc ion, (c) the oxide ion, and (d) the bromide ion?

5.24 What is a valid generalization about the charges on monatomic anions? What is a valid generalization about the charges on polyatomic anions containing oxygen and another element?

5.25 Draw an electron dot diagram for each of the following:

(a) K   (b) K^+ (c) N   (d) N^{3-}

5.26 Identify the type of bonding in each of the following:

(a) BrCl   (b) Br_2 (c) NaBr

Problems

5.1 Chemical Formulas

5.27 What is the difference between (a) 2 N and N_2? (b) N_2O_4 and 2 NO_2?

5.28 What is implied about bonding in the mercury(I) ion, Hg_2^{2+}?

5.29 How many atoms of each element are present in one formula unit of each of the following?

(a) $(NH_4)_3PO_4$ (b) Li_3N (c) $Al(C_2H_3O_2)_3$

5.30 How many atoms of each element are present in one formula unit of each of the following?

(a) $UO_2(ClO_4)_2$ (b) $CaCr_2O_7$ (c) $(NH_4)_2CrO_4$

(d) $KHCO_3 \cdot MgCO_3 \cdot 4H_2O$

5.31 What information (from Section 5.1) is conveyed by the formula $Zn_3(PO_4)_2$?

■ Problems

5.2 Ionic Bonding

5.32 Identify the ions in each of the following compounds:

    (a) SnO_2 (b) $CrPO_4$ (c) $CrSO_4$

    (d) $NaHCO_3$ (e) $CaHPO_4$

5.33 What difference, if any, is there between $Zn^{2+}O^{2-}$ and ZnO?

5.34 Identify the ions in each of the following compounds:

    (a) UO_2Cl_2 (b) K_3AsO_4 (c) NH_4HCO_3

    (d) $Co(NO_3)_2$

5.35 (a) Which metals form ions with 1+ charge? (b) Which metals form ions with 1+ charge only?

5.36 Complete the following table:

	Symbol	Atomic Number	No. of Protons	No. of Electrons	Net Charge
(a)	Cl^-	___	___	___	___
(b)	___	16	___	18	___
(c)	___	___	19	18	___
(d)	___	26	___	___	3+
(e)	___	___	78	___	2+

5.37 Complete the following table:

	Symbol	Atomic Number	No. of Protons	No. of Electrons	Net Charge
(a)	Zn^{2+}	___	___	___	___
(b)	___	13	___	___	3+
(c)	___	___	___	10	2−
(d)	___	___	34	___	2−
(e)	___	___	39	36	___

5.38 (optional) Write a detailed electronic configuration for each of the following ions:

    (a) Na^+ (b) Al^{3+} (c) Zn^{2+}

5.39 (optional) Write a detailed electronic configuration for each of the following ions:

    (a) N^{3-} (b) S^{2-} (c) Cl^-

5.40 (optional) Write a detailed electronic configuration for each of the following ions:

    (a) Co^{2+} (b) Cr^{3+} (c) Cu^{2+}

5.3 Lewis Electron Dot Diagrams

5.41 Draw an electron dot diagram for each of the following ions:

    (a) O^{2-} (b) Cl^- (c) N^{3-}

5.42 Draw an electron dot diagram for each of the following ions:

    (a) Na^+ (b) Ca^{2+} (c) Al^{3+} (d) Sn^{2+}

5.43 Draw electron dot diagrams for atoms of the following elements and the ions they produce when they combine:

    (a) Al and S   (b) Ca and Br   (c) Mg and N

5.44 Draw electron dot diagrams for atoms of the following elements and the ions they produce when they combine:

    (a) Li and F   (b) Be and H   (c) Al and H

5.4 Formulas for Ionic Compounds

5.45 Write the formula for the ion formed by each of the following metals in all of its compounds:

    (a) Lithium   (b) Calcium   (c) Zinc

    (d) Aluminum   (e) Scandium

5.46 Chromium forms ions of 2+ and 3+ charges. Write formulas for (a) two chlorides of chromium and (b) two oxides of chromium.

5.47 Write the formula for the compound formed between each of the following pairs of ions:

    (a) Al^{3+} and S^{2-}

    (b) Ag^+ and O^{2-}

    (c) N^{3-} and Mg^{2+}

5.48 Complete the following table by writing the formula of the compound formed by the cation on the left and the anion at the top:

	O^{2-}	Br^-	N^{3-}
K^+	___	___	___
Ca^{2+}	___	___	___
Al^{3+}	___	___	___

5.49 Complete the following table by writing the formula of the compound formed by the cation at the top and the anion on the left.

	Zn^{2+}	Cr^{3+}	NH_4^+
ClO_3^-	___	___	___
SO_4^{2-}	___	___	___
PO_4^{3-}	___	___	___
$Cr_2O_7^{2-}$	___	___	___

5.50 Write the formula for the compound formed between each of the following pairs:

    (a) Na and H   (b) Mg and H

5.51 For each of the following compounds, identify the individual ions, and indicate how many of each are present per formula unit:

    (a) $Zn(C_2H_3O_2)_2$ (b) $Al_2(CO_3)_3$

    (c) K_2SO_4 (d) NH_4HCO_3

5.52 Identify the individual ions in each of the following compounds:

(a) $CaBr_2$ (b) $MgSO_4$ (c) $Mg_3(PO_4)_2$

(d) $Al_2(SO_3)_3$ (e) K_2O_2 (f) $Sr(CN)_2$

(g) $Pb(ClO_3)_2$

5.53 Write the formula for the compound formed by each of the following pairs of elements:

(a) Mg and N   (b) Mg and P   (c) Ca and S

(d) Al and N   (e) Na and I   (f) Al and P

(g) Li and S   (h) Mg and Br   (i) Zn and Cl

5.54 Write the formula for the compound formed by each of the following pairs of elements:

(a) Zinc and sulfur   (b) Lithium and nitrogen

(c) Barium and chlorine   (d) Silver and iodine

(e) Oxygen and scandium   (f) Fluorine and calcium

5.55 Complete the following table by writing the formula of the compound formed by the metal at the left and the nonmetal at the top:

	Nitrogen	Sulfur	Bromine
Aluminum	_____	_____	_____
Cadmium	_____	_____	_____
Silver	_____	_____	_____

5.56 Identify the individual ions in each of the following compounds:

(a) LiH   (b) $Zn(ClO_3)_2$ (c) Rb_2O_2

(d) $NaClO_3$ (e) $BaCl_2$ (f) $Hg_2(NO_3)_2$

(g) $(NH_4)_2HPO_4$

5.57 How many valence electrons does a Pb^{2+} ion have?

5.58 What individual ions are present in (a) Cu_2O and (b) CuO?

5.59 Identify the anion and *both* cations in each of the following pairs of compounds:

(a) PtO and PtO_2

(b) Fe_2O_3 and FeO

(c) $CrSO_4$ and $Cr_2(SO_4)_3$

5.60 Complete the following table by writing the formula of the compound formed by each cation on the left with each anion at the top:

	NO_3^-	SO_4^{2-}	$Cr_2O_7^{2-}$	PO_4^{3-}
Na^+	_____	_____	_____	_____
Mg^{2+}	_____	_____	_____	_____
Zn^{2+}	_____	_____	_____	_____
Fe^{3+}	_____	_____	_____	_____

5.61 Complete the following table by writing the formula of the compound formed by each cation on the left with each anion at the top:

	ClO_2^-	SO_4^{2-}	PO_4^{3-}	$P_2O_7^{4-}$
NH_4^+	_____	_____	_____	_____
Fe^{2+}	_____	_____	_____	_____
Al^{3+}	_____	_____	_____	_____

5.62 Identify the cation and the anion in each of the following compounds:

(a) $Lu(CN)_3$ (b) $K_2Cr_2O_7$ (c) $(NH_4)_2SO_4$

(d) VO_2NO_3 (e) $VOSO_4$ (f) $Ba(MnO_4)_2$

(g) $KBrO_2$ (h) NH_4HSO_3 (i) $K_2S_2O_8$

5.63 Write the formula for the compound of each of the following pairs of ions:

(a) PO_4^{3-} and Fe^{3+}

(b) SO_3^{2-} and NH_4^+

(c) CO_3^{2-} and Ag^+

5.64 Write the formula of each ion in each of the following compounds:

(a) $(CH_3NH_3)_2SO_4$ (b) VO_2ClO_4

(c) $K_4P_2O_7$ (d) $UO_2(ClO_3)_2$

(e) $Ce(SO_4)_2$ (f) $MgCrO_4$

(g) $Ba(OCN)_2$ (h) $Na_2S_2O_3$

5.65 For each of the following compounds, identify the individual ions, and indicate how many of each are present per formula unit:

(a) $AlCl_3$ (b) Al_2O_3 (c) $Mg(HCO_3)_2$

(d) $Sr_3(PO_4)_2$ (e) $(NH_4)_2SeO_4$ (f) $(NH_4)_2SO_4$

(g) PbO_2

5.66 Identify the formulas of the ions in each of the following:

(a) $Sn_3(PO_4)_4$ (b) UO_2SO_4

5.67 Write formulas for the ions in each of the following compounds:

(a) KSCN   (b) $Cu(C_2H_3O_2)_2$ (c) $ZnSO_4$

(d) $(NH_4)_2CrO_4$ (e) NH_4NCS (f) KMn

(g) $Co(OH)_2$ (h) $(NH_4)_2Cr_2O_7$

5.5 Covalent Bonding

5.68 Explain v' double b

5.69 Which involve

(a) P_2

(d) C

5.70 What similarities and differences are there between a molecule and a polyatomic ion?

5.71 Draw an electron dot diagram for each of the following:

(a) SO_3^{2-} (b) N_3^- (c) CaO

5.72 Draw an electron dot diagram for each of the following:

(a) NH_4^+ (b) OCN^- (c) SO_4^{2-}

(d) N_2 (e) ONCl (nitrogen is the central atom)

(f) CO

5.73 Write an electron dot diagram for each of the following ions:

(a) HCO_3^- (b) HPO_4^{2-} (c) IO^-

5.74 What familiar ion is in each of the following compounds? Write the formula for the other ion present also.

(a) $Ba(BrO_3)_2$ (b) $(NH_4)_2SO_4$ (c) $K_2C_2O_4$

5.75 What is the difference between SO_3 and SO_3^{2-}? Draw an electron dot diagram for each.

5.76 Draw an electron dot diagram for each of the following:

(a) Ethylene, C_2H_4

(b) Hydrogen peroxide, H_2O_2

(c) Methyl alcohol, CH_3OH

5.77 Draw an electron dot diagram for each of the following compounds. Indicate any double or triple bonds.

(a) C_2H_2 (b) C_3H_6 (c) C_3H_8

5.78 Draw structural formulas for the compounds in the prior problem.

5.79 Draw resonance structures for each of the following:

(a) SO_3 (b) CO_3^{2-} (c) O_3

5.80 Draw an electron dot diagram for each of the following compounds:

(a) CH_2Br_2 (b) CH_5N

(c) CH_4O (d) HCN

5.81 Draw structural formulas for the compounds in the prior problem.

5.82 Draw a structural formula for each of the following:

(a) CH_2O (b) CCl_4

(c) NO_2Cl (nitrogen is the central atom)

5.83 Draw an electron dot diagram for each of the following compounds. In each of the last four compounds, the hydrogen atom is bonded to an oxygen atom.

(a) HCl   (b) HClO   (c) $HClO_2$

(d) $HClO_3$ (e) $HClO_4$

General Problems

5.84 Briefly define each of the following terms:

(a) Ion   (b) Anion   (c) Octet

(d) Lone pair   (e) Ozone

(f) Monatomic ion   (g) Noble gas configuration

(h) Polyatomic ion   (i) Triple bond

5.85 Draw an electron dot diagram for SCN^-, in which the carbon atom is the central atom.

5.86 (a) How many total valence electrons are in an ammonium ion?

(b) How many electrons, if any, should that ion share with other ions in its compounds?

5.87 Draw electron dot diagrams for (a) $CoCl_2$ and (b) $COCl_2$.

Draw an electron dot diagram for the ammonium ion, NH_4^+. Try to draw an electron dot diagram for the "ammonium molecule," NH_4, which does not exist. What
?

dot diagram for (a) O_2^{2-}, the perox- the azide ion.

ram for each of the following:

(c) $CH_3CH_2NH_2$

5.91 Write the formula for the compound composed of each of the following pairs of ions:

(a) Ca^{2+} and HCO_3^-

(b) Mn^{2+} and ClO_3^-

(c) NH_4^+ and AsO_4^{3-}

(d) Ag^+ and SO_3^{2-}

5.92 (optional) State the octet rule in terms of detailed electronic configurations.

5.93 Carbon does not have lone pairs of electrons in the great majority of its compounds. (Exceptions are C_2^{2-}, CN^-, and CO.) Draw electron dot diagrams for each of two different compounds, having the non-hydrogen atoms connected in different ways, each having the formula (a) C_2H_6O, (b) C_2H_7N.

5.94 Draw electron dot diagrams for C_2^{2-}, CN^-, and CO. Comment on their similarity.

5.95 (optional) Write detailed electronic configurations for (a) N^{3-}, (b) Mg^{2+}, and (c) O^{2-}.

5.96 (optional) Write detailed electronic configurations for (a) Cr^{2+}, (b) Fe^{3+}, and (c) Ni^{2+}.

158

5.97 Draw an electron dot diagram for each of the following pairs of elements and their compounds:

(a) Calcium and bromine

(b) Magnesium and nitrogen

Contrast this problem with Problem 5.43, parts (b) and (c).

5.98 A certain ionic compound contains eight oxygen atoms, one nickel atom, and two chlorine atoms per formula unit. Identify the ions that make up the compound.

5.99 Draw a structural formula for each of the following:

(a) H_2SO_3 (b) Na_2SO_3

(c) $SO_3{}^{2-}$ (d) SO_3

5.100 Which of the following have any ionic bonds?

C_2H_6 $Mg(ClO)_2$ $(NH_4)_3PO_4$ Pure HCl NH_3

5.101 Complete the following table:

Symbol	Atomic Number	No. of Protons	No. of Electrons	Net Charge
K	___	___	___	___
___	8	___	___	2−
___	___	15	18	___
N^{3-}	___	___	___	___
___	20	___	18	___
___	___	___	18	1−

5.102 Write formulas for the two new compounds formed if each of the following pairs of compounds traded anions:

(a) $Pb(ClO_3)_2$ and K_2S

(b) $CuCl_2$ and $AgC_2H_3O_2$

(c) KCl and $AgNO_3$

(d) $Pb(ClO_3)_2$ and $Al_2(SO_4)_3$

5.103 Draw a structural formula for (a) C_2F_2 and (b) CF_4.

5.104 Draw a structural formula for cyclohexane, C_6H_{12}, in which the six carbon atoms are bonded in a ring and each has two hydrogen atoms bonded to it.

5.105 Relatively speaking, how many atoms are covalently bonded in a diamond crystal?

5.106 What is the charge on the only monatomic cation of bismuth?

5.107 Write the formulas for the ions represented in each of the following:

(a) $(VO)_3(PO_4)_2$ (b) $NH_4H_2PO_4$

(c) $Na_{12}Si_6O_{18}$

5.108 Identify the cation in each of the following compounds:

(a) CuBr   (b) $FePO_4$ (c) $FeSO_4$

5.109 Which one of the following is ionic? $NiCl_2$ $NICl_2$

5.110 Complete the following table:

Symbol	Atomic Number	No. of Protons	No. of Electrons	Net Charge
Zn^{2+}	___	___	___	___
Cl^-	___	___	___	___
___	___	19	18	___
___	___	___	18	2+
___	___	___	36	2−
___	___	81	___	3+

5.111 In which of the following are there any covalent bonds?

$NaHCO_3$ MgO PCl_5 C_2H_6

5.112 (optional) We deduce the electronic configuration of copper from the periodic table, the $n + \ell$ rule, or other rules or memory devices to be

$$1s^2 \, 2s^2 \, 2p^6 \, 3s^2 \, 3p^6 \, 4s^2 \, 3d^9$$

The actual configuration is

$$1s^2 \, 2s^2 \, 2p^6 \, 3s^2 \, 3p^6 \, 4s^1 \, 3d^{10}$$

Starting with *each* of these configurations, deduce the electronic configuration of Cu^{2+}, and compare the results.

5.113 Write formulas for *both* kinds of ions in each of the following compounds:

(a) Mg_3N_2 (b) K_3PO_4 (c) $KClO_4$

5.114 (optional) (a) Write the outer electronic configuration of lead.

(b) On the basis of its configuration, explain why lead forms both a 2+ ion and a 4+ ion.

5.115 (a) How many oxygen atoms are covalently bonded to each silicon atom in SiO_2 (Figure 5.12)?

(b) How many silicon atoms are bonded to each oxygen? (*Hint:* Look at the top silicon atom and the oxygen atoms attached below it.)

5.116 Consult Figure 5.12 to determine how many carbon atoms are bonded to a given carbon atom in (a) diamond and (b) graphite. (*Hint:* Look in the middle of each figure, not at the edges.)

5.117 The formulas that follow represent compounds with ionic bonds only, with X representing one of the main group elements. In each case, state whether X is a metal or non-metal, and determine to which main group X belongs.

(a) Na_3X (b) XBr   (c) X_2O_3

(d) XO   (e) XF_4 (f) XCl_3

5.118 List two or more ions that have two atoms of the same element covalently bonded together.

5.119 How many atoms of each element are in one formula unit of (a) $Ni(CO)_4$ and (b) $(CH_3NH_3)_2SO_4$?

6

Nomenclature

Microscopic view of an antibiotic

■ **6.1** **Binary Nonmetal-Nonmetal Compounds**

■ **6.2** **Naming Ionic Compounds**

■ **6.3** **Naming Acids and Acid Salts**

■ **6.4** **Hydrates**

Review Clues

Section 6.1   Sections 1.4, 1.5, 5.1
Section 6.2   Sections 1.4, 3.3, 5.2, 5.4

Objectives

6.1 To name and write formulas for binary compounds of nonmetals

6.2 To name and write formulas for cations, anions, and ionic compounds

6.3 To name and write formulas for acids and acid salts

6.4 To name hydrates

So far in this book, we have used names for some simple chemical compounds, but we have not yet considered **nomenclature**—how to name compounds systematically. The great variety of compounds requires a systematic approach to naming them. Unfortunately, three or four different naming systems are used to name different types of compounds. Memorization of a few simple rules will allow naming of a great many compounds, but in addition to learning the rules, we must be sure to learn *when to use each one*. Learning generalities will help us to handle great quantities of information and to respond to specific questions. Even having four different systems for naming compounds is much better than using the trivial names that were first used, such as washing soda for Na_2CO_3, calomel for Hg_2Cl_2, lime for CaO, laughing gas for N_2O, Epsom salts for $MgSO_4 \cdot 7H_2O$, and so forth. Imagine having to learn for each compound a name that does not even give a clue as to the elements that make it up.

This chapter covers the basic rules for naming many compounds and ions and writing formulas for them. Section 6.1 considers the naming of binary nonmetal-nonmetal compounds. The naming of ionic compounds is addressed in Section 6.2. First, the naming of cations and anions is discussed, leading into the naming of complete compounds. Section 6.3 covers the naming of acids and acid salts. Hydrates are considered briefly in Section 6.4. Tables and figures in the chapter summarize how to name compounds in a systematic way.

6.1   Binary Nonmetal-Nonmetal Compounds

> The element farther to the left or farther down in the periodic table is named first.

Except for compounds of hydrogen, the formulas for compounds of two nonmetals are written and named with the element farther to the left or lower in the periodic table given first. If one element is below and to the right of the other in the periodic table, the one to the left is given first, unless that element is oxygen or fluorine.

Binary compounds of hydrogen that are not acids are given special names. Two very important examples are water, H_2O, and **ammonia,** NH_3 (Figure 6.1). (Other much less important hydrogen-containing binary compounds are also known by common names. These include phosphine, PH_3, and arsine, AsH_3.) Hydrogen compounds that are acids in aqueous solution are named, and their formulas are written in special ways (see Section 6.3).

EXAMPLE 6.1

Which element is named first in a binary compound of each of the following pairs of elements?

(a) S and Cl   (b) O and S   (c) S and I

(d) O and Cl   (e) O and Xe

Solution

The positions of the elements in the periodic table are used to determine the order of naming.

(a) Because sulfur lies to the left of chlorine in the periodic table (in the same period), sulfur is named first.

(b) Because sulfur lies below oxygen in the periodic table (in the same group), sulfur is named first.

(c) Because sulfur lies to the left of iodine in the periodic table, sulfur is named first (despite being above iodine).

(d) Even though oxygen lies to the left of chlorine in the periodic table, chlorine is named first. Oxygen is an exception to the rule that a position toward the left is more important than a position lower in the table.

(e) Even though oxygen lies to the left of xenon in the periodic table, xenon is named first. (Oxygen is always named last except in its compounds with fluorine.)

Practice Problem 6.1   Which element has its symbol written first in a binary compound of each of the following pairs of elements?

(a) F and Xe   (b) O and F   (c) O and N

Figure 6.1   Household Ammonia

A solution of (gaseous) ammonia in water.

To name a binary compound of two nonmetals,

• Name the first element.

• Use the root of the second element with the ending changed to -ide.

• In addition, add a **prefix** before each name to indicate the number of atoms of each element. The prefixes are given in Table 6.1. However, if there is only one atom of the *first* element, omit the prefix *mono-* for that element. Also, if hydrogen is the first element, omit the prefix for *both* elements.

• When the name of the element starts with an *o* and the prefix ends in *a* or *o*, the *a* or *o* is usually dropped.

EXAMPLE 6.2

Name the compound with formula containing (a) four atoms of chlorine and one atom of silicon, (b) one atom of sulfur and three atoms of oxygen, (c) two atoms of bromine and one atom of sulfur, (d) two atoms of phosphorus and three atoms of sulfur.

Table 6.1   Prefixes Used in Naming Binary Nonmetal-Nonmetal Compounds

Number of Atoms	Prefix*
1	mon(o)-
2	di-
3	tri-
4	tetr(a)-
5	pent(a)-
6	hex(a)-
7	hept(a)-
8	oct(a)-
9	non(a)-
10	dec(a)-

*The last *o* or *a* of the prefix is usually dropped when the element name begins with *o*.

Solution

(a) Silicon tetrachloride (Silicon is written first since it lies to the left of chlorine.)

(b) Sulfur trioxide (Sulfur is named first since it lies below oxygen.)

(c) Sulfur dibromide (Sulfur is written first since it lies left of bromine, even though bromine is below it.)

(d) Diphosphorus trisulfide (The prefix *di-* is attached to the first element since there is more than one atom of that element.)

Practice Problem 6.2   Name the compound with formula containing (a) two atoms of chlorine and three atoms of oxygen, (b) four atoms of sulfur and four atoms of nitrogen, (c) two atoms of phosphorus and five atoms of sulfur, (d) two atoms of fluorine and one atom of sulfur.

EXAMPLE 6.3

Name each of the following compounds:

(a) IF   (b) NO   (c) SO_3 (d) CO_2 (e) As_2O_5

(f) Br_2O_3 (g) PBr_5 (h) P_4O_{10} (i) H_2S (j) $SiCl_4$

Solution

(a) Iodine monofluoride (Iodine is written first because it lies below fluorine in the periodic table. The ending of *fluorine* is changed to *-ide*. The prefix *mono-* is added to *fluoride* to show that only one fluorine atom is present in the molecule, but not to iodine.)

(b) Nitrogen monoxide (Nitrogen is named first because it lies to the left of oxygen. The last *o* of the prefix *mono-* is dropped because the second element's name starts with *o*.)

(c) Sulfur trioxide   (d) Carbon dioxide

(e) Diarsenic pentoxide   (f) Dibromine trioxide

(g) Phosphorus pentabromide   (h) Tetraphosphorus decoxide

(i) Hydrogen sulfide   (j) Silicon tetrachloride

Practice Problem 6.3   Name each of the following compounds:

(a) P_4O_6 (b) B_2O_3 (c) N_2O

(d) ICl_5 (e) IF_7 (f) PCl_3

EXAMPLE 6.4

Write formulas for

(a) Dinitrogen pentoxide   (b) Diboron trioxide

(c) Chlorine dioxide   (d) Tetraarsenic hexoxide

Solution

(a) N_2O_5 (b) B_2O_3 (c) ClO_2 (d) As_4O_6

Practice Problem 6.4   Write formulas for (a) disulfur decafluoride and (b) iodine trioxide.

Snapshot Review

ChemSkill Builder 3.2

❏ Binary compounds of nonmetals are named with a set of classical prefixes, not used for most other compounds.
❏ If there is only one atom of the first element, no prefix is used.
❏ If the element is named first in a compound, its symbol is written first in the formula, and vice versa.

A. Name (a) Cl_2O and (b) SiF_4.

B. Write formulas for (a) iodine pentafluoride and (b) diphosphorus trisulfide.

6.2 Naming Ionic Compounds

In most cases, naming ionic compounds involves simply naming both ions. A huge majority of ionic compounds are made up of one type of cation plus one type of anion. Thus, to name most ionic compounds, we name the cation first and then the anion. The more difficult part of the process is learning to name cations and anions themselves.

The charges on the ions allow us to deduce the formula from the name of a compound, even though the numbers of each type of ion are not stated in the name. Writing formulas for ionic compounds requires deducing how many of each type of ion must be present to have a neutral compound (see Section 5.2).

> The number of each type of ion is *not* stated explicitly in the name.

Naming Cations

We learned in Chapter 5 that some metals always form monatomic ions having one given charge in all their compounds. In this book, we will call this type of ion the constant type. Other metals form monatomic ions with different charges (see Figure 5.11). We will call this type the variable type. There are also some polyatomic cations, but only three of these are important for this course. Thus, the first step in naming a cation is to decide which of these three types it is: polyatomic, constant type, or variable type. We name them in different ways.

POLYATOMIC CATIONS

Only three polyatomic cations are important in this course. The **ammonium ion** (NH_4^+) is very important and the mercury(I) ion (Hg_2^{2+}) is fairly important. The hydronium ion (H_3O^+) is important in Chapter 19. Others may be introduced in more advanced texts.

CONSTANT TYPE CATIONS

Naming the constant type of cation involves naming the element and adding the word *ion,* unless a compound is being named. For example, K^+ is the potassium ion, and Ca^{2+} is the calcium ion; KCl is potassium chloride. The alkali metals, the alkaline earth metals, zinc, cadmium, aluminum, and silver are the most important metals that form ions of the constant type (Figure 6.2). Each of these metals forms the same ion in any of its compounds, and the charge on the ion is equal to the classical periodic group number.

VARIABLE TYPE CATIONS

Naming ions of metals that form ions of more than one charge requires distinguishing between the possibilities. For example, iron forms Fe^{2+} and Fe^{3+} ions. We cannot call both of these "iron ion" because no one would know which of the two we meant. For *monatomic* cations of variable type, the *charge* in the form of a Roman numeral is attached to the element's name to indicate which ion we are talking about. For example, Fe^{2+} is called iron(II) ion and Fe^{3+} is called iron(III) ion. This system of nomenclature is called the **Stock system.**

Figure 6.2 Cations with Constant Charges and Cations with Varying Charges

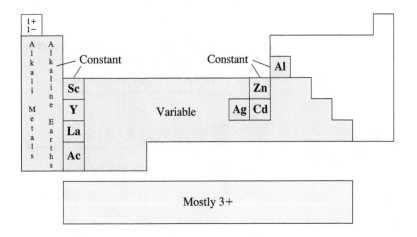

Mostly 3+

EXAMPLE 6.5

Name Co^{2+} and Co^{3+}.

Solution

Cobalt(II) ion and cobalt(III) ion, respectively.

EXAMPLE 6.6

How can we tell whether the chromium ion in the compound $CrCl_2$ has a 2+ or 3+ charge?

Solution

We know that the chloride ion has a 1− charge; the chromium ion must have a 2+ charge to balance the charge on two chloride ions and make the compound neutral. (See Section 5.4.)

Practice Problem 6.6   What is the charge on the anion in $(NH_4)_3VO_4$?

In writing formulas for ionic compounds from their names, we must remember the rules from Chapter 5. Be sure to balance the number of positive and negative charges! The charges on the cations are implied for some cations (the constant type) and stated explicitly in the name for the others. The charge on a monatomic anion is equal to the group number minus 8 (see Section 5.2).

EXAMPLE 6.7

Write the formula for each of the following compounds:

(a) Magnesium sulfide   (b) Sodium iodide

(c) Lead(IV) oxide   (d) Aluminum oxide

Solution

(a) MgS (The magnesium, in group II, has a charge of 2+, the sulfide, in group VI, has a charge of 2−.)

(b) NaI   (c) PbO_2 (not Pb_2O_4)   (d) Al_2O_3

EXAMPLE 6.8

Name (a) Cr_2O_3, (b) P_2O_3, and (c) Al_2O_3.

Solution

(a) Chromium(III) oxide   (b) Diphosphorus trioxide

(c) Aluminum oxide

Each of these compounds, with formulas that look so similar, is named in a different way.

(a) Chromium forms both Cr^{2+} and Cr^{3+} ions (see Figure 5.11), so the name must have a Roman numeral to distinguish which of the two is present.

(b) Phosphorus and oxygen form a binary nonmetal-nonmetal compound, so the oxygen is named with the prefix *tri-* added to it, and its ending is changed to *-ide*. The prefix *di-* is added to the phosphorus.

(c) Aluminum always forms a 3+ ion *in its compounds,* so no prefix or Roman numeral is necessary to tell its charge.

> Note that not only is it necessary to remember the rules for the different types of compounds but, just as important, *when to use each rule!*

| Not only is it necessary to remember the rules for the different types of compounds, but just as important, *when to use each rule!* |

Practice Problem 6.8   Name (a) IBr, (b) NaBr, and (c) CuBr.

EXAMPLE 6.9

Name each of the following compounds:

(a) CuS   (b) Cu_2S

Solution

(a) Copper(II) sulfide   (b) Copper(I) sulfide

In Cu_2S, the two copper ions are balanced by one sulfide ion with a 2− charge; the charge on each copper ion must be 1+. In CuS, only one copper ion is present to balance the 2− charge on the sulfide ion; the charge on the copper ion is 2+. Note that the Roman numerals in the names of monatomic cations denote the *charges on the ions.* The Arabic numerals appearing as subscripts in formulas denote the *number of atoms* of that element present per formula unit. Either of these numbers can be used to deduce the other, but they are not the same!

| Roman numerals in names denote charges on ions; Arabic numerals in formulas tell the number of atoms or ions present per formula unit. |

Practice Problem 6.9   Write the formula for (a) platinum(II) oxide and (b) platinum(IV) oxide.

Table 6.2 Classical Names of Some Common Cations

Periodic Group	Ion of Lower Charge	Ion of Higher Charge
VIB	Cr^{2+}, chromous	Cr^{3+}, chromic
VIIB	Mn^{2+}, manganous	Mn^{3+}, manganic
VIII	Fe^{2+}, ferrous	Fe^{3+}, ferric
VIII	Co^{2+}, cobaltous	Co^{3+}, cobaltic
VIII	Ni^{2+}, nickelous	Ni^{3+}, nickelic
IB	Cu^{+}, cuprous	Cu^{2+}, cupric
IB	Au^{+}, aurous	Au^{3+}, auric
IIB	Hg_2^{2+}, mercurous	Hg^{2+}, mercuric
IVA	Sn^{2+}, stannous	Sn^{4+}, stannic
IVA	Pb^{2+}, plumbous	Pb^{4+}, plumbic

An older nomenclature system (known as the classical system) uses suffixes to distinguish metal ions of the variable type. As Figure 5.11 shows, there are two possible monatomic cations for each variable metal listed. The ion with the higher charge is named with the ending changed to *-ic*. The ion of lower charge has its ending changed to *-ous*. For example, Cr^{2+} is called chromous ion, and Cr^{3+} is called chromic ion. For many elements, the Latin names are used instead of the English names. For example, Fe^{2+} is called ferrous ion—from *ferrum,* the Latin for iron. Table 6.2 lists classical names for some important monatomic cations. This older system is more difficult to use in two ways: (1) we must remember the other possible charge on an ion in addition to the one given, and (2) we must remember a Latin name for many of the elements.

EXAMPLE 6.10

Name V^{2+} using the Stock system. Explain why use of the classical system would be harder.

Solution

The Stock system name—vanadium(II) ion—is easy. To use the classical system, we must know the answers to at least three questions: (1) What is the charge on the other monatomic ion of vanadium? (2) Is the Latin name for vanadium used in the classical system? (3) If the Latin name is used, what is that name? The Stock system was invented to make naming easier.

Practice Problem 6.10 Name Ti^{3+}.

Naming Anions

Just as for cations, there are three types of anions for naming purposes. Monatomic anions are easy to name. A second type, **oxoanions,** are anions that contain oxygen covalently bonded to another element. Table 6.3 presents some important

Table 6.3 Names of Some Important Oxoanions*

Hypo ____ ite (Two Fewer Oxygen Atoms)		ite (One Fewer Oxygen Atom)		ate		Per ____ ate (One More Oxygen Atom)	
ClO^-	hypochlorite	ClO_2^-	chlorite	ClO_3^-	**chlorate**	ClO_4^-	perchlorate
BrO^-	hypobromite	BrO_2^-	bromite	BrO_3^-	**bromate**	BrO_4^-	perbromate
IO^-	hypoiodite	IO_2^-	iodite	IO_3^-	**iodate**	IO_4^-	periodate
PO_2^{3-}	hypophosphite	PO_3^{3-}	phosphite	PO_4^{3-}	**phosphate**		
		NO_2^-	nitrite	NO_3^-	**nitrate**		
		SO_3^{2-}	sulfite	SO_4^{2-}	**sulfate**		
				CO_3^{2-}	**carbonate**		

*The ions do not exist where there are spaces in the table.

Table 6.4 Names of Special Anions

Formula	Name
OH^-	Hydroxide
CN^-	Cyanide
O_2^{2-}	Peroxide
CrO_4^{2-}	Chromate
$Cr_2O_7^{2-}$	Dichromate
MnO_4^-	Permanganate
$C_2H_3O_2^-$	Acetate

> The charge on each *monatomic* anion except for H^- is its classical group number minus 8.

oxoanions in a format designed to make their names easier to learn. Several other important anions, referred to as special anions in this book, are listed in Table 6.4.

MONATOMIC ANIONS

All monatomic anions are named by changing the ending of the element's name to *-ide*. For example, I^-, H^-, and O^{2-} are called iodide ion, hydride ion, and oxide ion, respectively. (The names of a few special anions also end in *-ide*; among the most important are hydroxide and cyanide ions, listed in Table 6.4.) The charge on any monatomic anion is constant and, except for that on H^-, is equal to the classical group number minus 8 (see Figure 5.11).

EXAMPLE 6.11

Why do monatomic anions (except the hydride ion) have charges equal to their group numbers minus 8?

Solution

For the nonmetals, the group number is equal to the number of valence electrons (see Chapter 5). The number of additional electrons required to form an octet is therefore 8 minus the group number. Since each electron has a single negative charge, the charge on the ions is equal to the group number minus 8. For example, sulfur in group VI has 6 valence electrons and needs $8 - 6 = 2$ more to form an octet. Since each of the 2 electrons has a negative charge, the ion has a 2− charge (equal to $6 - 8$).

Practice Problem 6.11 Why does the hydride ion have a single negative charge?

OXOANIONS

In many important anions, oxygen atoms are covalently bonded to a central atom. These ions have extra electrons from some source, which give them their negative charges. They are called oxoanions but were formerly known as oxyanions. For the seven most important oxoanions, the name is that of the root of the central element with the ending -*ate* added. They are listed in the third column of Table 6.3. Once we have learned the names and formulas of these ions, we can deduce the formulas of the corresponding ions with fewer or more oxygen atoms. Ions ending in -*ite* have one fewer oxygen atom than the corresponding -*ate* ions. In four cases, removal of two oxygen atoms from an ion ending in -*ate* results in an ion named with the prefix *hypo-* and the ending -*ite*. For three ions that end with -*ate*, addition of one oxygen atom yields an ion named with the prefix *per-* and the ending -*ate*. Note in Table 6.3 that all the ions with a given central atom have the same charge. Note also that the charge on each third through fifth period oxoanion is equal to the classical group number minus 8, just as for the monatomic anions, but the charge on each *second* period oxoanion has *two fewer* negative charges (CO_3^{2-}, NO_3^-, and NO_2^-). See Figure 5.13.

> Oxoanions of even group elements have even charges (2−) and those of odd group elements have odd charges (1− or 3−).

EXAMPLE 6.12

Name Br^-, BrO_3^-, BrO_2^-, BrO^-, and BrO_4^-.

Solution

The names are bromide ion, bromate ion, bromite ion, hypobromite ion, and perbromate ion.

Practice Problem 6.12   Write the formula for (a) iodite ion and (b) hypoiodite ion.

EXAMPLE 6.13

What are the formulas for (a) sulfate ion and (b) carbonate ion?

Solution

The formulas are (a) SO_4^{2-} and (b) CO_3^{2-}.

Practice Problem 6.13   Write the formula for each of the following ions:

(a) Sulfite ion   (b) Chlorate ion

(c) Nitrate ion   (d) Nitrite ion

SPECIAL ANIONS

Other important anions that don't fit into the prior two categories are called special anions in this book. They are listed in Table 6.4. Names for anions that contain oxygen but are not included in Table 6.3 may sometimes be determined because of a periodic relationship between their central element and that of an ion in that table. For example, MnO_4^- is analogous to ClO_4^- because both central elements are in periodic groups numbered VII. Its name is permanganate, which is analogous to perchlorate. Similarly, CrO_4^{2-} and SO_4^{2-} both have central atoms that are in periodic groups numbered VI. The name of CrO_4^{2-} is chromate, analogous to sulfate. (Not all such analogies are valid, however.)

We may wish to use the following memory device to remember the formula of the dichromate ion: Double the chromate ion and remove an oxygen atom and two charges (an "oxide ion").

$$2(CrO_4^{2-}) - O^{2-} = Cr_2O_8^{4-} - O^{2-} = Cr_2O_7^{2-}$$

EXAMPLE 6.14

Name SeO_4^{2-}.

Solution

Selenium is just below sulfur in the periodic table. We can guess that the SeO_4^{2-} ion is named analogously to the SO_4^{2-} ion. The name is selenate ion.

Practice Problem 6.14   Name AsO_4^{3-}.

Naming and Writing Formulas for Ionic Compounds

Naming ionic compounds involves first naming the cation and then naming the anion. Therefore, the name of such a compound leads directly to its formula.

EXAMPLE 6.15

Name $NaNO_3$.

Solution

The cation is Na^+ and the anion is NO_3^-. The name of the compound is sodium nitrate.

Practice Problem 6.15   Name $BaSO_4$.

EXAMPLE 6.16

Name (a) Cu_2S and (b) $(NH_4)_2SO_4$.

Solution

(a) Each cation is Cu^+; the anion is S^{2-}. It is important to recognize that each cation is a monatomic ion and that the two together do not make up a different ion. The compound is copper(I) sulfide. Note that the name of the compound does not explicitly mention that there are two copper(I) ions per sulfide ion.

(b) Each of the cations is NH_4^+, the ammonium ion; the anion is the sulfate ion. The compound is ammonium sulfate.

Practice Problem 6.16   Name (a) $Al(C_2H_3O_2)_3$ and (b) $Co(ClO_3)_3$.

EXAMPLE 6.17

Write the formula for (a) zinc nitrate and (b) cobalt(III) hypochlorite.

Solution

(a) The zinc ion is Zn^{2+}; the nitrate ion is NO_3^-. The formula of the compound must balance positive charges and negative charges; it is $Zn(NO_3)_2$.

(b) The cobalt(III) ion is Co^{3+}; the hypochlorite ion is ClO^-. The compound is $Co(ClO)_3$. Parentheses are needed around the formula for the hypochlorite ion so that the subscript 3 indicates that three such ions are present. (If the parentheses were not written, the formula would appear to contain a chlorate ion, ClO_3^-.)

Practice Problem 6.17   Write the formula for (a) lead(IV) sulfate and (b) aluminum sulfide.

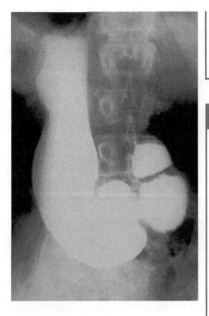

Figure 6.3   *X-Ray Film of the Stomach*

Barium sulfate, which is not soluble in water, is administered to humans to absorb X-rays and outline organs. Barium salts that are soluble are poisonous.

The differences in the names of compounds can be life-and-death details. For example, physicians sometimes prescribe a barium sulfate slurry or barium sulfate enema for patients who are about to have a stomach or intestinal X-ray film taken. The barium sulfate is opaque to X-rays and outlines the stomach or colon clearly (Figure 6.3). However, barium ion is poisonous to humans. Barium sulfate is safe only because it is too insoluble to be harmful. However, if barium *sulfite* were given instead of barium *sulfate,* the compound would dissolve in the stomach or colon, and the patient might die. The one-letter difference in the name is critical.

Snapshot Review

ChemSkill Builder 3.2, 3.3, 3.4

❏ Cations are named first, then anions.
❏ Learning the types of cations and anions enables us to choose the proper name endings for them.
❏ We must learn not only the rules, but when to use each one!
❏ The proper formulas must be written according to the rules presented in Chapter 5.

A. Name (a) $CaCl_2$, (b) $NiCl_2$, and (c) $(NH_4)_2SO_3$.
B. Write formulas for (a) lead(II) hypochlorite, (b) magnesium nitride, and (c) aluminum phosphite.

6.3   Naming Acids and Acid Salts

Acids are a special group of hydrogen-containing compounds whose properties will be covered more fully in Chapter 8. One of their most important properties is their reaction with **bases** to form **salts** (Section 8.4). Pure acids are covalent compounds, but they react to varying extents with water to form ions in solution. The hydrogen atoms that react with water to form ions are said to be **ionizable hydrogen atoms.** The formulas of acids have the ionizable hydrogen atoms written first. In beginning courses, all compounds (except for water and hydrogen peroxide) with hydrogen written first are acids. Thus, HCl is an acid with one ionizable hydrogen atom per molecule, and H_2SO_4 is an acid with two ionizable hydrogen atoms per molecule. CH_4 and NH_3 are not acids. (In fact, NH_3 acts as a base in aqueous solution.) In other words, the appearance of hydrogen first in a formula is *not* based on hydrogen's relative position in the periodic table, as is true for other elements, but only on whether the compound is an acid.

> The appearance of hydrogen first in a formula indicates that the compound is an acid.

EXAMPLE 6.18

How many hydrogen atoms per molecule of propanoic acid, $HC_3H_5O_2$, are ionizable?

Solution

One, represented by the first H, is ionizable. The other five hydrogen atoms of this compound are not ionizable, which is why they are written after the carbon atoms in the formula.

Practice Problem 6.18 How many hydrogen atoms per molecule of phthalic acid, $H_2C_8H_4O_4$, are ionizable?

Acids are related to their anions by exchanging hydrogen atoms of the acids for the same number of negative charges on the anions. For example,

Acid	*Anion*
HCl	Cl^-
H_2SO_4	SO_4^{2-}
H_3PO_4	PO_4^{3-}
$HC_2H_3O_2$	$C_2H_3O_2^-$

Naming Acids

Acids generally do not have the word "hydrogen" in their names. They are named by replacing the ending of the related anion by an ending including the word *acid*, as follows:

> Compounds named as acids do not include the word *hydrogen* in the name. The word *acid* implies the presence of hydrogen.

Name of anion	*Name of acid*
Per _____ ate	Per _____ ic acid
-ate	-ic acid
-ite	-ous acid
Hypo _____ ite	Hypo _____ ous acid
-ide	Hydro _____ ic acid

Note that if the anion has a prefix *hypo-* or *per-,* so does the acid.

If the acid is a binary hydrogen compound, including HF, HCl, HBr, HI, and H_2S, the pure compound is named as if hydrogen were an alkali metal. For example, pure HCl is named hydrogen chloride, and H_2S is named hydrogen sulfide, with no prefixes for either element in either case. When the hydrogen halides are dissolved in water, they are usually named as acids. Thus HCl in water is referred to as hydrochloric acid. H_2S is one of very few acids usually named like an alkali metal-nonmetal compound even when dissolved in water. It is called hydrogen sulfide, but the name hydrosulfuric acid (analogous to hydrochloric acid) may be used for its aqueous solution.

EXAMPLE 6.19

Name the following acids:

(a) HNO_3 (b) H_3PO_3 (c) H_2SO_3

(d) $HBrO$ (e) $HClO_4$ (f) HI

Solution

(a) Nitric acid. The ending -*ate* of the nitrate ion is changed to -*ic acid*.

(b) Phosphorous acid. The ending -*ite* of the phosphite ion is changed to -*ous acid*. In this case, the stem is also changed to *phosphor*.

(c) Sulfurous acid. The ending -*ite* is changed to -*ous acid*, and the stem is changed from *sulf* to *sulfur*.

(d) Hypobromous acid. The ending -*ite* is changed to -*ous acid*. The prefix *hypo-* on the anion makes no difference to the suffix; the prefix is included in the acid name.

(e) Perchloric acid. The ending -*ate* of perchlorate ion is changed to -*ic acid*; the prefix *per-* is not changed.

(f) Hydroiodic acid. The prefix *hydro-* distinguishes this binary acid from HIO_3.

Practice Problem 6.19   Name the following acids:

(a) HIO_3 (b) H_2SO_4 (c) $HClO_2$

Formulas for acids can be written by replacing every negative charge on the corresponding anion with one hydrogen atom. For example, SO_4^{2-} has two negative charges; therefore, sulfuric acid has two ionizable hydrogen atoms (and no charge): H_2SO_4. If the ion is an oxoanion, the acid is an **oxoacid.**

EXAMPLE 6.20

Write the formula for each of the following acids:

(a) Hypophosphorous acid   (b) Chloric acid   (c) Perbromic acid

Solution

(a) H_3PO_2 (b) $HClO_3$ (c) $HBrO_4$

Practice Problem 6.20   Write the formulas for (a) nitrous acid and (b) sulfuric acid.

Figure 6.4 and Table 6.5 outline a systematic procedure for naming many compounds and ions. One of these presentations may be very helpful, especially at first. (Use only one of these as needed.)

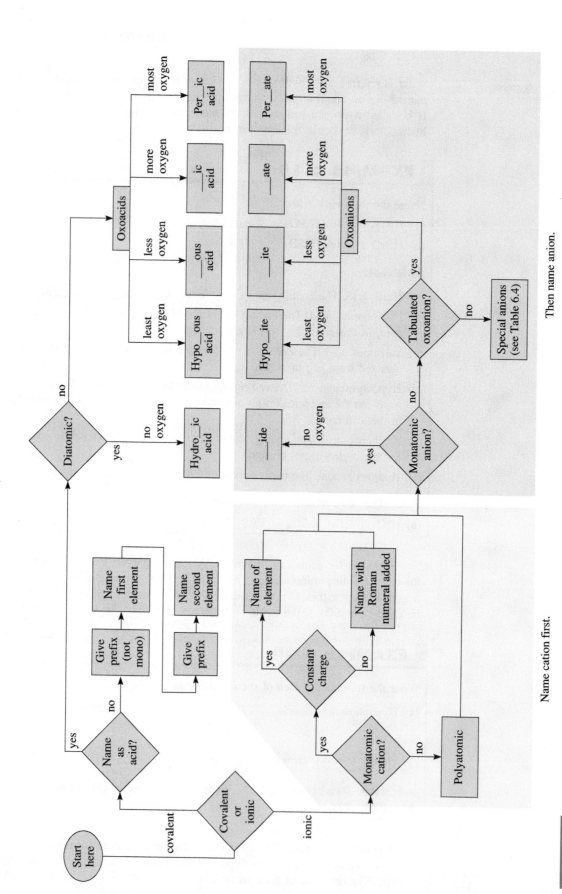

Name cation first.

Then name anion.

Figure 6.4 Flow Chart Summarizing the Naming of Compounds and Ions
Use this chart or the outline of Table 6.5 if it helps you.

Table 6.5 Outline for Nomenclature*

Is the compound (I) covalent or (II) ionic?
I. Covalent: Is the compound (A) an acid or (B) a binary compound of two nonmetals?
   A. Acid: Name the compound using a suffix and possibly a prefix related to the name of the analogous anion (IIB). Add the word *acid*.
   B. Binary compound: Name the first element with a prefix from Table 6.1 if there are two or more atoms. Then name the second element with a prefix from Table 6.1 (even if there is only one atom), and with the ending changed to *-ide*.
II. Ionic: Name *both* (A) the cation and then (B) the anion.
   A. Cation: Is the cation (1) polyatomic, (2) a metal forming ions with more than one charge, or (3) a metal with only one ion?
      1. Polyatomic: Name the ion.
      2. Variable: Use the name of the metal with a Roman numeral to indicate the charge.
      3. Constant: Use the name of the metal only.
   B. Anion: Is the anion (1) monatomic, (2) a tabulated oxoanion, or (3) something else?
      1. Monatomic: Change the ending of the element name to *-ide*.
      2. Oxoanion: See Table 6.3.
      3. Special: See Table 6.4.

*Use this outline or Figure 6.4; you don't need both.

Naming Acid Salts

In Section 8.4, we will see that an acid with more than one ionizable hydrogen atom can react with bases in steps, with all but the last step yielding compounds called **acid salts.** Such salts consist of a cation, such as a sodium ion, plus an anion that has one or two hydrogen atoms still attached. Just as the hydrogen atoms are covalently bonded in the pure acid, the ones that remain in the acid salt are still covalently bonded. The anion is named with the word **hydrogen** followed by the name of the parent anion. For example, $NaHCO_3$ has a sodium cation, Na^+, and the hydrogen carbonate anion, HCO_3^-. The compound is sodium hydrogen carbonate. Acid salts of acids with three hydrogen atoms, such as phosphoric acid, require specification of how many hydrogen atoms remain. The prefixes *mono-* and *di-* are used for one and two hydrogen atoms, respectively. Thus, NaH_2PO_4 is sodium dihydrogen phosphate, and Na_2HPO_4 is sodium monohydrogen phosphate (or disodium hydrogen phosphate).

> Acid salts, and their anions, have the word *hydrogen* in their names.

> The total of the number of hydrogen atoms plus negative charges is the same for the parent acid, the anion, and any hydrogen-containing anions.

EXAMPLE 6.21

Name (a) NaHS and (b) HS^-.

Solution

(a) Sodium hydrogen sulfide   (b) Hydrogen sulfide ion

Including the word *ion* in the name in part (b) is important to distinguish this ion from hydrogen sulfide, H_2S.

Practice Problem 6.21   Write the formula for (a) sodium monohydrogen phosphate and (b) magnesium dihydrogen phosphate.

Figure 6.5   Baking Soda
Ordinary baking soda is sodium hydrogen carbonate.

An older nomenclature system, still in use to some extent, uses the word "acid" to denote an acid salt. Also, the prefix *bi-* may be used for an acid salt of an acid with two ionizable hydrogen atoms. Thus, $NaHCO_3$ can be called sodium bicarbonate or sodium acid carbonate instead of sodium hydrogen carbonate (Figure 6.5).

Snapshot Review

ChemSkill Builder 3.5

❑ Acids have hydrogen written first in their formulas, but do not have the word "hydrogen" in their names.
❑ Acids are related to anions; for every hydrogen atom removed from the formula of an acid, one negative charge is added in the resulting anion.
❑ The names of acids and anions are also related:

Anion suffix	*Acid suffix (and prefix)*
-ate	-ic acid
-ite	-ous acid
-ide	hydro _____ ic acid

A. Name the following acids: (a) H_3PO_3, (b) $HClO$, and (c) HNO_2.
B. Write formulas for the following compounds: (a) sulfuric acid and (b) sodium dihydrogen phosphite

6.4   Hydrates

Hydrates are stable crystalline compounds consisting of other compounds that are stable in their own right, with certain numbers of water molecules attached (see Section 5.1). Naming and writing formulas for hydrates is easy. We simply name the compound first and then combine a Table 6.1 prefix that identifies the number of water molecules with the word "hydrate" to indicate the presence of the water molecules. For example, $CuSO_4 \cdot 5H_2O$ is called copper(II) sulfate pentahydrate. $CuSO_4$ may be called *anhydrous* copper(II) sulfate, if we wish to emphasize that no water is attached.

Snapshot Review

❏ Hydrates—compounds with water attached—are named with a prefix from Table 6.1 attached to the word "hydrate" to denote the number of water molecules.

A. Name $BaI_2 \cdot 2H_2O$.
B. Write the formula for chromium(III) phosphate dihydrate.

Key Terms

Key terms are defined in the Glossary.

acid (6.3)	hydrogen (6.3)	prefix (6.1)
acid salt (6.3)	ionizable hydrogen atom (6.3)	salt (6.3)
ammonia (6.1)	nomenclature (intro)	Stock system (6.2)
ammonium ion (6.2)	oxoacid (6.3)	
base (6.3)	oxoanion (6.2)	

Prefixes/Suffixes

-ate (6.2)	hypo- (6.2)	octa- (6.1)
bi- (6.3)	-ic (6.2)	-ous (6.2)
deca- (6.1)	-ic acid (6.3)	-ous acid (6.3)
di- (6.1)	-ide (6.1)	penta- (6.1)
hepta- (6.1)	-ite (6.2)	per- (6.2)
hexa- (6.1)	mono- (6.1)	tetra- (6.1)
hydro- (6.3)	nona- (6.1)	tri- (6.1)

Summary

Metal-nonmetal compounds and ammonium compounds (containing the NH_4 group within a formula) are ionic. Other compounds are covalent, except that acids are ionized, some completely, when dissolved in water. The acids are named with a special system of their own, but pure binary acids can be named similarly to alkali metal-nonmetal compounds.

Different systems are used for naming binary covalent compounds and ionic compounds, and acids are named still other ways. For binary nonmetal-nonmetal compounds (which are covalent), name the leftmost or lower element in the periodic table first, and then name the other element. Change the ending of the second element to -ide, and indicate the number of atoms of that element in the molecule by a prefix (Table 6.1). If more than one

atom of the first element is present per molecule, use a prefix for that element, too. (Section 6.1)

To name an ionic compound, name the cation first and then the anion. Use just the name of the element for monatomic cations of elements that form only one cation. For monatomic cations of elements that can form more than one cation, indicated the charge on the cation by a Roman numeral in parentheses added to the name of the element. Polyatomic cations have special names, ammonium ion being the most important.

The names of monatomic anions have the ending of the element's name changed to -ide. The charge on any monatomic anion (except H^-) is equal to the classical group number minus 8. The charge on each second-period oxoanion has two fewer negative charges than the classical group number minus 8, and the charge on each third-through fifth-period oxoanion is equal to the classical group number minus 8, just as for the monatomic anions. The names of most familiar oxoanions end in -ate or -ite, depending on the relative number of oxygen atoms per ion. Ions with more oxygen atoms than those whose names end in -ate have the prefix per- added to the name; ions with fewer oxygen atoms than those whose names end in -ite have the prefix hypo- added to the name. Names of other anions must be learned based on periodic table relationships or individually.

A Roman numeral in parentheses in the *name* of the compound designates the charge on a cation and an Arabic numeral as a subscript in the *formula* designates the number of atoms or ions. The charges enable us to deduce the numbers of ions, and vice versa, but the Roman numerals and the Arabic numerals do not represent the same quantities. (Section 6.2)

Acids can be recognized by the fact that the ionizable hydrogen atoms are written first in their formulas. The word "hydrogen" does not appear in their names; the word "acid" implies the presence of the hydrogen. Name oxoacids like the corresponding oxoanions, with the ending -ate changed to -ic acid or the ending -ite changed to -ous acid. Names of binary acids have the ending -ide of the corresponding anion changed to -ic acid and the prefix hydro- added. For example, Cl^- is chloride; HCl is hydrochloric acid.

Name acid salts as ionic compounds, but put the word "hydrogen" in the name of the anion (perhaps with a prefix) to indicate that at least one ionizable hydrogen atom is still present. For example, $NaHCO_3$ is sodium hydrogen carbonate. (Section 6.3)

Name hydrates with a prefix from Table 6.1 before the word "hydrate," to indicate the number of water molecules. For example, $CuSO_4 \cdot 5H_2O$ is named copper(II) sulfate pentahydrate. (Section 6.4)

Items for Special Attention

■ The following list summarizes the types of compounds and ions we have learned to name in this chapter:

Binary nonmetal-nonmetal compounds

Ionic compounds
    Cations
        Monatomic cations
            Variable charge
            Constant charge
        Polyatomic cations
    Anions
        Monatomic anions
        Oxoanions
        Special anions
Acids
Acid salts
Hydrates

■ The prefixes in Table 6.1 are used only for naming binary nonmetal-nonmetal compounds, acid salts, and hydrates.

■ It is critical to specify the charges in formulas for ions and to include the word "ion" if the name without that word means something else, such as sodium ion or hydrogen sulfide ion.

■ Roman numerals in names stand for charges, and subscripts in formulas represent numbers of atoms.

■ All monatomic anions have names ending in -ide, but not all anions with names ending in -ide are monatomic. Hydroxide ion, OH^-, and cyanide ion, CN^-, are important examples of diatomic ions with names ending in -ide.

■ Parentheses are used when two or more polyatomic ions are present in a given formula, as in $Mg(ClO)_2$. The subscript after the parentheses indicates the number of these ions present. In certain cases, the parentheses also distinguish between familiar ions, such as the ClO^- ions in $Mg(ClO)_2$ and the ClO_2^- ion in $KClO_2$.

■ That hydrogen is present in an acid is implied in the name by the word "acid," not by the word "hydrogen". For example, HCl is hydrochloric *acid*. The word "hydrogen" is used in names of acid salts, such as sodium hydrogen carbonate, $NaHCO_3$.

■ In naming the binary compounds of hydrogen in which hydrogen is written first in the formula, *name* the compound as if hydrogen were an alkali metal (despite the fact that it is not, and that the compound is covalent). For example, HCl is named hydrogen chloride and H_2S is named hydrogen sulfide. [These compounds do form ions to a greater or lesser extent when they are dissolved in water. (Section 8.4)]

Answers to Snapshot Reviews

6.1 A. (a) Dichlorine monoxide   (b) Silicon tetrafluoride
    B. (a) IF_5 (b) P_2S_3
6.2 A. (a) Calcium chloride   (b) Nickel(II) chloride
    (c) Ammonium sulfite
    B. (a) $Pb(ClO)_2$ (b) Mg_3N_2 (c) $AlPO_3$

6.3 A. (a) Phosphorous acid   (b) Hypochlorous acid
    (c) Nitrous acid
    B. (a) H_2SO_4 (b) NaH_2PO_3
6.4 A. Barium iodide dihydrate
    B. $CrPO_4 \cdot 2H_2O$

Self-Tutorial Problems

6.1 Use the Table of Elements on the inside of the back cover, if necessary, to name each of the following substances:

(a) Hf (b) HF (c) NO (d) No

6.2 What is the difference in the meanings of the prefixes *bi-* and *di-* (as used in this chapter)?

6.3 Which metals form cations of the constant type? What are the charges on these cations?

6.4 What is the difference between ClO_2 and ClO_2^-? Name each one.

6.5 What are the rules for remembering the charges on (a) monatomic anions and (b) oxoanions?

6.6 Classify each of the following as ionic or covalent, and name each:

(a) $CaCl_2$ (b) CO_2 (c) CrO (d) CCl_4

6.7 Name the following ions:

(a) SO_4^{2-} (b) NO_3^- (c) PO_4^{3-} (d) S^{2-}

6.8 Name the following ions:

(a) SO_3^{2-} (b) NO_2^- (c) PO_2^{3-} (d) Br^-

6.9 What can we tell from each of the following?

(a) The charges on the two ions making up a compound

(b) The fact that hydrogen is written first in a formula

(c) The fact that the name for a compound or ion ends in *-ite*

6.10 Classify the metal in each of the following compounds as constant type or variable type, and then name each compound:

(a) $CrSO_4$ (b) $CoSO_4$ (c) $CaSO_4$

(d) $AlCl_3$ (e) $FeSO_4$ (f) K_2SO_4

6.11 Classify each of the following compounds as ionic, covalent, or both: (a) NH_4Cl, (b) $CuCl_2$, (c) $KMnO_4$, (d) SCl_2.

6.12 (a) What is the difference between hydrogen ion and hydride ion?

(b) Explain why H^+ is called the hydrogen ion rather than the hydrogen(I) ion, even though hydrogen can form two different ions.

6.13 Write formulas for (a) chloride ion, (b) chlorate ion, and (c) chlorite ion.

6.14 What is the difference between NH_3 and NH_4^+? Name each one.

6.15 In which one(s) of the following nomenclature classes is the word "hydrogen" used?

(a) acids (b) acid salts

(c) binary hydrogen-nonmetal compounds

6.16 Pure HBr may be named as a binary nonmetal-nonmetal compound, whereas pure H_2SO_4 is always named as an acid. Explain why H_2SO_4 is not named like HBr is named.

6.17 What are the differences in the following, as used in naming compounds?

(a) Hypo- (b) Hydro- (c) Hydrogen

6.18 Name (a) Na_2SO_4 and (b) H_2SO_4.

6.19 What is the difference between the two names for HCl: hydrogen chloride and hydrochloric acid?

6.20 Write the formula for (a) ammonium hydrogen carbonate, (b) ammonium bicarbonate, (c) ammonium acid carbonate.

6.21 Name each member of the following pairs, and compare the names:

(a) NaCl and HCl (pure)

(b) Na_2S and H_2S (pure)

6.22 Name each of the following acids:

(a) $HBrO_4$ (b) $HBrO_3$ (c) $HBrO_2$

(d) HBrO (e) HBr

6.23 What is the charge on each of the following?

(a) The hydrogen sulfite ion

(b) The dihydrogen phosphate ion

(c) The monohydrogen phosphite ion

Problems

6.1 Binary Nonmetal-Nonmetal Compounds

6.24 Name each of the following compounds:

(a) N_2O_5 (b) CF_4 (c) P_2S_3

(d) SF_4 (e) BrF_3

6.25 Write the formula for each of the following compounds:

(a) Carbon dioxide (b) Hydrogen bromide

(c) Silicon tetrafluoride (d) Iodine pentafluoride

(e) Bromine dioxide (f) Hydrogen sulfide

(g) Dinitrogen trioxide

6.26 Name the following substances:

(a) HCl (pure) (b) H_2Se (c) HI (pure)

6.27 Write the formula for each of the following compounds:

(a) Chlorine monofluoride   (b) Ammonia

(c) Arsenic trifluoride   (d) Sulfur trioxide

(e) Phosphorus pentachloride   (f) Water

6.28 Name each of the following compounds:

(a) SO_2 (b) SiF_4 (c) AsF_3

(d) S_2Cl_2 (e) XeF_6

6.29 Write the formula for each of the following compounds:

(a) Sulfur hexafluoride   (b) Sulfur tetrafluoride

(c) Sulfur difluoride

6.30 Write the formula for each of the following compounds:

(a) Iodine dioxide

(b) Diiodine trioxide

(c) Diiodine monoxide

(d) Diiodine heptoxide

6.31 Name each of the following compounds:

(a) NH_3 (b) P_4S_{10} (c) CO_2

(d) P_2O_5 (e) CO

6.32 Write the formula for each of the following compounds:

(a) Tetraarsenic hexoxide

(b) Bromine monochloride

(c) Tetrasulfur tetranitride

(d) Diphosphorus pentasulfide

6.2 Naming Ionic Compounds

6.33 Explain why chemists often refer to S^{2-} as "sulfide" (without the word "ion") but do not refer to K^+ as "potassium" (without the word "ion").

6.34 Name each of the following cations:

(a) Ca^{2+} (b) Ag^+ (c) Al^{3+}

6.35 Write the formula for each of the following ions:

(a) Copper(I) ion   (b) Nickel(II) ion

(c) Lithium ion   (d) Ammonium ion

(e) Gold(I) ion

6.36 Name each of the following cations:

(a) V^{2+} (b) Al^{3+} (c) Mn^{2+}

6.37 Name each of the following anions:

(a) Cl^- (b) P^{3-} (c) O^{2-} (d) N^{3-}

6.38 Write the formula for each of the following ions:

(a) Nitrite ion   (b) Perchlorate ion

(c) Cyanide ion   (d) Phosphite ion

(e) Dichromate ion   (f) Hypoiodite ion

6.39 Name each of the following anions:

(a) PO_4^{3-} (b) SO_4^{2-} (c) CO_3^{2-}

6.40 Name each of the following anions:

(a) $C_2H_3O_2^-$ (b) CrO_4^{2-}

(c) MnO_4^- (d) $Cr_2O_7^{2-}$

(e) CN^- (f) O_2^{2-}

6.41 Name each of the following compounds:

(a) $Co_2(SO_4)_3$ (b) $Ca_3(PO_4)_2$ (c) $(NH_4)_2SO_3$

6.42 Write the formula for each of the following compounds:

(a) Cobalt(III) oxide   (b) Nickel(II) sulfate

(c) Lithium hydroxide   (d) Copper(II) carbonate

(e) Magnesium cyanide   (f) Ammonium chlorate

6.43 Name each of the following compounds:

(a) Cu_2O (b) CuS

6.44 Name each of the following compounds:

(a) $FePO_4$ (b) $MnSO_4$

(c) $(NH_4)_2SO_3$

6.45 Write the formula for each of the following compounds:

(a) Potassium peroxide   (b) Gold(III) chromate

(c) Nickel(II) hydroxide   (d) Copper(I) cyanide

(e) Aluminum acetate   (f) Ammonium dichromate

6.46 Complete the following table by writing the formula for each ionic compound whose cation is given on the left and whose anion is given at the top:

	Nitrate	Sulfate	Acetate	Phosphate
Ammonium	____	____	____	____
Calcium	____	____	____	____
Vanadium(III)	____	____	____	____
Lead(IV)	____	____	____	____

6.47 Complete the following table by writing the formula for each ionic compound whose cation is given on the left and whose anion is given at the top:

	Chloride	Hypochlorite	Phosphate
Lithium	____	____	____
Mercury(II)	____	____	____
Iron(II)	____	____	____
Cobalt(III)	____	____	____

6.48 Complete the following table by writing the formula for each ionic compound whose cation is given on the left and whose anion is given at the top:

	Hydroxide	Cyanide	Chromate	Permanganate
Sodium	____	____	____	____
Copper(II)	____	____	____	____
Iron(III)	____	____	____	____

6.49 An instructor tells the students in a class that Mg^{2+} is the only stable ion of magnesium and that Mg^+ cannot be prepared in a solid. What name should the instructor use for Mg^+?

6.50 Name each of the following cations two ways:

(a) Cr^{3+} (b) Co^{2+} (c) Au^+ (d) Pt^{4+}

6.3 Naming Acids and Acid Salts

6.51 Write the formula for each of the following acids:

(a) Phosphoric acid   (b) Hydrobromic acid

(c) Chloric acid   (d) Hydrosulfuric acid

6.52 Name each of the following acids:

(a) H_2SO_4 (b) $HClO_4$ (c) H_3PO_3

6.53 What is the difference between iodous acid and hypoiodous acid?

6.54 What is the difference between hypobromous acid and hydrobromic acid?

6.55 What is the difference between hydroiodic acid and periodic acid?

6.56 Name each of the following compounds as an acid and also as a pure compound:

(a) HBr   (b) H_2S (c) HCl

6.57 Classify each of the following as an acid, an acid salt, or a regular salt, and name each:

(a) H_3PO_4 (b) KH_2PO_4

(c) Na_2HPO_4 (d) $(NH_4)_3PO_4$

6.58 Complete the following table by writing the formula for each ionic compound whose cation is given on the left and whose anion is given at the top:

	Monohydrogen Phosphate	Hydrogen Sulfate	Dihydrogen Phosphate
Magnesium	_____	_____	_____
Chromium(III)	_____	_____	_____
Ammonium	_____	_____	_____
Copper(II)	_____	_____	_____

6.59 What is the difference between the names "phosphorus," and "phosphorous"?

6.4 Hydrates

6.60 Name (a) $Ba(ClO)_2 \cdot 2H_2O$ (b) $Na_2CO_3 \cdot 7H_2O$, and (c) $FeBr_3 \cdot 6H_2O$

6.61 Write the formula for (a) iron(II) sulfate monohydrate and (b) barium bromide dihydrate.

General Problems

6.62 Name each of the following:

(a) SO_3 (b) SO_3^{2-} (c) Na_2SO_3

(d) H_2SO_3 (e) K_2SO_3

6.63 Name (a) CuS and (b) Cu_2S.

6.64 Name each of the following compounds:

(a) CoS   (b) Na_2O_2

(c) HI (in water)   (d) $NiSO_4$

(e) P_4O_{10} (f) Cl_2O_3

(g) Na_2SO_4 (h) K_2CrO_4

6.65 Name each of the following compounds:

(a) XeF_6 (b) XeF_2 (c) XeF_4

6.66 Select all of the following compounds that should be named using the prefixes of Table 6.1, all that should be named with Roman numerals, and all that should have neither. Name each.

(a) CCl_4 (b) Na_2CO_3 (c) NCl_3

(d) $Co(ClO_3)_2$ (e) Na_2SO_4 (f) SO_2

6.67 Which of the following pure compounds have covalent bonds only?

$CaCO_3$ H_2SO_3 N_2O_3 $NH_4C_3H_5O_2$ AlF_3

6.68 Complete the following table by writing the formula and name of each compound formed from an anion at the top and a cation on the left:

	NO_3^-	SO_4^{2-}	PO_4^{3-}
Potassium	_____	_____	_____
	_____	_____	_____
	_____	_____	_____
Iron(II)	_____	_____	_____
	_____	_____	_____
	_____	_____	_____
Titanium(III)	_____	_____	_____
	_____	_____	_____
	_____	_____	_____

6.69 Name the following ions by the Stock system, using Table 6.2 if necessary:

(a) Nickelous ion   (b) Cuprous ion

(c) Ferric ion   (d) Cupric ion

(e) Plumbous ion

6.70 Name (a) Na_2HPO_4, (b) NaH_2PO_4, (c) H_3PO_4, and (d) Na_3PO_4.

6.71 Which of the following compounds have acid properties?

HNO_2 NaH_2PO_4 NH_3 $NaHSO_3$ CH_4
NaOH

6.72 Write formulas for (a) platinum(II) monohydrogen phosphate and (b) platinum(II) dihydrogen phosphate.

6.73 Write formulas for the following ions, as well as formulas and names for the corresponding acids and anions (with no hydrogen):

(a) Hydrogen sulfate ion

(b) Hydrogen carbonate ion

(c) Hydrogen sulfide ion

(d) Dihydrogen phosphate ion

6.74 Write formulas for the following substances:

(a) Vanadium(V) oxide

(b) Chlorous acid

(c) Sodium dichromate

(d) Hypoiodous acid

(e) Platinum(II) oxide

6.75 Name each of the following compounds:

(a) XeF_2 (b) FeF_2 (c) CaF_2

6.76 Which transition metal ions have a charge of $1+$?

6.77 Name each of the following compounds:

(a) Al_2O_3 (b) Cr_2O_3 (c) N_2O_3

6.78 Name (a) HCl (as an acid), (b) HCl (pure), and (c) NaCl.

6.79 Name each of the following ions:

(a) $SO_4{}^{2-}$ (b) $SeO_4{}^{2-}$

(c) $PO_4{}^{3-}$ (d) $AsO_4{}^{3-}$

6.80 Write the formula of each of the following:

(a) Calcium oxide   (b) Sodium peroxide

(c) Lead(IV) oxide   (d) Potassium peroxide

6.81 Complete the following table by writing the formula and name of each compound formed from an anion at the top and a cation on the left:

	Carbonate	Chlorate	Arsenate
Fe^{2+}	_____	_____	_____
	_____	_____	_____
	_____	_____	_____
Ca^{2+}	_____	_____	_____
	_____	_____	_____
	_____	_____	_____
Cr^{3+}	_____	_____	_____
	_____	_____	_____
	_____	_____	_____

6.82 Give a more modern name for each of the following:

(a) Nickelous bicarbonate   (b) Chromic chloride

(c) Ferric sulfate   (d) Cobaltic oxide

6.83 Write the formula for sodium bisulfide.

6.84 Name each of the following substances:

(a) Cu_2O (b) $Mn(OH)_2$ (c) BrF_5

(d) HNO_3 (e) AgBr   (f) BF_3

(g) H_3PO_3 (h) Mn_2O_3 (i) CoF_2

(j) Ag_2O

6.85 Write the formulas for

(a) Magnesium nitride

(b) Aluminum sulfate

(c) Lead(IV) oxide

6.86 Write formulas for hydrogen sulfide, hydrogen sulfide ion, and hydrosulfuric acid.

6.87 Name the cation in each of the following compounds:

(a) $(NH_4)_2SeO_4$ (b) K_2MoO_4

(c) $CoPO_4$ (d) $CoSO_4$

6.88 Name the anion in each of the following compounds:

(a) $VOSO_4$ (b) VO_2NO_3 (c) $Ba_3(PO_4)_2$

6.89 Write formulas for (a) magnesium arsenate, (b) calcium selenate, and (c) acetic acid.

6.90 Name each of the following compounds:

(a) H_2SO_3 (b) N_2O (c) XeF_6

(d) CrF_3 (e) NH_3

6.91 Name (a) K_2O_2 and (b) PbO_2. (*Hint:* Peroxide ion generally exists only in combination with metals in the form of their ion of highest charge.)

6.92 Name (a) $KClO_3$ and (b) $Co(ClO)_3$.

6.93 Name and write formulas for both ions in (a) $CaCl_2$ and (b) Na_2O_2.

6.94 Name each of the following:

(a) Sb_2S_3 (b) $(NH_4)_3PO_4$ (c) IF_5

(d) $HBrO_2$ (e) TiO_2

6.95 Identify the type of substance, using the following symbols. Then name each.

IV for Ionic compounds containing metal ion of Variable type

IC for Ionic compounds containing metal ions of Constant type

A for Acids or acid salts

C for other binary Covalent compounds

E for Elements

		Type	Name
(a)	FeF_3	____	____
(b)	NiO	____	____
(c)	ICl_3	____	____
(d)	NaH	____	____
(e)	Au_2S	____	____
(f)	$Mg(OH)_2$	____	____
(g)	HNO_3	____	____
(h)	$(NH_4)_2SO_4$	____	____
(i)	$MgSO_3$	____	____
(j)	H_3PO_3	____	____
(k)	HCl	____	____
(l)	K_2CO_3	____	____
(m)	$(NH_4)_2Cr_2O_7$	____	____

6.96 Identify the type of substance using the symbols of Problem 6.95, and write the formula for each.

(a) Cobalt(II) carbonate

(b) Phosphorus triiodide

(c) Sulfurous acid

(d) Ammonium bromate

(e) Manganese(IV) oxide

(f) Sulfur hexafluoride

(g) Barium phosphate

(h) Nitrous acid

(i) Carbon tetrachloride

(j) Iron(II) chloride

(k) Diphosphorus pentasulfide

6.97 Identify the type of substance using the symbols of Problem 6.95, and write the formula for each.

(a) Sodium permanganate

(b) Potassium peroxide

(c) Barium dichromate

(d) Vanadium(III) acetate

(e) Iron(III) hydrogen carbonate

(f) Sulfur dioxide

(g) Copper(II) arsenate

(h) Tetraphosphorus hexoxide

(i) Iodine heptafluoride

(j) Ammonium monohydrogen phosphate

(k) Diarsenic pentoxide

(l) Chloric acid

(m) Ammonium chlorate

(n) Bromic acid

6.98 Identify the type of substance using the symbols of Problem 6.95, and name each.

(a) KOH (b) $(NH_4)_2SO_3$ (c) $Cu_3(PO_4)_2$

(d) CO_2 (e) Na_2CO_3 (f) ICl_5

(g) NH_4ClO_3 (h) SO_2 (i) $AlPO_4$

6.99 Identify the type of substance using the symbols of Problem 6.95, and name each.

(a) PbO_2 (b) $HBrO_2$ (c) $Ca(OH)_2$

(d) $HC_2H_3O_2$ (e) CS_2 (f) MnO_2

(g) N_2O_3

6.100 Name each of the following:

(a) CrS (b) Hg_2Cl_2 (c) Mg_3N_2

(d) Ag_2S (e) CaH_2 (f) $Co_3(PO_4)_2$

(g) $Zn(ClO_4)_2$ (h) PCl_3 (i) $BaCl_2$

(j) $CuSO_4$ (k) $NH_4C_2H_3O_2$

6.101 Name the following substances:

(a) CaO (b) HNO_3 (c) $Ti(OH)_3$

(d) $MnCrO_4$ (e) $Ni(NO_3)_2$ (f) $K_2Cr_2O_7$

(g) $CrCl_3$ (h) NF_3 (i) SF_4

(j) H_2SO_3

6.102 Write formulas for the following substances:

(a) Iron(II) bromide

(b) Iron(III) chloride

(c) Ammonium sulfite

(d) Xenon tetrafluoride

(e) Iodine trichloride

(f) Magnesium hydride

(g) Ammonia

(h) Manganese(III) fluoride

(i) Lithium nitrate

(j) Barium peroxide

6.103 Name each of the following:

(a) N_2O (b) CaS (c) HNO_3

(d) $Ca(NO_2)_2$ (e) $Fe(NO_3)_3$ (f) $Ni(ClO_3)_2$

(g) $HClO_3$ (h) KNO_3 (i) PI_3

(j) $(NH_4)_3PO_4$ (k) Li_3PO_4

6.104 Name the following substances:

(a) Li_2SO_3 (b) HCl (c) NI_3

(d) $CaCO_3$ (e) $NaOH$ (f) $NH_4H_2PO_4$

(g) $(NH_4)_2SeO_4$ (h) Na_3AsO_4 (i) $HClO_3$

(j) KCN

6.105 Write formulas for the following substances:

    (a) Iron(III) oxide   (b) Cobalt(III) oxide

    (c) Bromine trifluoride   (d) Lithium hydride

    (e) Gold(III) bromide   (f) Magnesium perchlorate

    (g) Lithium nitride   (h) Carbon tetrachloride

    (i) Calcium hydride

6.106 Write formulas for the following substances:

    (a) Silicon tetrafluoride

    (b) Gold(I) chloride

    (c) Phosphoric acid

    (d) Silver sulfide

    (e) Lead(IV) sulfate

    (f) Copper(II) permanganate

    (g) Tricarbon dioxide

    (h) Potassium carbonate

    (i) Chloric acid

    (j) Nickel(II) cyanide

6.107 From Figure 6.4, give the route by which you would name (a) $Al(ClO_3)_2$, (b) BrF_5, and (c) $(NH_4)_2Cr_2O_7$.

6.108 If oxalate ion is $C_2O_4{}^{2-}$, what are the formula and name of its parent acid?

6.109 (a) Azide ion has the formula $N_3{}^-$. Write the formula for the corresponding acid.

    (b) What is the name of that acid?

6.110 Name the following substances:

    (a) $CaSO_4$ (b) $HC_2H_3O_2$ (c) PCl_5

    (d) $BrCl_3$ (e) CuO (f) $HClO_4$

    (g) $KHSO_4$ (h) $HBrO_2$ (i) HNO_2

    (j) $Pb(HPO_4)_2$

6.111 Write formulas for the following substances:

    (a) Ammonium hydrogen sulfide

    (b) Magnesium chlorite

    (c) Iodine heptafluoride

    (d) Oxygen difluoride

    (e) Lithium chlorite

    (f) Cobalt(II) hydroxide

    (g) Gold(III) chloride

    (h) Ammonium sulfite

    (i) Manganese(II) oxide

    (j) Lead(II) sulfide

6.112 Why do most oxoanions have the same charges as the corresponding monatomic anions?

7

Formula Calculations

- 7.1 **Formula Masses**
- 7.2 **Percent Composition**
- 7.3 **The Mole**
- 7.4 **Empirical Formulas**
- 7.5 **Molecular Formulas**

A liquid sample, a solid sample, and a gaseous sample

Review Clues

Objectives

7.1 To calculate a formula mass

7.2 To calculate the percent composition by mass from the formula of a compound

7.3 To use the basic chemical quantity—the mole—to make calculations convenient

7.4 To determine the empirical formula from percent composition or other mass-ratio data

7.5 To determine the molecular formula from percent composition and molecular mass data or from the empirical formula and molecular mass data

The meaning of a chemical formula was discussed in Chapter 5, and we learned how to interpret formulas in terms of the numbers of atoms of each element per formula unit. In this chapter, we will learn how to calculate the number of grams of each element in any given quantity of a compound from its formula and to do other calculations involving formulas. Formula masses are presented in Section 7.1, and percent composition is considered in Section 7.2. Section 7.3 discusses the mole—the basic chemical quantity of any substance. Moles can be used to count atoms, molecules, or ions and to calculate the mass of any known number of formula units of a substance. Section 7.4 shows how to use relative mass data to determine empirical formulas, and the method is extended to molecular formulas in Section 7.5.

7.1   Formula Masses

Because each symbol in a formula represents an atom, which has a given average atomic mass, the formula as a whole represents a collection of atoms with a given formula mass. The **formula mass** (also called **formula weight**) is the sum of the atomic masses of all atoms of every element (not merely each type of atom) in a formula unit. In general, formula masses should be calculated to as many significant digits as are given in any data presented in a problem. For problems in which no data are given, at least three significant digits should be used in values from the periodic table. For example, we can calculate the formula mass for acetic acid, the major acid in vinegar, $HC_2H_3O_2$, as follows:

Number of atoms per formula unit	Atomic mass		
4 H	$4 \times$ 1.01 amu	=	4.04 amu
2 C	$2 \times$ 12.0 amu	=	24.0 amu
2 O	$2 \times$ 16.0 amu	=	32.0 amu
	Formula mass	=	60.0 amu

Because calculation of formula mass is essentially adding two or more numbers, the numbers to be added may be rounded to the same number of decimal places. For example, the four H atoms in the preceding calculation might have been included as 4.0 amu. Prior multiplication might affect the number of decimal places we retain in the atomic masses (see Problem 7.14).

The three types of formula masses correspond to the three types of formula units: (1) atomic masses (also called atomic weights), (2) **molecular masses** (also called **molecular weights**), and (3) formula masses for ionic compounds (also called formula weights). The term "atomic mass" may be used whether an atom is combined or not, but it always refers to the mass of one atom of an element.

EXAMPLE 7.1

(a) What is the atomic mass of nitrogen?

(b) What is the molecular mass of nitrogen?

Solution

(a) 14.00 amu.

(b) 28.00 amu because nitrogen molecules contain two atoms each.

EXAMPLE 7.2

Why is it incorrect to refer to the molecular mass of $(NH_4)_2SO_4$?

Solution

$(NH_4)_2SO_4$ is an ionic compound. It does not have molecules, and thus does not have a molecular mass.

Practice Problem 7.2 Which of the following have molecular masses?

$$Cl_2O \qquad Na_2SO_3 \qquad NH_3 \qquad NH_4Cl$$

EXAMPLE 7.3

Calculate the formula mass of (a) $(NH_4)_2SO_3$ and (b) $Fe(NO_3)_2$.

Solution

(a) 2 N   2 × 14.01 amu = 28.02 amu

  8 H   8 × 1.008 amu = 8.06 amu

  1 S   1 × 32.06 amu = 32.06 amu

  3 O   3 × 16.00 amu = 48.00 amu

  Formula mass = 116.14 amu

(b) 1 Fe   1 × 55.85 amu = 55.85 amu

  2 N   2 × 14.01 amu = 28.02 amu

  6 O   6 × 16.00 amu = 96.00 amu

  Formula mass = 179.87 amu

Practice Problem 7.3 Calculate the formula mass of (a) $Zn(C_2H_3O_2)_2$ and (b) $Na_2Cr_2O_7$.

Snapshot Review

❏ The formula mass—atomic mass for atoms, molecular mass for molecules, and formula mass for ionic substances—is merely the sum of the atomic masses of every *atom* in the formula unit.

A. Calculate the formula mass for each of the following substances and state which is an atomic mass, which is a molecular mass, and which is neither: (a) Ni, (b) NI_3, and (c) $Ni(IO_3)_2$.

7.2 Percent Composition

If we know the total mass of each element in a formula unit and we also know the mass of the entire formula unit, we can calculate the **percent composition** of the compound. We simply divide the total mass of each element by the total mass of the formula unit and multiply each quotient by 100% to convert it to a percentage. Together, all the percentages constitute the percent composition.

EXAMPLE 7.4

Calculate the percent composition of $Fe(NO_3)_2$.

Solution

The iron in one formula unit has a mass of 55.85 amu in a total mass of 179.87 amu, as calculated in Example 7.3(b). Iron's percent by mass is 100% times the mass of an iron atom divided by the formula mass:

$$\text{Percentage of iron} = \frac{\text{mass of iron}}{\text{mass of Fe(NO}_3)_2} \times 100.00\%$$

$$= \left(\frac{55.85 \text{ amu}}{179.87 \text{ amu}}\right) \times 100.00\% = 31.05\% \text{ Fe}$$

The percentages of nitrogen and oxygen are calculated in the same way:

$$\text{Percentage of nitrogen} = \left(\frac{28.02 \text{ amu}}{179.87 \text{ amu}}\right) \times 100.00\% = 15.58\% \text{ N}$$

$$\text{Percentage of oxygen} = \left(\frac{96.00 \text{ amu}}{179.87 \text{ amu}}\right) \times 100.00\% = 53.37\% \text{ O}$$

Notice that the *total* mass of nitrogen or oxygen in the formula unit, not the atomic mass of nitrogen or oxygen, is used in the calculation.

The sum of all the percentages of elements in any compound should be 100%:

$$31.05\% + 15.58\% + 53.37\% = 100.00\%$$

In general, the sum may not be exactly 100% because of prior rounding to the proper number of significant digits. If we get a total of 98% or 105%, we must look for an error. (Getting 100% does not guarantee that our percentages are correct, but getting a sum that is significantly different from 100% guarantees that something is *incorrect*.)

Practice Problem 7.4 Calculate the percent composition of $(NH_4)_3PO_4$.

Snapshot Review

ChemSkill Builder
4.2, 4.5

❏ The percentage of an element in a compound is 100% times the ratio of the total mass of the element divided by the formula mass. The percent composition of the compound is the percentages of all the elements.

❏ It does not matter if the compound is covalent or ionic.

A. Calculate the percent composition of each of (a) methyl alcohol, CH_4O, and (b) TNT, $C_7H_5N_3O_6$.

7.3 The Mole

The atomic mass unit (amu) is an extremely small unit, suitable for measuring masses of individual atoms and molecules. However, to measure masses on laboratory balances takes a huge number of atoms, molecules, or formula units. Chemists have to weigh a large collection of formula units, so that the total mass is measurable on a laboratory balance. (If we try to weigh one grain of rice on a scale designed to weigh people, we will get an inkling of the problem of measuring the mass of one atom or molecule. See Figure 3.7.)

> The mole is the basic unit of quantity of chemical substance.

The **mole** (abbreviated mol) is the standard chemical unit used to measure the quantity of a substance. A mole is defined as the number of ^{12}C atoms in *exactly* 12 g of ^{12}C. The mole is equal to 6.0221367×10^{23} particles. Thus the mole is a number, essentially like a dozen, except very much larger. This number is about the number of grains of sand that would fit into a sphere the size of the Earth. (See Problem 2.154.) This number is known as **Avogadro's number.** Remember the value of this number to at least three significant digits.

Avogadro's number was set at 6.0221367×10^{23} so that the atomic mass of each element and the number of grams per mole of that element have the same numeric value, although in different units. The atomic mass of ^{12}C is 12.00 amu, and 12.00 g is the mass of 1.000 mol of ^{12}C. The formula mass of any compound or element is also equal to its number of grams per mole. The formula mass of a substance in units of grams per mole is called the **molar mass** of the substance. (Molar mass can be abbreviated MM.)

> The molar mass of any substance is equal to the number of grams per mole of that substance.

ENRICHMENT

It is also possible to think of a mole as the number of atomic mass units in 1 gram.

The number of atomic mass units per gram is equal to Avogadro's number.

EXAMPLE 7.5

Use the value of Avogadro's number, the mass of one ^{12}C atom (exactly 12 amu), and the definition of a mole to calculate the number of atomic mass units per gram.

Practice Problem 7.5 Calculate the number of inches in 1 foot, knowing that a certain shoe box is 4.00 in. tall and that a stack of 1 dozen of these boxes is 4.00 ft tall.

Solution

$$\underbrace{\frac{6.022 \times 10^{23}\,^{12}C\text{ atoms}}{1\text{ mol }^{12}C}}_{\text{Avogadro's number}} \underbrace{\left(\frac{1\text{ mol}^{12}C}{12.000\text{ g}}\right)}_{\substack{\text{Mass of}\\1\text{ mol}}} \underbrace{\left(\frac{12.000\text{ amu}}{1\,^{12}C\text{ atom}}\right)}_{\substack{\text{Mass of}\\1\text{ atom}}}$$

$$= 6.022 \times 10^{23}\text{ amu/g}$$

7.3 ■ The Mole

Figure 7.1 Some Conversions Involving Moles

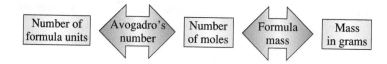

EXAMPLE 7.6

Knowing that the formula mass of ethyl alcohol, C_2H_6O, is 46.0 amu, show that C_2H_6O has a molar mass equal to 46.0 g/mol.

Solution

$$\frac{46.0 \text{ amu}}{1 \text{ formula unit}} \underbrace{\left(\frac{6.02 \times 10^{23} \text{ formula units}}{1 \text{ mol}}\right)}_{\text{Avogadro's number}} \underbrace{\left(\frac{1.00 \text{ g}}{6.02 \times 10^{23} \text{ amu}}\right)}_{\text{From Example 7.5}} = \frac{46.0 \text{ g}}{1 \text{ mol}}$$

Practice Problem 7.6   The formula mass of H_3PO_4 is 98.0 amu. What is its molar mass (in grams per mole)?

We can use Avogadro's *number* as a conversion factor to convert moles to *numbers* of formula units, and vice versa. We can use the molar *mass* to convert moles to *masses,* and vice versa (Figure 7.1).

EXAMPLE 7.7

(a) Calculate the number of molecules in 0.445 mol of C_4H_8.
(b) Calculate the mass of 0.445 mol of C_4H_8.

Solution

(a) $0.445 \text{ mol } C_4H_8\left(\dfrac{6.02 \times 10^{23} \text{ molecules } C_4H_8}{1 \text{ mol } C_4H_8}\right)$

$$= 2.68 \times 10^{23} \text{ molecules } C_4H_8$$

(b) The molar mass of C_4H_8 is 4(12.01 g) + 8(1.008 g) = 56.104 g.

$$0.445 \text{ mol } C_4H_8\left(\frac{56.104 \text{ g } C_4H_8}{1 \text{ mol } C_4H_8}\right) = 25.0 \text{ g } C_4H_8$$

Practice Problem 7.7

(a) Calculate the number of moles of C_5H_{12} in 41.9 g of C_5H_{12}.
(b) Calculate the number of moles of C_5H_{12} in a sample containing 7.15×10^{23} C_5H_{12} molecules.

EXAMPLE 7.8

Calculate the number of molecules of SO_2 in 41.31 g of SO_2.

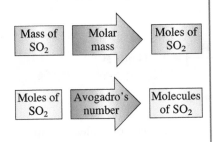

Solution

The molar mass of SO_2 is 32.06 g + 2(16.00 g) = 64.06 g. (The molar mass is calculated to four significant digits because the data in the problem are given to four significant digits.)

$$41.31 \text{ g } SO_2 \left(\frac{1 \text{ mol } SO_2}{64.06 \text{ g } SO_2} \right) = 0.64486 \text{ mol } SO_2$$

$$0.64486 \text{ mol } SO_2 \left(\frac{6.022 \times 10^{23} \text{ molecules}}{1 \text{ mol } SO_2} \right) = 3.883 \times 10^{23} \text{ molecules } SO_2$$

or

$$41.31 \text{ g } SO_2 \left(\frac{1 \text{ mol } SO_2}{64.06 \text{ g } SO_2} \right) \left(\frac{6.022 \times 10^{23} \text{ molecules } SO_2}{1 \text{ mol } SO_2} \right)$$
$$= 3.883 \times 10^{23} \text{ molecules } SO_2$$

Practice Problem 7.8   Calculate the mass of 6.63×10^{24} molecules of diethyl ether, $C_4H_{10}O$.

The chemical formula for a compound gives the ratio of atoms of each element in the compound to atoms of every other element in the compound. It also gives the ratio of dozens of atoms of each element in the compound to dozens of atoms of every other element in the compound. Moreover, it gives the ratio of *moles* of atoms of each element in the compound to *moles* of atoms of every other element in the compound. For example, a given quantity of H_2O has 2 mol of H atoms for every mole of O atoms, and a given quantity of CH_4 has 1 mol of C atoms for every 4 mol of H atoms. The mole ratio from the formula can be used as a factor to convert from moles of any element in the formula to moles of any other element or to moles of the formula unit as a whole. In Figure 7.2, these additional conversions have been added to those already presented in Figure 7.1.

Figure 7.2   Additional Conversions Involving Moles

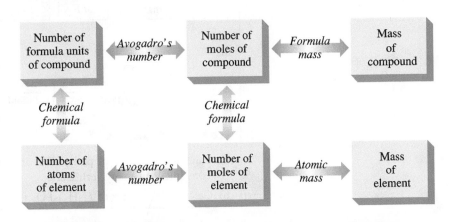

EXAMPLE 7.9

Calculate the number of moles of hydrogen atoms in 6.170 mol of H_2O.

Solution

$$6.170 \text{ mol } H_2O \left(\frac{2 \text{ mol } H}{1 \text{ mol } H_2O} \right) = 12.34 \text{ mol } H$$

Factor from
chemical formula

Practice Problem 7.9 Calculate the number of moles of aspirin, $C_9H_8O_4$, that contains 4.21×10^{23} oxygen atoms.

EXAMPLE 7.10

(a) Calculate the number of grams of fluorine in 7.197 g of CaF_2.

(b) Calculate the mass of CaF_2 that contains 7.197 g of fluorine.

Solution

(a) The molar mass (atomic mass in grams per mole) of fluorine is 19.00 g/mol; the molar mass of CaF_2 is 78.08 g/mol.

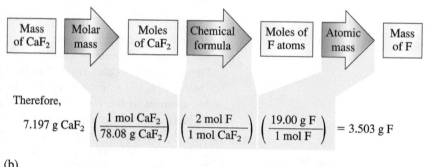

Therefore,

$$7.197 \text{ g } CaF_2 \left(\frac{1 \text{ mol } CaF_2}{78.08 \text{ g } CaF_2} \right) \left(\frac{2 \text{ mol } F}{1 \text{ mol } CaF_2} \right) \left(\frac{19.00 \text{ g } F}{1 \text{ mol } F} \right) = 3.503 \text{ g } F$$

(b)

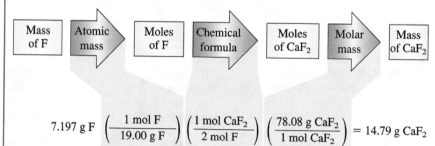

$$7.197 \text{ g } F \left(\frac{1 \text{ mol } F}{19.00 \text{ g } F} \right) \left(\frac{1 \text{ mol } CaF_2}{2 \text{ mol } F} \right) \left(\frac{78.08 \text{ g } CaF_2}{1 \text{ mol } CaF_2} \right) = 14.79 \text{ g } CaF_2$$

Practice Problem 7.10

(a) Calculate the mass of phosphorus in 1.50 kg of $(NH_4)_3PO_4$, a principal constituent of many fertilizers.

(b) Calculate the mass of $(NH_4)_3PO_4$ that contains 1.50 kg of phosphorus.

The percent composition of a compound can be calculated in terms of molar masses instead of formula masses.

EXAMPLE 7.11

Calculate the percent composition of nitroglycerine, $C_3H_5N_3O_9$, using molar masses instead of formula masses.

Solution

The mass of a mole of $C_3H_5N_3O_9$ is

$$3(12.01 \text{ g}) + 5(1.008 \text{ g}) + 3(14.01 \text{ g}) + 9(16.00 \text{ g}) = 227.1 \text{ g}$$

The percentage of each element is given by

$$\left(\frac{3(12.01 \text{ g}) \text{ C}}{227.1 \text{ g } C_7H_5N_3O_6}\right) \times 100.0\% = 15.87\% \text{ C}$$

$$\left(\frac{5(1.008 \text{ g}) \text{ H}}{227.1 \text{ g } C_7H_5N_3O_6}\right) \times 100.0\% = 2.219\% \text{ H}$$

$$\left(\frac{3(14.01 \text{ g}) \text{ N}}{227.1 \text{ g } C_7H_5N_3O_6}\right) \times 100.0\% = 18.51\% \text{ N}$$

$$\left(\frac{9(16.00 \text{ g}) \text{ O}}{227.1 \text{ g } C_7H_5N_3O_6}\right) \times 100.0\% = 63.41\% \text{ O}$$

$$\text{Total} = 100.01\%$$

Practice Problem 7.11   Calculate the percent composition of trinitrotoluene, TNT, $C_7H_5N_3O_6$.

Snapshot Review

ChemSkill Builder 4.1

❑ The mole is Avogadro's number of formula units—equal to 6.02×10^{23} units.

❑ A mole of a substance has a mass (in grams) equal to its formula mass, called the *molar mass,* which can be used as a factor in solving problems.

A. A mole of a substance with formula mass 52.4 amu has (a) how many formula units? (b) what mass?

B. Calculate the mass of 3.50 mol of the amino acid alanine, $C_3H_7NO_2$.

C. Calculate the number of molecules in 3.50 mol of alanine.

7.4 Empirical Formulas

The **empirical formula** of a compound is the formula that gives the lowest whole-number ratio of atoms of all the elements. For example, the empirical formula of fruit sugar, fructose, $C_6H_{12}O_6$, is CH_2O. The simplest ratio of carbon to hydrogen to oxygen atoms in fructose is 1 to 2 to 1. An empirical formula always has the smallest integral subscripts that give the correct ratio of atoms of the elements.

EXAMPLE 7.12

Write the empirical formulas for the compounds containing carbon and hydrogen in the following ratios:

(a) 2 mol carbon to 3 mol hydrogen

(b) 1.0 mol carbon to 1.5 mol hydrogen

(c) 0.1712 mol carbon to 0.2568 mol hydrogen

Solution

(a) The mole ratio is 2:3, so the empirical formula is C_2H_3.

(b) The mole ratio given is not integral, but we can multiply each value by 2 to get an integral ratio of 2:3. The empirical formula is again C_2H_3.

(c) This mole ratio is not integral, and this time it is more difficult to make it so. If we divide both values by the magnitude of the smaller one, we can get closer to an integral ratio:

$$\frac{0.1712 \text{ mol C}}{0.1712} = 1.000 \text{ mol C} \qquad \frac{0.2568 \text{ mol H}}{0.1712} = 1.500 \text{ mol H}$$

Now multiply by 2, as in part (b):

$$\frac{1.000 \text{ mol C}}{1.500 \text{ mol H}} = \frac{2 \text{ mol C}}{3 \text{ mol H}}$$

This ratio is also 2:3, and again the empirical formula is C_2H_3.

Practice Problem 7.12   Write the empirical formula for a compound consisting of elements A and B, for each ratio of A to B:

(a) 1:1   (b) 1:1.5   (c) 1:1.33   (d) 1:1.67

(e) 1:1.25   (f) 1:1.75   (g) 1:1.20   (h) 1:1.40

We can find the empirical formula from percent composition data. The empirical formula represents a ratio; therefore, it does not depend on the size of the sample under consideration. Because the empirical formula reflects a *mole* ratio, and percent composition data are given in terms of *mass,* we have to convert the masses to moles. We then convert the mole ratio, which is unlikely to be an integral ratio, to the smallest possible whole-number ratio, from which we write the empirical formula.

The steps we take to obtain an empirical formula from percent composition data are given in the left column (Steps) that follows. In the right column (Example), the empirical formula of a compound containing 39.2% phosphorus and 60.8% sulfur is calculated.

Steps

Step 1: Change the percentages to numbers of grams (by assuming that 100.00 g of sample is present). (On exams, state that assumption.)

Step 2: For each element, convert the number of grams to the number of moles.

Step 3: Try to get an integral ratio by dividing *all* the numbers of moles by the magnitude of the smallest number of moles. This will make at least one number an integer.

Step 4: If necessary, multiply *all* the numbers of moles by the same small integer to clear fractions. Round off the result to an integer only when the number of moles is within 1% of the integer. Always use at least three significant digits in empirical formula calculations; otherwise, rounding errors may produce an incorrect empirical formula.

Never round off more than 1%.

Example

Because the size of the sample does not matter in determining an empirical formula, we can assume a 100.00-g sample. That way, the percentages given are automatically equal numerically to the numbers of grams of the elements. For example:

$$100.00 \text{ g compound}\left(\frac{39.2 \text{ g P}}{100.00 \text{ g compound}}\right) = 39.2 \text{ g P}$$

From the percentage

39.2 g P and 60.8 g S

$$39.2 \text{ g P}\left(\frac{1 \text{ mol P}}{30.97 \text{ g P}}\right) = 1.266 \text{ mol P}$$

$$60.8 \text{ g S}\left(\frac{1 \text{ mol S}}{32.06 \text{ g S}}\right) = 1.896 \text{ mol S}$$

$$\frac{1.266 \text{ mol P}}{1.266} = 1.00 \text{ mol P}$$

$$\frac{1.896 \text{ mol S}}{1.266} = 1.50 \text{ mol S}$$

$$1.00 \text{ mol P} \times 2 = 2.00 \text{ mol P}$$

$$1.50 \text{ mol S} \times 2 = 3.00 \text{ mol S}$$

The empirical formula is P_2S_3.

EXAMPLE 7.13

Determine the empirical formula of a compound that has a percent composition of 43.7% P and 56.3% O.

Solution

Merely change the percentage signs to grams:

43.7 g P   and   56.3 g O

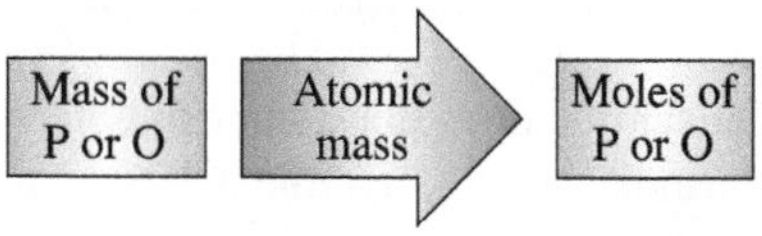

Then convert the numbers of grams to moles:

$$43.7 \text{ g P} \left(\frac{1 \text{ mol P}}{30.97 \text{ g P}} \right) = 1.41I \text{ mol P}$$

$$56.3 \text{ g O} \left(\frac{1 \text{ mol O}}{16.00 \text{ g O}} \right) = 3.519 \text{ mol O}$$

That gives the mole ratio of oxygen to phosphorus,

$$1.41I \text{ mol P} \qquad \text{to} \qquad 3.519 \text{ mol O}$$

but it is not an integral ratio. The best way to try to get an integral ratio is to divide *each* of the numbers of moles by the magnitude of the lower number of moles:

$$\frac{1.41I \text{ mol P}}{1.41I} \qquad \text{to} \qquad \frac{3.519 \text{ mol O}}{1.41I}$$

which simplifies to

$$1.00 \text{ mol P} \qquad \text{to} \qquad 2.494 \text{ mol O}$$

The numbers of moles are still not all integers, but we can see that if we multiply *each* of them by 2, we will get an integral ratio:

$$2(1.00) \text{ mol P} \qquad \text{to} \qquad 2(2.494) \text{ mol O}$$

which simplifies to

$$2 \text{ mol P} \qquad \text{to} \qquad 5 \text{ mol O}$$

The ratio is 2 mol P to 5 mol O, and the empirical formula is P_2O_5. (Remember to write the P first, as stated in Section 5.1.)

Note that we do *not* use the molecular mass of an oxygen *molecule* (or any other diatomic molecule) in empirical formula calculations because we are interested in the mole ratio involving oxygen *atoms*. Molecular oxygen, O_2, has nothing to do with empirical formula calculations.

Practice Problem 7.13 Determine the empirical formula of manganese(II) pyrophosphate, a compound containing 38.71% Mn, 21.82% P, and 39.46% oxygen.

We can obtain an empirical formula from mass data instead of a percent composition.

EXAMPLE 7.14

Determine the empirical formula of a compound if a sample of the compound contains 3.524 g of iron, 3.034 g of sulfur, and 4.542 g of oxygen.

Solution

Because the data are given in grams rather than percentages, we do not have to do the first step of changing to grams. Simply change the grams to moles:

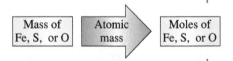

$$3.524 \text{ g Fe}\left(\frac{1 \text{ mol Fe}}{55.85 \text{ g Fe}}\right) = 0.06310 \text{ mol Fe}$$

$$3.034 \text{ g S}\left(\frac{1 \text{ mol S}}{32.06 \text{ g S}}\right) = 0.09464 \text{ mol S}$$

$$4.542 \text{ g O}\left(\frac{1 \text{ mol O}}{16.00 \text{ g O}}\right) = 0.2839 \text{ mol O}$$

The mole ratios are

   0.06310 mol Fe   to   0.09464 mol S   to   0.2839 mol O

Dividing by the magnitude of the smallest number of moles yields

      1.000 mol Fe   to   1.500 mol S   to   4.499 mol O

Multiplying each of these numbers by 2 yields

         2 mol Fe   to   3 mol S   to   9 mol O

and the empirical formula is $Fe_2S_3O_9$.

Practice Problem 7.14   Determine the empirical formula of "hypo," a compound used in photographic development, if a sample contains 2.453 g of sodium, 3.422 g of sulfur, and 2.561 g of oxygen.

Most ionic compounds such as NaCl, $MgBr_2$, Al_2S_3, and NH_4NO_3 are identified by their empirical formulas, and such formulas are used for calculations involving these compounds. Compounds such as K_2O_2, Hg_2Cl_2, $K_2C_2O_4$, and $Na_2S_2O_8$, having certain polyatomic ions, are exceptions. For molecular substances, empirical formulas are used as a basis in determining molecular formulas, as described in the next section.

Snapshot Review

ChemSkill Builder 4.6

❑ An empirical formula—the simplest formula for a compound—is obtained from the integral mole ratio of its elements.
❑ To determine an empirical formula, calculate the number of moles of each element in a sample (arbitrarily choose 100 g if percentages are given), divide each of them by the smallest number of moles, and then multiply by some small integer if necessary to get integral numbers of moles.

A. Calculate the empirical formula of a compound consisting of 87.73% C and 12.27% H.

● ●

ITEM OF INTEREST

A forensic chemist analyzes some white pills found in an aspirin bottle on an unidentified dead body. One pill is found to consist of 60.05% potassium, 18.44% carbon, and 21.51% nitrogen. A second pill contains 60.00% carbon, 4.48% hydrogen, and 35.53% oxygen and has a molar mass of 180 g/mol. Can these data help the forensic chemist deduce whether the death was accidental, murder, or suicide?

The percent composition shows that the first pill is KCN—potassium cyanide. The second pill — $C_9H_8O_4$ — could be aspirin. It looks like murder because a cyanide pill is not likely to get into an aspirin bottle accidentally, and a person committing suicide is not likely to put a cyanide pill in an aspirin bottle. As in most human affairs, however, there is no certainty to this conclusion, given only the data presented.

7.5 Molecular Formulas

> The molecular formula gives the number of atoms of each element in one molecule.

The **molecular formula** gives the number of atoms of each element in one molecule. This information includes (1) the ratio of atoms of each element to atoms of every other element in a compound, (2) the ratio of atoms of each element to molecules of the compound, and (3) the corresponding mole ratios. For example, C_2H_4 has a ratio of 2 mol of carbon atoms to 4 mol of hydrogen atoms (or more simply 1 mol of carbon atoms to 2 mol of hydrogen atoms). It also has a ratio of 2 mol of carbon atoms to 1 mol of C_2H_4 molecules and 4 mol of hydrogen atoms to 1 mol of C_2H_4 molecules. The molecular formula is always an integral multiple (1, 2, 3, . . .) of the empirical formula. Thus, the molecular formula gives all the information that the empirical formula gives plus the ratio of the number of moles of each element to moles of the compound. Molecular formulas can be written only for compounds that exist in the form of molecules.

If we calculated the percent compositions of C_2H_2 and C_6H_6 (Figure 7.3), we would find that both have the same percentages of carbon and the same percentages of hydrogen (compare Problem 7.100 at the end of the chapter). Both have the same empirical formula—CH. This result means that we cannot tell these two compounds apart from percent composition data alone. However, if we also have a molar mass, we can use that information with the percent composition data to determine not only the empirical formula but also the molecular formula.

Determining the molecular formula of a compound involves first determining the empirical formula and then determining how many empirical formula units are in a molecule of the compound.

Figure 7.3 Percent Compositions of Acetylene and Benzene

Consider a sample containing three molecules of acetylene, C_2H_2, and another sample containing one molecule of benzene, C_6H_6. Because both samples have the same number of carbon atoms (six) and both have the same number of hydrogen atoms (six), both obviously have the same percent composition. Because percent composition is an intensive property, the two compounds have the same percent composition, no matter how many molecules are present.

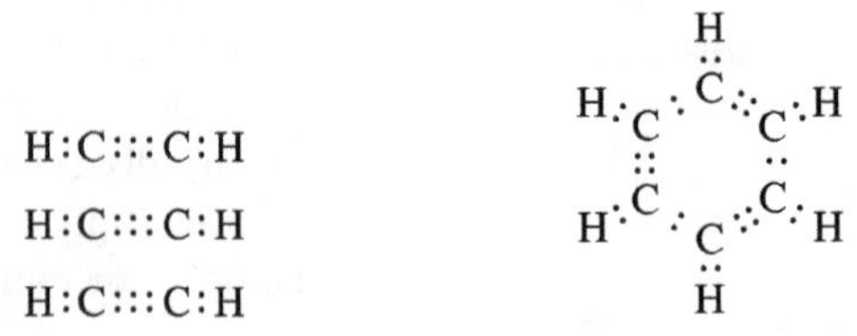

H:C:::C:H

H:C:::C:H

H:C:::C:H

Three molecules of acetylene

One molecule of benzene

EXAMPLE 7.15

Determine the molecular formula of styrene, used to prepare the plastic wrapping material polystyrene. It is a compound of carbon and hydrogen only that contains 92.26% carbon, and has a molar mass of 104 g/mol.

Solution

Because the total of the percentages must be 100.00%, the percentage of hydrogen in the compound must be 100.00% total -92.26% C $= 7.74\%$ H.

$$92.26 \text{ g C}\left(\frac{1 \text{ mol C}}{12.01 \text{ g C}}\right) = 7.682 \text{ mol C}$$

$$7.74 \text{ g H}\left(\frac{1 \text{ mol H}}{1.008 \text{ g H}}\right) = 7.68 \text{ mol H}$$

The ratio is 1 mol C to 1 mol H. The empirical formula is CH. Next, the molar mass (the number of grams per mole) is divided by the mass of a mole of empirical formula units to get the number of empirical formula units per molecule. The mass of 1.00 mol of CH formula units is

$$12.01 \text{ g} + 1.008 \text{ g} = 13.02 \text{ g}$$

Thus,

$$\frac{104 \text{ g/mol of molecules}}{13.02 \text{ g/mol of empirical formula units}} = \frac{8 \text{ mol of empirical formula units}}{1 \text{ mol of molecules}}$$

The empirical formula CH is multiplied by 8 to get the molecular formula, C_8H_8.

Practice Problem 7.15 Determine the molecular formula of a hydrocarbon (a compound of carbon and hydrogen only) that contains 89.94% carbon and has a molar mass of 80.2 g/mol.

| Mass of C, H, or O | Atomic mass | → | Moles of C, H, or O |

   One important use of molecular formulas is to identify molecular compounds. If a chemist isolates a useful substance from a plant or animal source, the chemist wants to know the formula so that the compound can be made in the laboratory. Making a compound is often more convenient and more economical than obtaining it from its natural source. Certain vitamins and penicillin are examples of such compounds.

ChemSkill Builder 4.6

Snapshot Review

❒ Molecular formulas apply to covalent substances only.
❒ A molecular formula may be calculated from the empirical formula and the molecular mass by dividing the molecular mass by the mass of one empirical formula unit, which gives the number of empirical formula units per molecule.

A. Calculate the molecular formula of a compound whose empirical formula is CH_2 and whose molecular mass is 126 amu.
B. One allotropic form of sulfur has a formula S_x, where x is a small integer. Its molecular mass is 256 amu. Calculate its molecular formula.

Key Terms

Key terms are defined in the Glossary.

Avogadro's number (7.3)   molar mass (7.3)   molecular mass (7.1)
empirical formula (7.4)   mole (7.3)   molecular weight (7.1)
formula mass (7.1)   molecular formula (7.5) percent composition (7.2)
formula weight (7.1)

Symbols/Abbreviations

MM (molar mass) (7.3)   mol (mole) (7.3)

Summary

The formula mass (formula weight) of a substance is determined by adding the atomic masses (atomic weights) of each *atom* (not each element) in a formula unit. Molecular mass is one type of formula mass (for substances that form molecules) and is calculated in the same way as the formula mass for an ionic compound. For example, the formula mass of NH_3 is 17.0 amu, the atomic mass of three hydrogen atoms plus that of one nitrogen atom. Three or more significant digits should be used to report formula masses. (Section 7.1)

The percent composition is the percentage of each element in a compound. The percentage of an element in a compound is calculated by finding the ratio of the total mass of that element to the formula mass and multiplying that ratio by 100%. The percentages of all the elements in a compound should total 100% (within less than 1%). (Section 7.2)

The mole is defined as the number of ^{12}C atoms in exactly 12 g of ^{12}C, which is 6.02×10^{23}—Avogadro's number. Equal numbers of moles of two (or more) different substances have the same number of formula units but *not* the same mass. The molar mass is the mass in grams of one mole of a substance. The number of grams per mole—the molar mass—is a frequently used conversion factor, used for converting between grams and moles. (Section 7.3)

An empirical formula gives the lowest integral mole ratio of atoms of all the elements in a compound. An empirical formula may be determined from a percent composition by changing the percentages to numbers of grams (by assuming a 100-g sample) and then dividing the number of grams of each element by its atomic mass in grams. The nonintegral mole ratio that results is converted to an integral mole ratio by dividing each of the numbers of moles by the magnitude of the smallest, and then, if necessary, multiplying every one of the quotients by the same small whole number. Never round off by more than 1% during this procedure. If data are given in grams rather than as a percent composition, simply omit the first step. (Section 7.4)

Molecular formulas give all the information that empirical formulas do, plus the ratio of the number of moles of each element to the number of moles of the compound. (Molecular formulas are used only for molecular substances, not ionic substances.) A molecular formula can be determined from the empirical formula of the compound and its formula mass: First, divide the formula mass by the mass in amu of one empirical formula unit, which will result in a small integer. Then, multiply each subscript of the empirical formula by that integer. (Section 7.5)

Items for Special Attention

■   A formula gives the mole ratio of one element to another and the mole ratio of each element to 1 mol of compound. With atomic masses and a chemical formula, we can calculate mass ratios—for example, percent by mass—rather easily.

■   To convert to or from moles, use Avogadro's *number* for *numbers* of formula units, or the molar *mass* to convert to or from a *mass*. Use the subscripts in the formula to convert from moles of atoms of an element to or from moles of atoms of another element or moles of entire formula units (see Figure 7.2). We must consider the units (for example, moles of atoms versus number of individual atoms versus mass of the atoms) as well as the species (for example, atoms of an element versus molecules of that element). These differences are apparent in the questions: "How many *atoms* of oxygen are in 2.00 *mol* of oxygen *molecules?*" and "What is the *mass* of the *oxygen atoms* in 1.00×10^{23} *water molecules?*"

■ The most important skill learned in this chapter may be the ability to convert from grams to moles of a substance, and vice versa.

■ Do not use the term "molecule" or "molecular mass" when discussing ionic compounds, because they do not exist as molecules.

■ The unit usually used for the mass of a small number of atoms, molecules, or formula units is the amu, which is a very small fraction of a gram (about 10^{-24} g). The unit ordinarily used for the mass of molar quantities of a substance is the gram.

■ The percentages of the elements making up any compound must total 100%. If the percentages of all but one element are given, the percentage of that element can easily be calculated.

Answers to Snapshot Reviews

7.1 A. (a) 58.71 amu, atomic mass
(b) 394.7 amu, molecular mass
(c) 408.5 amu, neither
All three are formula masses.

7.2 A. (a) $\%C = \left(\dfrac{12.01 \text{ amu}}{32.04 \text{ amu}}\right)100\% = 37.48\% \text{ C}$

$\%H = \left(\dfrac{4.032 \text{ amu}}{32.04 \text{ amu}}\right)100\% = 12.58\% \text{ H}$

$\%O = \left(\dfrac{16.00 \text{ amu}}{32.04 \text{ amu}}\right)100\% = 49.94\% \text{ O}$

(b) $\%C = \left(\dfrac{7[12.01 \text{ amu}]}{227.14 \text{ amu}}\right)100\% = 37.01\% \text{ C}$

$\%H = \left(\dfrac{5[1.008 \text{ amu}]}{227.14 \text{ amu}}\right)100\% = 2.219\% \text{ H}$

$\%N = \left(\dfrac{3[14.01 \text{ amu}]}{227.14 \text{ amu}}\right)100\% = 18.50\% \text{ N}$

$\%O = \left(\dfrac{6[16.00 \text{ amu}]}{227.14 \text{ amu}}\right)100\% = 42.26\% \text{ O}$

7.3 A. (a) 6.02×10^{23} (b) 52.4 g

B. $3.50 \text{ mol C}_3\text{H}_7\text{NO}_2\left(\dfrac{89.0 \text{ g C}_3\text{H}_7\text{NO}_2}{1 \text{ mol C}_3\text{H}_7\text{NO}_2}\right)$
$= 312 \text{ g C}_3\text{H}_7\text{NO}_2$

C.

$3.50 \text{ mol C}_3\text{H}_7\text{NO}_2\left(\dfrac{6.02 \times 10^{23} \text{ molecules C}_3\text{H}_7\text{NO}_2}{1 \text{ mol C}_3\text{H}_7\text{NO}_2}\right)$
$= 2.11 \times 10^{24} \text{ molecules C}_3\text{H}_7\text{NO}_2$

7.4 A. $87.73 \text{ g C}\left(\dfrac{1 \text{ mol C}}{12.01 \text{ g C}}\right) = 7.305 \text{ mol C}$

$12.27 \text{ g H}\left(\dfrac{1 \text{ mol H}}{1.008 \text{ g H}}\right) = 12.17 \text{ mol H}$

The mole ratio of H to C is
$12.17/7.305 = 1.666/1 = 5/3$.
The empirical formula is C_3H_5.

7.5 A. The empirical formula mass is 14.0 amu and the molecular mass is 126 amu, so there are (126 amu)/(14.0 amu) = 9 empirical formula units per molecule. The molecular formula is C_9H_{18}.

B. The empirical formula for sulfur is S, with mass 32.06 amu. There are 256 amu/32.06 amu = 8 empirical formula units per molecule. S_8 is the molecular formula.

Self-Tutorial Problems

7.1 What small integer should we multiply each of the following ratios by to get a whole-number ratio? What ratio results in each case?

(a) $\dfrac{1.50}{1}$ (b) $\dfrac{2.25}{1}$ (c) $\dfrac{3.33}{1}$

(d) $\dfrac{3.67}{1}$ (e) $\dfrac{2.75}{1}$ (f) $\dfrac{1.20}{1}$

7.2 What small integer should we multiply each of the following ratios by to get a whole-number ratio? What ratio results in each case?

(a) $\dfrac{2.50}{1}$ (b) $\dfrac{1.33}{1}$ (c) $\dfrac{1.40}{1}$

(d) $\dfrac{3.25}{1}$ (e) $\dfrac{2.167}{1}$ (f) $\dfrac{1.75}{1}$

7.3 For each of the following, select the proper units from the following list: amu, grams, grams/mole.

    (a) Mass   (b) Atomic mass

    (c) Molecular mass   (d) Formula mass

    (e) Molar mass

7.4 For this problem, assume that all the socks are identical.

    (a) How many pairs of socks are in 1.5 dozen pairs of socks?

    (b) How many socks are in 1.5 dozen socks?

    (c) How many pairs of socks are in 1.5 dozen socks?

    (d) How many socks are in 1.5 dozen pairs of socks?

    (e) How many dozen pairs of socks are in 1.5 dozen socks?

    (f) How many dozen socks are in 1.5 dozen pairs of socks?

7.5 (a) How many chlorine molecules are in 1.50 mol of chlorine molecules?

    (b) How many chlorine atoms are in 1.50 mol of chlorine, atoms?

    (c) How many chlorine molecules are in 1.50 mol of bonded chlorine atoms?

    (d) How many chlorine atoms are in 1.50 mol of chlorine molecules?

    (e) How many moles of chlorine molecules are in 1.50 mol of bonded chlorine atoms?

    (f) How many moles of chlorine atoms are in 1.50 mol of chlorine molecules?

7.6 A 100-g sample of a certain compound contains 92.3% carbon. What percentage of carbon is contained in a 29.7-g sample of the same compound? What mass?

7.7 (a) Compare the mass of two dozen socks rolled into pairs with the mass of the same socks unrolled.

    (b) Compare the mass of two dozen socks with the mass of two dozen pairs of socks.

    (c) Compare the mass of 2.00 mol of nitrogen atoms with that of the same atoms bonded into N_2 molecules.

    (d) Compare the mass of 2.00 mol of nitrogen atoms with that of 2.00 mol of nitrogen molecules.

7.8 (a) If a certain atom has a mass of 19.0 amu, what is the mass in grams of 1.00 mol of these atoms?

    (b) If a certain atom has a mass of 12.0 amu, what is the mass in grams of 1.00 mol of these atoms?

    (c) If a certain atom has a mass of 238 amu, what is the mass in grams of 1.00 mol of these atoms?

    (d) Explain your results.

7.9 (a) Which weighs more—a dozen grapefruit or a dozen cherries? Which contains the greater number of fruits?

    (b) Which weighs more—a mole of iodine atoms or a mole of fluorine atoms? Which contains more atoms?

7.10 (a) If a shirt box is 1.0 in. high, how many feet high is a stack of a dozen shirt boxes?

    (b) If a shoe box is 4.0 in. high, how many feet high is a stack of a dozen shoe boxes?

    (c) If a hat box is 7.0 in. high, how many feet high is a stack of a dozen hat boxes?

    (d) Explain your results.

7.11 What information do you need to determine each of the following?

    (a) A formula mass   (b) An empirical formula

    (c) A molecular formula

7.12 What conversion factor is used to convert a number of moles of a substance to (a) the number of grams of the substance? (b) the number of formula units of the substance?

7.13 What conversion factor(s) is (are) used to convert a number of formula units of a substance to a mass of that substance?

7.14 Calculate the formula mass of each of the following to two decimal places twice, first by rounding each atomic mass to two decimal places, and second by using the entire number of significant digits in the atomic masses and rounding the formula mass:

    (a) $C_{12}H_{26}$ (b) $KClO_4$ (c) PCl_3

7.15 Which of the following substances have molecular masses? Which have molar masses?

    BaH_2 CCl_4 C_2H_4 Ne S_8

7.16 Which of the following substances have molecular masses? Which have molar masses?

    NaCl P_2O_3 $(NH_4)_2SO_4$ Hg

7.17 What is a synonym for molar mass (a) for molecules? (b) for atoms? (c) for ionic compounds? What is a synonym for formula mass (d) for molecules? (e) for atoms? (f) for ionic compounds?

7.18 How many moles of chlorine atoms are present in 1.00 mol of $Al(ClO_3)_3$?

7.19 How many moles of $(NH_4)_2SO_4$ contain 1.00 mol of hydrogen atoms?

7.20 Is molar mass an intensive or extensive property?

7.21 What is the molar mass of (a) a 3.00 mol sample of NH_3? (b) a 1.50 mol sample of NH_3? (c) a 0.125 mol sample of NH_3?

7.22 (a) What is the difference between the atomic mass of nitrogen and the molecular mass of nitrogen?

    (b) Why is the phrase "molar mass of nitrogen" ambiguous?

    (c) To what does "molar mass of nitrogen gas" refer?

7.23 Which of the following are empirical formulas?

CH $\quad$ C$_5$H$_9$ $\quad$ C$_4$H$_6$ $\quad$ C$_6$H$_{15}$ $\quad$ C$_9$H$_{17}$

7.24 Which of the following are empirical formulas?

C$_3$H$_6$ $\quad$ C$_2$H$_3$ $\quad$ C$_5$H$_8$ $\quad$ C$_4$H$_{10}$ $\quad$ C$_3$H$_5$

7.25 Which of the following formulas identify ionic compounds but are not empirical formulas?

C$_2$H$_6$ $\quad$ P$_4$O$_6$ $\quad$ ZnCl$_2$O$_6$ $\quad$ K$_2$S$_2$O$_8$ $\quad$ K$_2$O$_2$

7.26 What is the empirical formula of each of the following?

(a) C$_8$H$_{12}$ $\qquad$ (b) C$_8$H$_{12}$O$_4$

(c) C$_3$H$_6$O$_3$ $\qquad$ (d) C$_{12}$H$_{22}$O$_{11}$

7.27 State whether the percent composition, the empirical formula, or the molecular formula gives the information specified in each of the following parts.

(a) Ratio of moles of each element to moles of compound

(b) Ratio of moles of each element to each other element, and no more

(c) Ratio of masses of each element to mass of compound

7.28 What can we determine from percent composition data?

7.29 What information is given in the formula Na$_2$Cu(CN)$_4$?

7.30 Which of the following formulas identify ionic compounds but are not empirical formulas?

Hg$_2$Cl$_2$ $\qquad$ K$_2$O $\qquad$ C$_8$H$_6$Cl$_2$ $\qquad$ P$_4$O$_6$

7.31 Calculate the molar mass of a compound if 2.50 mol has a mass of 155 g.

7.32 How many moles of atoms of each element are present in 1.00 mol of each of the following compounds?

(a) CH$_3$CH$_2$NH$_2$ $\qquad$ (b) In(C$_2$H$_3$O$_2$)$_3$

(c) Na$_3$CoF$_6$ $\qquad$ (d) Co(NH$_3$)$_6$PO$_4$

7.33 How many moles of atoms of each element are present in 1.00 mol of each of the following compounds?

(a) KHCO$_3$·MgCO$_3$·4H$_2$O $\qquad$ (b) (NH$_4$)$_2$C$_2$O$_4$

(c) C$_6$H$_{12}$O$_6$ $\qquad$ (d) Co$_2$(CO)$_9$

7.34 How many moles of atoms of each element are present in 1.00 mol of each of the following compounds?

(a) Iron(III) chlorate

(b) Ammonium sulfate

(c) Barium sulfide

Problems

7.1 Formula Masses

7.35 What is the smallest formula mass known for (a) any atom and (b) any molecule?

7.36 Calculate the formula mass of each of the following compounds to one decimal place:

(a) NaHCO$_3$ $\qquad$ (b) Ca(CNS)$_2$

(c) (NH$_4$)$_2$SO$_3$ $\qquad$ (d) Na$_3$PO$_4$

(e) C$_8$H$_{18}$ $\qquad$ (f) AsCl$_3$

7.37 Calculate the formula mass of each of the following substances:

(a) Ba(CN)$_2$ $\qquad$ (b) (NH$_4$)$_2$Cr$_2$O$_7$

(c) Co(ClO$_3$)$_3$ $\qquad$ (d) UF$_6$

(e) BaCO$_3$ $\qquad$ (f) P$_4$

7.38 Calculate the formula mass of (a) CuSO$_4$·5H$_2$O (b) PbSiF$_6$·4H$_2$O.

7.39 Calculate the formula mass of each of the following compounds to one decimal place:

(a) Ammonium sulfite

(b) Cobalt(II) sulfate

(c) Arsenic tribromide

7.2 Percent Composition

7.40 Calculate the percent composition of thiamine (a vitamin of the B complex family), C$_{12}$H$_{17}$N$_4$OSCl.

7.41 Calculate the percent composition of cholesterol, C$_{27}$H$_{45}$OH.

7.42 Calculate the percent composition of aspirin, C$_9$H$_8$O$_4$.

7.43 Calculate the percent composition of vitamin B$_{12}$, C$_{63}$H$_{90}$CoN$_{14}$P.

7.44 Calculate the percent compositions of pentene, C$_5$H$_{10}$, and cycloheptane, C$_7$H$_{14}$. Compare the values, and explain the results.

7.45 Calculate the percent compositions of cyclooctatetrene, C$_8$H$_8$, and benzene, C$_6$H$_6$. Compare the values, and explain the results.

7.46 Calculate the percent composition of ammonium monohydrogen phosphate.

7.47 Calculate the percent composition of (a) sodium dichromate and (b) potassium permanganate.

7.48 Calculate the percent composition of ethylene glycol, C$_2$H$_6$O$_2$, commonly used as a permanent antifreeze in cars.

7.49 Calculate the percent chlorine in DDT, $C_{14}H_9Cl_5$, an insecticide that has been discontinued because it does not biodegrade.

7.50 Calculate the percent composition of niacin, a B-complex vitamin, $C_6H_5NO_2$.

7.51 Calculate the percent composition of vitamin E, $C_{29}H_{50}O_2$.

7.3 The Mole

7.52 Calculate the formula mass and the molar mass of each of the following compounds to three significant figures:

(a) $(NH_4)_2CO_3$ (b) $Ba(ClO_3)_2$ (c) CaC_2O_4

7.53 Calculate the number of grams of acetic acid, $HC_2H_3O_2$, in 1.76 mol of acetic acid.

7.54 Calculate the number of moles of butane, C_4H_{10}, in 151 g of butane.

7.55 Calculate the mass of 1.25 mol of (a) unbonded oxygen atoms, (b) oxygen atoms bonded into O_2 molecules, and (c) O_2 molecules.

7.56 Calculate the number of moles of glucose, a simple sugar, $C_6H_{12}O_6$, in 283.5 g (10.00 oz).

7.57 Calculate the number of grams of acetaldehyde, C_2H_4O, in 0.848 mol of acetaldehyde.

7.58 Calculate the number of moles of methane (natural gas), CH_4, in 175 g of methane.

7.59 Calculate the number of moles in 12.9 g of a compound with a molar mass of 62.0 g/mol.

7.60 Calculate the number of moles in 1.93 g of a compound with a molar mass of 98.0 g/mol.

7.61 Calculate the mass in grams of (a) one oxygen atom. (b) one oxygen molecule.

7.62 Calculate the number of molecules in 12.9 g of a compound with a molar mass of 64.0 g/mol.

7.63 Calculate the mass of a sample of fruit sugar, fructose, $C_6H_{12}O_6$, containing 2.65×10^{20} molecules.

7.64 Calculate the number of grams in 2.76 mol of ethyl alcohol, C_2H_5OH.

7.65 Calculate the number of molecules in 6.50 mol of CH_4.

7.66 (a) Calculate the number of moles that contain 9.25×10^{20} formula units of $(NH_4)_2SO_4$.

(b) Calculate the number of molecules in 1.67 mol of trinitrotoluene, TNT, $C_7H_5N_3O_6$.

7.67 Calculate the mass of a sample of table sugar, sucrose, $C_{12}H_{22}O_{11}$, containing 1.91×10^{24} molecules.

7.68 Calculate the mass of 6.68×10^{23} molecules of PCl_3.

7.69 (a) Calculate the number of moles of C_2H_4 in 44.7 g of C_2H_4.

(b) Calculate the number of moles of carbon atoms in 44.7 g of C_2H_4.

(c) Calculate the number of individual carbon atoms in 44.7 g of C_2H_4.

7.70 Calculate the number of carbon atoms in 1.77 mol of butene, C_4H_8.

7.71 Calculate the number of hydrogen atoms in 1.11 mol of acetaldehyde, C_2H_4O.

7.72 Calculate the number of grams of hydrogen in 4.11 mol of ammonia.

7.73 Calculate the mass of hydrogen in 6.92 g of CH_4, methane (natural gas).

7.74 Calculate the number of grams of oxygen in 7.42 mol of Na_3BO_3.

7.75 Calculate the number of hydrogen atoms in 41.4 g of ethyl alcohol, C_2H_6O.

7.76 Calculate the number of moles of H_3PO_4 that contains 6.78×10^{24} oxygen atoms.

7.77 Calculate the number of moles of ammonium chloride that contains 1.37×10^{24} hydrogen atoms.

7.78 Calculate the mass of aluminum chloride that contains 2.22×10^{23} chlorine atoms.

7.79 Calculate the number of grams of oxygen in 1.63 mol of $Al(ClO_4)_3$.

7.80 Calculate the number of hydrogen atoms in 125 g of benzene, C_6H_6.

7.81 Calculate the mass of $Cr(ClO_2)_2$ that contains 5.57×10^{22} chlorine atoms.

7.82 Calculate the number of molecules of C_5H_{12} containing 1.44×10^{25} C atoms.

7.83 Calculate the mass of N in 4.75×10^{23} formula units of Mg_3N_2.

7.84 Calculate the number of chlorine atoms in (a) 1.77 g of SCl_2 and (b) 1.77 g of $SOCl_2$.

7.4 Empirical Formulas

7.85 Decide whether each of the following is an empirical formula:

(a) $C_2H_8N_2$ (b) $K_2S_2O_8$ (c) $Na_2Cr_2O_7$

(d) S_4N_4 (e) $C_{12}H_{21}$

7.86 Decide whether each of the following is an empirical formula:

(a) $K_4P_2O_7$ (b) C_3F_6 (c) $C_6H_{10}O_3$

(d) Hg_2Br_2 (e) $H_2C_2O_4$

7.87 Polyethylene a well-known plastic, is composed of 85.63% carbon and 14.37% hydrogen.

(a) How many grams of each element are in 100.0 g of polyethylene?

(b) How many moles of each element are in 100.0 g of polyethylene?

(c) What is the mole ratio in integers?

(d) What is the empirical formula?

7.88 Testosterone, a hormone, is composed of 79.12% carbon, 9.79% hydrogen, and 11.10% oxygen. What is its empirical formula?

7.89 Polypropylene, a well-known plastic, is composed of 85.63% carbon and 14.37% hydrogen. Determine its empirical formula.

7.90 Styrene, used in manufacturing a well-known plastic, is composed of 92.26% carbon and 7.74% hydrogen. Determine its empirical formula.

7.91 Determine an empirical formula from each of the following sets of percent composition data:

(a) 82.66% C, 17.34% H

(b) 72.03% Mn, 27.97% O

(c) 43.64% P, 56.36% O

(d) 37.82% C, 6.35% H, 55.83% Cl

(e) 54.53% C, 9.15% H, 36.32% O

7.92 Determine an empirical formula from each of the following sets of percent composition data:

(a) 47.05% K, 14.45% C, 38.50% O

(b) 77.26% Hg, 9.25% C, 1.17% H, 12.32% O

(c) 66.42% C, 5.57% H, 28.01% Cl

(d) 74.98% C, 5.24% H, 19.77% F

7.93 Determine an empirical formula from each of the following sets of percent composition data:

(a) 69.94% Fe, 30.06% O

(b) 77.73% Fe, 22.27% O

(c) 72.36% Fe, 27.64% O

7.94 Nitroglycerin is composed of 15.87% carbon, 2.22% hydrogen, 18.51% nitrogen, and 63.41% oxygen. Determine its empirical formula.

7.95 Calculate the empirical formula of each of the substances from the following analyses:

(a) 5.52 g C, 0.464 g H, 13.1 g F

(b) 75.95 g C, 9.57 g H, 224.2 g Cl

7.96 Calculate the empirical formula of each of the following substances. Name each.

(a) 9.07 g H, 288 g O, 144 g S

(b) 76.8 g Na, 80.1 g O, 53.4 g S

7.97 Calculate the empirical formula mass of each of the following:

(a) Hg_2Br_2 (b) $Na_2S_2O_3$ (hypo)

7.5 Molecular Formulas

7.98 What is the empirical formula mass and the molecular mass of each of the following?

(a) C_6H_6 (b) C_3H_6 (c) C_2H_6

7.99 What is the empirical formula mass and the molecular mass of each of the following?

(a) C_6H_{12} (b) C_4H_6 (c) C_6H_{10}

7.100 Calculate the percent compositions of ethyl naphthalene, $C_{12}H_{12}$, and cyclobutadiene, C_4H_4. Compare the values, and explain the results.

7.101 Calculate the percent compositions of butene, C_4H_8, and cyclooctane, C_8H_{16}. Compare the values, and explain the results.

7.102 Determine the molecular formula of a substance if its empirical formula is NO_2 and its molar mass is (a) 46.0 g/mol and (b) 92.0 g/mol.

7.103 Find the molecular formula of a substance with an empirical formula CH_2 and a molar mass (a) 56.0 g/mol, (b) 126 g/mol, (c) 210 g/mol, and (d) 78.0 g/mol.

7.104 Find the molecular formula of a substance if the empirical formula is CH and its molar mass is (a) 52.0 g/mol, (b) 104 g/mol, (c) 156 g/mol, and (d) 78.0 g/mol.

7.105 Determine the molecular formula of a sugar from its percent composition of 40.0% C, 6.67% H, 53.3% O, and its molar mass of 180 g/mol.

7.106 Find the molecular formula of a compound composed of 87.73% carbon and 12.27% hydrogen which has a molar mass of 82.1 g/mol.

7.107 Calculate the molecular formula of each of the substances from the following analyses:

(a) 36.93 g C, 8.27 g H, 49.20 g O, MM = 92.0 g/mol

(b) 3.72 g H, 44.1 g C, 118 g O, MM = 90.0 g/mol

(c) 8.65 g C, 0.484 g H, 3.36 g N, 11.5 g O, MM = 200 g/mol

(d) 42.87 g C, 7.20 g H, 38.08 g O, MM = 74.1 g/mol

7.108 White phosphorus is one form of elemental phosphorus. Its molar mass is 124 g/mol. Calculate its molecular formula.

7.109 The most widely used antifreeze, ethylene glycol, is composed of 38.70% carbon, 9.74% hydrogen, and 51.56% oxygen. Its molar mass is 62.07 g/mol. Find its molecular formula.

7.110 Calculate the molecular formula of a substance if its percent composition is 79.91% C and 20.09% H, and its molar mass is approximately 30 g/mol.

7.111 Calculate the molecular formula of a substance if its percent composition is 85.63% C and 14.37% H, and its molar mass is approximately 85 g/mol.

7.112 Calculate the molecular formula of a compound if a sample contains 135 g of phosphorus and 175 g of oxygen and its molar mass is 284.

7.113 Octane and heptane are two ingredients of gasoline. Octane has 84.12% carbon and 15.88% hydrogen, and heptane has 83.90% carbon and 16.10% hydrogen. Their molecular masses are 114 amu and 100 amu, respectively. What are their molecular formulas?

General Problems

7.114 A 6.09-mg sample of a hydrocarbon was burned in air. The products were 17.9 mg of CO_2 and 11.0 mg of H_2O.

   (a) What mass of oxygen was used in the combustion?

   (b) How many millimoles of carbon was present in the products, and in the sample?

   (c) How many millimoles of hydrogen was present in the products and in the sample?

   (d) What is the empirical formula of the sample?

7.115 A 17.1-mg sample of a hydrocarbon was burned in air. The products were 47.0 mg of CO_2 and 38.4 mg of water. What is the empirical formula of the hydrocarbon?

7.116 A certain carbohydrate (a compound containing carbon plus hydrogen and oxygen in a 2:1 atom ratio) is 40.0% carbon. Calculate its empirical formula.

7.117 Calculate the percent composition of soluble saccharin, $C_7H_4NNaO_3S$.

7.118 How many moles of carbon atoms is present in the quantity of C_2H_6O that contains 4.14 g of hydrogen?

7.119 Calculate the percent composition of ammonium cyanide.

7.120 Calculate the number of hydrogen atoms in 42.7 g of a compound that contains 91.25% carbon and 8.75% hydrogen.

7.121 Calculate the number of molecules in 2.79 g of a compound that has a molar mass of 92.13 g/mol and contains 91.25% carbon and 8.75% hydrogen.

7.122 Calculate the number of hydrogen atoms in 12.8 g of a compound whose percent composition is 15.88% H and 84.12% C.

7.123 Calculate the number of hydrogen atoms in 41.8 g of a compound that contains 4.14% hydrogen.

7.124 Calculate the number of molecules in 31.7 g of a compound that has a molar mass of 82.2 g/mol.

7.125 Calculate the number of carbon atoms in 1.000 gallon of octane, C_8H_{18}, a major component of gasoline (1 gallon = 3.785 L; density = 0.7025 g/mL).

7.126 Calculate the number of molecules of vitamin A, $C_{20}H_{30}O$, in 2.34 g of vitamin A.

7.127 (a) Vitamin B_{12} has one cobalt atom per formula unit. The compound is 4.348% Co. Calculate its molar mass.

   (b) Vitamin D_1 has two oxygen atoms per formula unit. The compound is 4.03% O. Calculate its molar mass.

7.128 A sample is 39.2% KCl by mass, and the rest is water. Calculate the number of molecules of water in 14.4 g of the sample.

7.129 A 6.055-g sample of a hydrate of copper(II) sulfate, $CuSO_4 \cdot xH_2O$, is heated until all the water is driven off. After the anhydrous salt cools, its mass is 3.870 g. Calculate the value of x. (*Hint:* Treat this problem as an empirical formula problem with one of the "elements" H_2O.)

7.130 A scientist isolates a pure substance from a newly discovered plant in the Amazon River basin. What data does the scientist need to start to determine whether the substance is a new compound and what its formula is?

7.131 Calculate the percent error in rounding off the atomic mass of each of the following elements to three significant digits:

   (a) Hydrogen   (b) Sulfur

   (c) Lead   (d) Neon

   (e) Carbon   (f) Fluorine

7.132 A different method may be used to calculate the molecular formula from percent composition data plus a molar mass: First, calculate the mass of each element in 1.00 mol of compound. Next, calculate the number of moles of each of the elements in the mole of compound. Those results yield the molecular formula. Use this method to calculate the molecular formula of a hydrocarbon (a compound of carbon and hydrogen only) that contains 87.73% C and has a molar mass of 82.0 g/mol.

8

Chemical Reactions

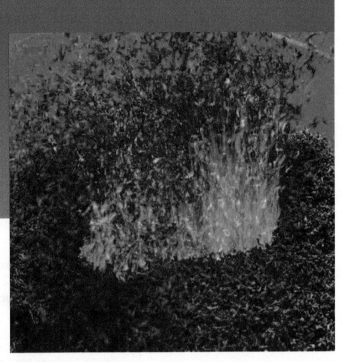

A reaction liberating energy

Review Clues

Objectives

8.1 To interpret a balanced chemical equation in terms of mole ratios of reactants and products

8.2 To balance chemical equations—that is, to get the same number of atoms of each element on each side

8.3 To predict the products of thousands of chemical reactions by categorizing reactions

8.4 To predict the products of the reactions of acids with bases and metals, and to use a specialized nomenclature for acid-base reactions

In Chapter 7, we learned how to do numerical calculations for compounds, using their formulas as a basis. This chapter lays the foundation for doing similar calculations for chemical reactions, using the balanced equation as a basis. The chemical equation is introduced in Section 8.1, and methods for balancing equations are presented in Section 8.2. To write equations, we must often be able to predict the products of a reaction from a knowledge of the properties of the reactants. Section 8.3 shows how to classify chemical reactions into types to predict the products of thousands of reactions. An important type of reaction—the acid-base reaction—is discussed in Section 8.4.

8.1   The Chemical Equation

In a chemical reaction, the substances that react are called **reactants,** or sometimes, **reagents.** The substances that are produced are called **products.** During the reaction, some or all of the atoms of the reactants change their bonding. For example, two hydrogen molecules can react with an oxygen molecule to form two water molecules (Figure 8.1). In a less familiar example—the reaction of MgI_2 with $AgNO_3$—the products are $Mg(NO_3)_2$ and AgI. The metal ions have merely traded anions. All of the ions are still present after the reaction; they have just "changed partners." We can describe the reaction, pictured in Figure 8.2, in words:

> Magnesium iodide plus silver nitrate yields magnesium nitrate plus silver iodide.

We use formulas to represent the substances involved in a reaction when we write a chemical equation. In an **equation,** the formulas for reactants are placed on the left side of the arrow and those for products are placed on the right side. Either substance may be written first on each side of the equation:

$$MgI_2 + AgNO_3 \rightarrow Mg(NO_3)_2 + AgI \qquad \textit{(Not balanced)}$$

Even better, we can write a **balanced equation,** which shows the relative numbers of atoms of each of the elements involved. The unbalanced equation just presented seems to indicate that an iodide ion has disappeared during the reaction and that a nitrate ion has appeared from nowhere. As written, that equation violates the law of conservation of mass. Thus, we must always write balanced equations for reactions. The word "equation" is related to the word "equal"; an equation must have equal numbers of atoms of each element on each side. Such an equation is said to be *balanced.*

We must always write *balanced* chemical equations.

Figure 8.1 Reaction of Hydrogen and Oxygen

The bonds in the diatomic molecules H_2 and O_2 are broken, and new bonds are formed between hydrogen and oxygen atoms.

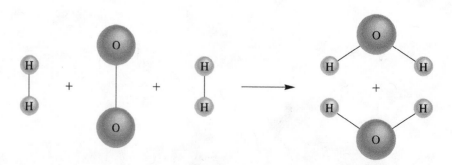

Figure 8.2 Reaction of Aqueous Magnesium Iodide with Aqueous Silver Nitrate to Produce the Insoluble Silver Iodide and Aqueous Magnesium Nitrate

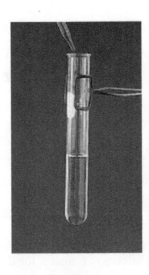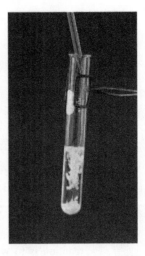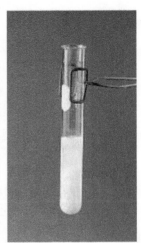

Coefficients—numbers that are written before the formulas—tell the relative numbers of formula units of reactants and products involved in a reaction and balance the number of atoms of each element involved. The coefficient does not imply any chemical bonding. *The coefficient multiplies everything in the formula:*

$$MgI_2 + 2\,AgNO_3 \rightarrow Mg(NO_3)_2 + 2\,AgI \qquad \textit{(Balanced)}$$

Coefficients

In a balanced chemical equation, the absence of a coefficient before a formula implies a coefficient of 1. The two formula units of $AgNO_3$ are composed of two Ag^+ ions and two NO_3^- ions. The two NO_3^- ions in the one formula unit of $Mg(NO_3)_2$ produced come from the two formula units of $AgNO_3$.

The balanced equation for the reaction of hydrogen and oxygen, illustrated in Figure 8.1, is

$$2\,H_2 + O_2 \rightarrow 2\,H_2O$$

The coefficients in a balanced equation give the *ratio* of *moles* of each substance in the reaction to *moles* of any other substance. They also give the ratio of formula units of each substance to formula units of any other substance. The balanced chemical equation is the cornerstone from which we can calculate how much of one substance reacts with or is produced by a certain quantity of another substance (Chapter 10).

> The coefficients in a balanced equation give the ratio of moles of each reactant and product to moles of any other reactant or product.

Reaction conditions are often written above or below the arrow, as in

$$MgCO_3 \xrightarrow{\text{Heat}} MgO + CO_2$$

Snapshot Review

ChemSkill Builder 5.4

❑ A balanced equation gives the mole ratios of reactants and products as well as the ratios of formula units.

A. For the reaction $PCl_5 + 4\,H_2O \rightarrow H_3PO_4 + 5\,HCl$, (a) How many molecules of HCl will be produced from three molecules of PCl_5? (b) How many moles of HCl will be produced from 3.0 mol of PCl_5?

B. What difference, if any, is there between the following equations?

$$R + Q \rightarrow T + Z$$

$$Q + R \rightarrow Z + T$$

8.2 Balancing Equations

Our first major task of this chapter is to learn to balance equations for chemical reactions. Balancing simple equations will be covered in this chapter; equations for more complicated oxidation-reduction reactions will be considered in Chapter 16.

The first step in writing a complete and balanced equation for a chemical reaction is to write correct formulas for the reactants and products. To help us as we learn, we might write the equation in words and later write the formulas. Correct formulas cannot be changed to make an equation balance! Only after the correct formulas have been written can we go on to the next step. Then, we use coefficients to change the numbers of formula units to get the same number of atoms of each element on the two sides of the equation.

> To complete an equation for any type of reaction, write the proper formulas for the reactants and products before starting to balance the equation.

For example, the unbalanced equation for the reaction of sulfur dioxide with oxygen to give sulfur trioxide is

$$SO_2 + O_2 \rightarrow SO_3 \quad \textit{(Not balanced)}$$

Don't forget that elemental oxygen occurs as O_2. With one molecule of each substance, the numbers of oxygen atoms on the two sides of the equation are not equal, so the equation is not balanced. We can balance the equation by inserting proper coefficients in front of the formulas:

$$2\,SO_2 + O_2 \rightarrow 2\,SO_3 \quad \textit{(Balanced)}$$

The number 2 before the SO_2 indicates that there are two sulfur dioxide molecules, containing two sulfur atoms and four oxygen atoms. There are two more oxygen atoms in the O_2 molecule. Because there are two sulfur atoms and six oxygen atoms in the two SO_3 molecules, the equation is now balanced. We must always check an equation after we balance it to make sure that the numbers of atoms of each element on each side of the arrow are equal.

One of the problems encountered by students just learning to balance equations is that the absence of a coefficient in a balanced equation means a coefficient of 1, but the absence of a coefficient before the equation is fully balanced might mean that this substance has not yet been considered. To avoid any confusion, we can place a question mark before each formula when we start to balance an equation. (After we have had a lot of practice, we will not need to use the question marks.)

EXAMPLE 8.1

Balance the equation for the reaction of barium hydroxide and hydrobromic acid to give barium bromide and water.

Solution

| **Steps** | **Example** |

Step 1: Write correct formulas for the reactants and products, as discussed in Chapter 5. Do not write incorrect formulas to make balancing easier; write correct formulas!

$$Ba(OH)_2 + HBr \rightarrow BaBr_2 + H_2O$$
(Not balanced)

Step 2: Insert question marks before each formula except the most complicated one; place a 1 there.

$$1\ Ba(OH)_2 + ?\ HBr \rightarrow ?\ BaBr_2 + ?\ H_2O$$

Step 3: Balance one or more of the elements in the substance with the "1" coefficient by inserting coefficients in front of the formulas for other substances. In this case, the 1 Ba^{2+} in $Ba(OH)_2$ yields 1 $BaBr_2$ and the 2 O in $Ba(OH)_2$ yield 2 H_2O.

$$1\ Ba(OH)_2 + ?\ HBr \rightarrow 1\ BaBr_2 + 2\ H_2O$$

Step 4: Complete the equation using values already determined. In this case, the HBr is balanced by considering the 2 Br^- ions in 1 $BaBr_2$:

$$1\ Ba(OH)_2 + 2\ HBr \rightarrow 1\ BaBr_2 + 2\ H_2O$$

Step 5: Delete any coefficients equal to 1:

$$Ba(OH)_2 + 2\ HBr \rightarrow BaBr_2 + 2\ H_2O$$

Step 6: Check the numbers of atoms of each element on each side:

1 Ba, 2 O, 4 H, 2 Br on each side.

Practice Problem 8.1 Balance the equation for the reaction of ammonium iodide with lead(II) nitrate to yield ammonium nitrate and lead(II) iodide.

If the initial placement of the coefficient 1 yields fractional coefficients in the equation, we can get integer values by simply multiplying every coefficient (including the coefficients equal to 1) by the smallest integer that will clear the fractions.

EXAMPLE 8.2

Balance the equation for the reaction of $CoCl_2$ and Cl_2, which produces $CoCl_3$.

Solution

$$?\ CoCl_2 + ?\ Cl_2 \rightarrow 1\ CoCl_3$$

Balancing cobalt: $\quad 1\ CoCl_2 + ?\ Cl_2 \rightarrow 1\ CoCl_3$

Balancing chlorine: $\quad 1\ CoCl_2 + \frac{1}{2}\ Cl_2 \rightarrow 1\ CoCl_3$

Clearing the fraction: $\quad 2\ CoCl_2 + 1\ Cl_2 \rightarrow 2\ CoCl_3$

Final equation: $\quad 2\ CoCl_2 + \quad Cl_2 \rightarrow 2\ CoCl_3$

Check: 2 Co, 6 Cl on each side.

Practice Problem 8.2 Balance an equation for the reaction of octane, C_8H_{18}, with O_2 to yield CO_2 and H_2O.

When any element appears in more than one substance on the same side of the equation, we balance that element last.

EXAMPLE 8.3

Write a balanced equation for the following reaction:

$$KIO_3 + KI + HCl \rightarrow I_2 + H_2O + KCl$$

Solution

Place a 1 before KIO_3, the most complicated-looking formula, and a question mark before each of the other formulas:

$$1\ KIO_3 + ?\ KI + ?\ HCl \rightarrow ?\ I_2 + ?\ H_2O + ?\ KCl$$

Because potassium and iodine appear in two compounds on the left side of the equation, start working with oxygen, which appears in only one compound on each side, including the compound with the "1."

$$1\ KIO_3 + ?\ KI + ?\ HCl \rightarrow ?\ I_2 + 3\ H_2O + ?\ KCl$$

Knowing how many hydrogen atoms are on the right side of the equation, we can balance hydrogen next:

$$1\ KIO_3 + ?\ KI + 6\ HCl \rightarrow ?\ I_2 + 3\ H_2O + ?\ KCl$$

Now balance chlorine:

$$1\ KIO_3 + ?\ KI + 6\ HCl \rightarrow ?\ I_2 + 3\ H_2O + 6\ KCl$$

Balance the potassium, being careful to note that there is already one K^+ in the $1\ KIO_3$:

$$1\ KIO_3 + 5\ KI + 6\ HCl \rightarrow ?\ I_2 + 3\ H_2O + 6\ KCl$$

Finally, balance the iodine:

$$1\ KIO_3 + 5\ KI + 6\ HCl \rightarrow 3\ I_2 + 3\ H_2O + 6\ KCl$$

The coefficient 1 may now be deleted:

$$KIO_3 + 5\ KI + 6\ HCl \rightarrow 3\ I_2 + 3\ H_2O + 6\ KCl$$

Check: 6 K, 6 I, 3 O, 6 H, 6 Cl on each side.

Practice Problem 8.3 Balance an equation for the reaction of H_2O with N_2O_5 to yield HNO_3.

EXAMPLE 8.4

Write a balanced equation for the reaction of sodium hydroxide with phosphoric acid to produce sodium monohydrogen phosphate and water.

Solution

First, write the correct formulas for the reactants and products, place a 1 before the most complicated-looking formula, and place a question mark before every other formula:

$$? \text{NaOH} + ? \text{H}_3\text{PO}_4 \rightarrow 1 \text{Na}_2\text{HPO}_4 + ? \text{H}_2\text{O}$$

Balance the sodium and phosphorus atoms first, because oxygen and hydrogen appear in two substances on each side of the equation:

$$2 \text{NaOH} + 1 \text{H}_3\text{PO}_4 \rightarrow 1 \text{Na}_2\text{HPO}_4 + ? \text{H}_2\text{O}$$

Balance the hydrogen atoms:

$$2 \text{NaOH} + 1 \text{H}_3\text{PO}_4 \rightarrow 1 \text{Na}_2\text{HPO}_4 + 2 \text{H}_2\text{O}$$

The oxygen atoms have been balanced in the process. Finally, eliminate the coefficients equal to 1:

$$2 \text{NaOH} + \text{H}_3\text{PO}_4 \rightarrow \text{Na}_2\text{HPO}_4 + 2 \text{H}_2\text{O}$$

Check: 2 Na, 6 O, 5 H, 1 P on each side.

Practice Problem 8.4   Balance an equation for the reaction of ammonium sulfide with copper(II) chloride to yield copper(II) sulfide and ammonium chloride.

To make balancing some equations a little easier, we can balance any polyatomic ion that maintains its composition through an entire reaction as the entire ion, instead of balancing the individual atoms of the elements.

EXAMPLE 8.5

Balance the following equation using the polyatomic ions rather than the individual atoms.

$$\text{Ba(NO}_3)_2 + \text{Na}_2\text{CO}_3 \rightarrow \text{BaCO}_3 + \text{NaNO}_3$$

Solution

$$1 \text{Ba(NO}_3)_2 + ? \text{Na}_2\text{CO}_3 \rightarrow ? \text{BaCO}_3 + ? \text{NaNO}_3$$

Balance the barium ion and the nitrate ions:

$$1 \text{Ba(NO}_3)_2 + ? \text{Na}_2\text{CO}_3 \rightarrow 1 \text{BaCO}_3 + 2 \text{NaNO}_3$$

Balance the carbonate ion:

$$1 \text{Ba(NO}_3)_2 + 1 \text{Na}_2\text{CO}_3 \rightarrow 1 \text{BaCO}_3 + 2 \text{NaNO}_3$$

Clear the coefficients equal to 1:

$$\text{Ba(NO}_3)_2 + \text{Na}_2\text{CO}_3 \rightarrow \text{BaCO}_3 + 2 \text{NaNO}_3$$

Practice Problem 8.5   Balance the following equation:

$$(\text{NH}_4)_3\text{PO}_4 + \text{Mg(NO}_3)_2 \rightarrow \text{NH}_4\text{NO}_3 + \text{Mg}_3(\text{PO}_4)_2$$

Information about the **state** of a reactant or product (whether it is present as a solid, liquid, gas, or solute) may be given in a chemical equation. The following abbreviations are used: solid (s), liquid (ℓ), gas (g), and solute in aqueous solution (aq). An **aqueous solution** is a solution in water. Thus, the reaction of silver nitrate with ammonium chloride can be represented by the following equation:

$$AgNO_3(aq) + NH_4Cl(aq) \rightarrow AgCl(s) + NH_4NO_3(aq)$$

The reaction of aqueous lithium carbonate with a solution of hydrochloric acid can be represented by the following equation:

$$Li_2CO_3(aq) + 2\,HCl(aq) \rightarrow 2\,LiCl(aq) + H_2O(\ell) + CO_2(g)$$

Snapshot Review

ChemSkill Builder 5.4

❐ Because the balanced equation is a set of reacting ratios, one coefficient is rather arbitrary. We set the coefficient of the most complex formula to 1, but we might later have to adjust all the coefficients to get integers.

A. Balance the following equations: (a) $P_4O_6(s) + H_2O(\ell) \rightarrow H_3PO_3(\ell)$, (b) $TiCl_4(\ell) + H_2O(\ell) \rightarrow TiO_2(s) + HCl(g)$, and (c) $CoCl_3(aq) + Co(s) \rightarrow CoCl_2(aq)$.

8.3   Predicting the Products of Chemical Reactions

To the beginning student, the huge array of chemical reactions might seem bewildering. To memorize the products of each one by merely looking at the reactants would be impossible. Instead, we generalize a great number of reactions into five simple types that allows us at least to make an educated guess as to the products. To learn a few simple rules is much easier than to memorize each reaction independently. Thus we must

- Learn to classify reactions into their types by considering the reactants only.
- Learn what products might be produced by that type reaction.
- Learn how to predict if the expected reaction will actually proceed.

More complicated oxidation-reduction reactions will be presented in Chapter 16, and other complex reactions are covered in more advanced chemistry courses.

Simple chemical reactions can be divided into the following classes:

1. Combination reactions
2. Decomposition reactions
3. Single substitution (or single displacement) reactions
4. Double substitution (or double displacement) reactions

In addition, most elements and many compounds react with oxygen:

5. Combustion reactions

Combination Reactions

Combination reactions involve the reaction of two (or more) substances to form one compound. Perhaps the easiest combination reaction to recognize is one in which two free elements (at least one of which is a nonmetal) react with each other. The elements can do little except react with each other (or not react at all). For example, if we treat aluminum metal with chlorine gas, the elements can combine to form aluminum chloride:

$$2\,Al(s) + 3\,Cl_2(g) \rightarrow 2\,AlCl_3(s)$$

The formula for the product of a combination reaction must be written according to the rules presented in Chapter 5. *After* the product has been represented by the proper formula, the equation is balanced, as shown in Section 8.2.

EXAMPLE 8.6

Complete and balance an equation for the reaction of zinc metal and oxygen gas.

Solution

Step 1: Identify the product—zinc oxide.

Step 2: Write correct formulas for reactant(s) and product(s). Remember that oxygen is one of the seven elements that occur as diatomic molecules when uncombined with other elements (Figure 5.2):

$$Zn(s) + O_2(g) \rightarrow ZnO(s) \qquad \text{(Not balanced)}$$

Step 3: Balance the equation:

$$2\,Zn(s) + O_2(g) \rightarrow 2\,ZnO(s) \qquad \text{(Balanced)}$$

Practice Problem 8.6 Complete and balance an equation for the reaction of aluminum metal with oxygen gas.

When two nonmetallic elements combine, the product formed often depends on the relative quantities of the reactants present. For example, when carbon combines with oxygen, either of two possible compounds may be produced: carbon monoxide or carbon dioxide. When the supply of oxygen is limited, carbon monoxide is produced, but when excess oxygen is available, carbon dioxide results:

$$2\,C(s) + O_2(g, \text{limited quantity}) \rightarrow 2\,CO(g)$$

$$C(s) + O_2(g, \text{excess}) \rightarrow CO_2(g)$$

●●●●●●●●●●●●●●●●●●●●●●●

ITEM OF INTEREST

What happens in the atmosphere to the carbon monoxide generated in automobile engines? The carbon monoxide gas reacts slowly with the oxygen gas in the air to produce carbon dioxide gas:

$$2\,CO(s) + O_2(g) \rightarrow 2\,CO_2(g)$$

Of course, not every pair of elements will react with each other. For example, we know that the noble gases are quite stable in their elemental forms.

EXAMPLE 8.7

Predict what will happen when helium is treated with oxygen gas.

Solution

Nothing will happen; helium is too stable to react. In equation format,

$$He + O_2 \rightarrow N.R. \qquad \textit{(N.R. stands for "no reaction.")}$$

Practice Problem 8.7 Predict the products of the reaction, if any, of aluminum metal with zinc metal.

In another type of combination reaction, a compound may be able to combine with a particular free element to form another compound as the only product. This occurs most often when the free element is the same as one of the elements in the original compound. An example of such a combination reaction is

$$2 CrCl_2(s) + Cl_2(g) \rightarrow 2 CrCl_3(s)$$

Here, the element chlorine combines with a compound of chromium and chlorine—chromium(II) chloride—to form another compound of chromium and chlorine—chromium(III) chloride—in which the chromium ion has a different positive charge.

In yet another type of combination reaction, two compounds containing the same element may be able to combine to form a single, more complex compound. The element the reactants have in common is very often oxygen:

$$MgO(s) + CO_2(g) \rightarrow MgCO_3(s)$$

$$CaO(s) + H_2O(\ell) \rightarrow Ca(OH)_2(s)$$

Decomposition Reactions

Decomposition reactions have the opposite effect from combination reactions. In a decomposition reaction, a single compound can decompose to two elements, to an element and a simpler compound, to two simpler compounds, or (rarely) to another combination of products. **Ternary compounds,** compounds containing three elements, do not decompose into three uncombined elements. Decomposition reactions are easy to identify because there is only one reactant. Table 8.1 summarizes the most common types of decomposition reactions.

Table 8.1 Common Types of Decomposition Reactions

Reactant	Products	Example
Binary compound	→ Two elements	$2 H_2O \xrightarrow{\text{Electricity}} 2 H_2 + O_2$
Binary compound	→ Compound + element	$2 H_2O_2 \rightarrow 2 H_2O + O_2$
Ternary compound	→ Compound + element	$2 KClO_3 \xrightarrow{\text{Heat}} 2 KCl + 3 O_2$
Ternary compound	→ Two compounds	$CaCO_3 \xrightarrow{\text{Heat}} CaO + CO_2$

Input of energy in some form is usually required to get a compound to decompose:

$$2\,H_2O(\ell) \xrightarrow[\text{Na}_2\text{SO}_4(\text{aq})]{\text{Electricity}} 2\,H_2(g) + O_2(g)$$
Two elements

$$2\,H_2O_2(\ell) \xrightarrow{\text{Light}} 2\,H_2O(\ell) + O_2(g)$$
A simpler compound and an element

$$CaCO_3(s) \xrightarrow{\text{Heat}} CaO(s) + CO_2(g)$$
Two simpler compounds

To get compounds to decompose using electricity, ions must be present, and the sample must be in some liquid form. (Electricity does not pass through solid ionic compounds, even though they are composed of positive and negative ions.) The ions in a liquid are free to move and thus conduct the current. The liquid can be a **molten** (melted) ionic substance or a solution of an ionic substance in water or another liquid (Figure 8.3). If a solution is used, the compound that is more easily decomposed (the ionic compound or the water, for example) is the one that will react.

Note in the previous equations that the formulas of elemental hydrogen and oxygen are written as diatomic molecules: H_2 and O_2. Before equations are balanced, the formulas for all reactants and products must be written according to the rules given in Chapter 5.

Figure 8.3 *Electrolysis Reaction*

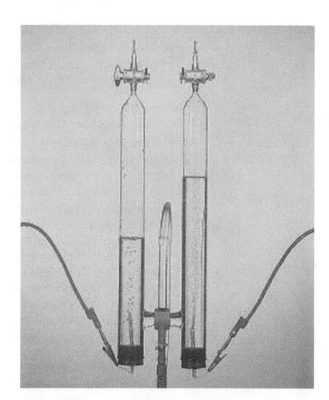

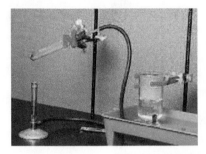

Figure 8.4 Decomposition of Potassium Chlorate

Decomposition reactions are often used to prepare elements. Joseph Priestley (1733–1804), the discoverer of oxygen, used the decomposition of mercury(II) oxide, HgO, to prepare elemental oxygen (and free mercury):

$$2\,HgO(s) \xrightarrow{Heat} 2\,Hg(\ell) + O_2(g)$$

Students often decompose potassium chlorate to produce oxygen in the laboratory (Figure 8.4). This reaction is usually carried out by heating that compound in the presence of manganese(IV) oxide, MnO_2. The MnO_2 is a **catalyst**—a substance that changes the speed of a chemical reaction without undergoing a permanent change in its own composition. A catalyst is conventionally written above or below the reaction arrow:

$$2\,KClO_3(s) \xrightarrow[Heat]{MnO_2} 2\,KCl(s) + 3\,O_2(g)$$

Single Substitution Reactions

The reaction of a free element with a compound of two (or more) other elements may result in the free element displacing one of the elements originally in the compound. A free metal can generally displace a less active metal in a compound; a free nonmetal can generally displace a less active nonmetal in a compound:

$$Cu(s) + 2\,AgNO_3(aq) \rightarrow Cu(NO_3)_2(aq) + 2\,Ag(s)$$
Copper (metal) displaces silver (metal).

$$Cl_2(g) + CaI_2(aq) \rightarrow CaCl_2(aq) + I_2(s)$$
Chlorine (nonmetal) displaces iodine (nonmetal).

In this class of reaction, called a **single displacement reaction,** or **single substitution reaction,** elements that are inherently more reactive can displace less reactive elements from their compounds, but the opposite process does not occur:

$$Ag(s) + Cu(NO_3)_2(aq) \rightarrow N.R. \qquad \textit{(N.R. stands for "no reaction")}$$

Chemicals tend to react to go to a more stable, lower energy state. When copper reacts with silver nitrate, $AgNO_3$, the system goes to a lower energy state. When an aqueous solution of copper(II) nitrate, $Cu(NO_3)_2$, is treated with silver metal, these chemicals are already in the lower energy state, so they have no tendency to produce copper metal and silver nitrate. We say that copper is more **active,** or more **reactive,** than silver, which indicates that it has a greater tendency to leave its elemental state and form compounds. This is due to atoms of copper having a greater tendency to lose electrons than those of silver do.

To predict which single substitution reactions will occur, we need to know a little about the *relative* reactivities of some of the important metals and nonmetals. Some metals and a few nonmetals are listed in Table 8.2 in order of decreasing reactivity. A more complete list is given in Section 17.2. Hydrogen is included in the list of metals because it can be displaced from aqueous acids by reactive metals (Figure 8.5) and can displace less active metals from their compounds:

$$Zn(s) + 2\,HCl(aq) \rightarrow H_2(g) + ZnCl_2(aq)$$

$$H_2(g) + CuCl_2(aq) \rightarrow Cu(s) + 2\,HCl(aq)$$

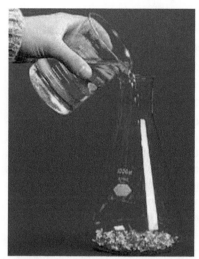

Table 8.2 Relative Reactivities of Uncombined Elements

	Metals	Nonmetals	
Most active	Alkali metals and	F_2	*Most active*
	alkaline earth metals	O_2	
	Al	Cl_2	
	Mn		
	Zn		
	Cr		
	Fe	Br_2	
	Sn		
	Pb		
	H*	I_2	*Less active*
	Cu		
	Ag		
Least active	Au		

*Hydrogen is included in the list of metals because it can be displaced from aqueous acids by reactive metals.

Very active metals can even displace hydrogen from water:

$$Ba(s) + 2 H_2O(\ell) \rightarrow Ba(OH)_2(aq) + H_2(g)$$

EXAMPLE 8.8

Using data from Table 8.2, predict which of the following pairs of substances will react. If they will react, write a balanced equation for the reaction. If they will not react, write N.R. on the right-hand side of the arrow.

(a) $Mn(s)$ and $Zn(NO_3)_2(aq)$ (b) $Ag(s)$ and $Pb(NO_3)_2(aq)$

(c) $HCl(aq)$ and $Cr(s)$ (d) $Sn(s)$ and $CuSO_4(aq)$

(e) $Ag(s)$ and $HC_2H_3O_2(aq)$

Solution

(a) $Mn(s) + Zn(NO_3)_2(aq) \rightarrow Mn(NO_3)_2(aq) + Zn(s)$

(b) $Ag(s) + Pb(NO_3)_2(aq) \rightarrow N.R.$ (Ag is less active than Pb.)

(c) $2 HCl(aq) + Cr(s) \rightarrow H_2(g) + CrCl_2(aq)$

(d) $Sn(s) + CuSO_4(aq) \rightarrow SnSO_4(aq) + Cu(s)$

(e) $Ag(s) + HC_2H_3O_2(aq) \rightarrow N.R.$ (Ag is less active than H.)

Practice Problem 8.8 Predict whether each of the following pairs of substances will react. If they will react, write a balanced equation for the reaction. If they will not react, write N.R. on the right-hand side of the arrow.

(a) $Ba(s)$ and $Al_2O_3(s)$ plus heat (b) $NaF(aq)$ and $Cl_2(g)$

Figure 8.5 Reaction of Zinc Metal with Hydrochloric Acid

Copper, silver, and gold—the coinage metals—have long been prized for their **stability,** or lack of reactivity (Figure 8.6). They can even occur uncombined in nature. Active metals do not occur naturally as free elements.

Double Substitution Reactions

The reaction of two compounds may yield two new compounds. Many reactions that occur in aqueous solution involve two ionic compounds trading anions. This class of reactions is called **double substitution reactions, double displacement reactions,** or **metathesis reactions.** As usual, the correct formulas must be written for the products before the equation is balanced. In a double substitution reaction, if the ions are not converted to covalent compounds, their charges do not change as they are converted from reactants to products.

> In a double substitution reaction, if the ions are not converted to covalent compounds, their charges do not change when they are converted from reactants to products.

EXAMPLE 8.9

Predict the products for reactions of the following pairs of reactants, and write balanced equations:

(a) Aqueous barium nitrate and aqueous iron(II) sulfate

(b) Aqueous iron(II) chloride and aqueous silver acetate

(c) Solid calcium hydroxide and aqueous hydrochloric acid

Solution

First, write the names of the products:

(a) Barium nitrate plus iron(II) sulfate yields barium sulfate plus iron(II) nitrate. The Ba^{2+} and Fe^{2+} cations trade anions.

(b) Iron(II) chloride plus silver acetate yields iron(II) acetate plus silver chloride. Here, the cations also trade anions; however, the Fe^{2+} ion requires two singly charged anions to satisfy its dipositive charge. Note that the iron ion had a 2+ charge and still has that charge. Iron(III) nitrate is not expected as a product, because the Fe^{2+} ion does not change to a Fe^{3+} ion in this type of reaction.

(c) Calcium hydroxide plus hydrochloric acid yields calcium chloride plus water. The charge on the calcium ion remains the same throughout the reaction; the charge on the hydrogen ion changes because the water formed is covalent, not ionic.

Next, write correct formulas for all reactants and products:

(a) $Ba(NO_3)_2(aq) + FeSO_4(aq) \rightarrow BaSO_4(s) + Fe(NO_3)_2(aq)$

(b) $FeCl_2(aq) + AgC_2H_3O_2(aq) \rightarrow Fe(C_2H_3O_2)_2(aq) + AgCl(s)$

(c) $Ca(OH)_2(s) + HCl(aq) \rightarrow CaCl_2(aq) + H_2O(\ell)$

Finally, balance the equations:

(a) $Ba(NO_3)_2(aq) + FeSO_4(aq) \rightarrow BaSO_4(s) + Fe(NO_3)_2(aq)$

(b) $FeCl_2(aq) + 2\,AgC_2H_3O_2(aq) \rightarrow Fe(C_2H_3O_2)_2(aq) + 2\,AgCl(s)$

(c) $Ca(OH)_2(s) + 2\,HNO_3(aq) \rightarrow Ca(NO_3)_2(aq) + 2\,H_2O(\ell)$

Figure 8.6   *Gold, Silver, and Copper Coins*

Silver tarnishes slowly in air to form silver sulfide, Ag_2S; it is more reactive than gold. Although copper is also used in coins, it is more reactive than the other coinage metals. Copper coins tarnish or corrode relatively quickly.

Practice Problem 8.9 Complete and balance the equation for each of the following reactions:

(a) $Ba(OH)_2(aq) + HC_2H_3O_2(aq) \rightarrow$ (b) $AlCl_3(aq) + AgNO_3(aq) \rightarrow$

In aqueous solution, neither H_2CO_3 (carbonic acid) nor NH_4OH (ammonium hydroxide) is stable; they decompose to yield water and CO_2 or NH_3 respectively. If either H_2CO_3 or NH_4OH is expected to be a product of a double substitution reaction, CO_2 plus H_2O, or NH_3 plus H_2O, will be produced instead. Other unstable compounds are encountered much less frequently.

EXAMPLE 8.10

Predict the products of the following reactions:

(a) $Li_2CO_3(aq) + HClO_3(aq) \rightarrow$ (b) $NH_4Cl(aq) + NaOH(aq) \rightarrow$

Solution

(a) Ordinarily, we would predict that the ions will trade partners to yield $LiClO_3$ and H_2CO_3. However, water and carbon dioxide are produced instead of H_2CO_3:

$$Li_2CO_3(aq) + 2\,HClO_3(aq) \rightarrow 2\,LiClO_3(aq) + H_2O(\ell) + CO_2(g)$$

(b) Ordinarily, we would predict that the ions will trade partners to yield $NaCl$ and NH_4OH. However, instead of ammonium hydroxide, water and ammonia are produced:

$$NH_4Cl(aq) + NaOH(aq) \rightarrow NaCl(aq) + H_2O(\ell) + NH_3(aq)$$

Practice Problem 8.10 Complete and balance the following equations:

(a) $(NH_4)_2CO_3(aq) + HClO_4(aq) \rightarrow$ (b) $(NH_4)_2CO_3(aq) + NaOH(aq) \rightarrow$

Table 8.3 Water Solubility of Some Common Ionic Compounds

Soluble in Water	Insoluble in Water
All chlorates	$BaSO_4$
All acetates	Most oxides
All nitrates	Most sulfides
All compounds of alkali metals	Most phosphates
All compounds containing the ammonium ion	
All chlorides except those listed in the next column	$AgCl$, $PbCl_2$, Hg_2Cl_2, and $CuCl$

The driving force behind double substitution reactions is the formation of a covalent compound (including water or a gaseous compound) or an insoluble ionic compound from ions in solution. A solid formed from ions in solution is called a **precipitate**. We can thus predict that a reaction will occur if soluble ionic compounds yield at least one insoluble ionic compound or one covalent compound. We need to be familiar with the **solubilities** of some common ionic compounds in water. Some types of ionic compounds that are soluble or insoluble in water are listed in Table 8.3. A more comprehensive tabulation of solubilities is presented in Table 8.4 for reference, not necessarily to be memorized.

EXAMPLE 8.11

Complete and balance the equation for each of the following reactions:

(a) $Ba(NO_3)_2(aq) + (NH_4)_2SO_4(aq) \rightarrow$

(b) $Pb(NO_3)_2(aq) + MgCl_2(aq) \rightarrow$

Table 8.4   Solubility Reference Table*

	ClO_3^- NO_3^- $C_2H_3O_2^-$	Cl^- Br^- I^-	SO_4^{2-}	CO_3^{2-} SO_3^{2-} PO_4^{3-} CrO_4^{2-} BO_3^{3-}	S^{2-}	OH^-	O^{2-}
Pb^{2+}	s	ss-i	i	i	i	i	i
Na^+, K^+, NH_4^+	s	s	s	s	s	s	d
Hg_2^{2+}	s	i	i	i	i	i	i
Hg^{2+}	s	s-i**	s	i	i	i	i
Ag^+	s	i	ss	i	i	i	i
Mg^{2+}	s	s	s	s	s	i	i
Ca^{2+}	s	s	i	i	s	s	d
Ba^{2+}	s	s	i	i	s	s	d

Key: s = soluble (greater than about 1 g solute/100 g of water)
   ss = slightly soluble (approximately 0.1–1 g solute/100 g of water)
   i = insoluble (less than about 0.1 g solute/100 g of water)
   d = decomposes in water
*Memorize this Table only if directed to do so by your instructor.
**$HgCl_2$ is soluble, $HgBr_2$ is less soluble, and HgI_2 is insoluble

Solution

(a) We see from Table 8.3 that $BaSO_4$ is insoluble in water. Thus, the following reaction will occur:

$$Ba(NO_3)_2(aq) + (NH_4)_2SO_4(aq) \rightarrow BaSO_4(s) + 2\,NH_4NO_3(aq)$$

Barium sulfate precipitates.

(b) $Pb(NO_3)_2(aq) + MgCl_2(aq) \rightarrow PbCl_2(s) + Mg(NO_3)_2(aq)$

Lead(II) chloride is insoluble in cold water (and only slightly soluble in hot water).

Practice Problem 8.11   Complete and balance the equation for each of the following reactions:

(a) $Li_2O(s) + H_2SO_4(aq) \rightarrow$ (b) $LiHCO_3(aq) + HBr(aq) \rightarrow$

In addition to learning the solubility rules, we also must be familiar with the nature of the bonding in compounds to be able to predict if double substitution reactions will proceed as written. We learned in Chapter 5 that covalent compounds have no metallic elements, and no ammonium ion in them. It might be helpful to note that formation of a covalent compound includes

(a) Formation of a gas (All gases at room temperature are covalent.)

(b) Formation of water

(c) Formation of a *weak* acid or *weak* base. (Weak acids and bases in solution are more than 95% covalent. They will be discussed in Section 8.4.) Weak acids include all acids *except* HCl, $HClO_3$, $HClO_4$, HBr, HI, HNO_3, and H_2SO_4. These acids are *strong,* that is, they are completely ionic in water solution. The weak base that we will focus on is ammonia, NH_3.

EXAMPLE 8.12

Complete and balance the following equations:

(a) $NaC_2H_3O_2(aq) + HNO_3(aq) \rightarrow$

(b) $Na_2CO_3(aq) + HNO_3(aq) \rightarrow$

Solution

(a) $NaC_2H_3O_2(aq) + HNO_3(aq) \rightarrow NaNO_3(aq) + HC_2H_3O_2(aq)$

HNO_3 is strong, and thus ionic. The salts are also ionic. However, acetic acid, $HC_2H_3O_2$, is weak, and the formation of this covalent compound causes this reaction to go.

(b) $Na_2CO_3(aq) + 2\,HNO_3(aq) \rightarrow 2\,NaNO_3(aq) + CO_2(g) + H_2O(\ell)$

The formation of the covalent compounds $CO_2(g)$ and $H_2O(\ell)$ drives this reaction. CO_2 is readily seen to be covalent because it is a gas.

Practice Problem 8.12   Complete and balance the following equations:

(a) $NH_4NO_3(aq) + NaOH(aq) \rightarrow$

(b) $NH_4I(aq) + Ba(OH)_2(aq) \rightarrow$

●●●●●●●●●●●●●●●●●●●●●●●●●

ITEM OF INTEREST

An industrial process called the *Solvay process* uses the following set of reactions to produce Na_2CO_3 (known as washing soda). The reactants are inexpensive, and Na_2CO_3 is a very important industrial compound used in the manufacture of soap, glass, paper, detergents, and other chemicals.

$$CaCO_3(s) \xrightarrow{\text{Heat}} CaO(s) + CO_2(g)$$

$$2\,CO_2(g) + 2\,H_2O(\ell) + 2\,NH_3(aq) \rightarrow 2\,NH_4HCO_3(aq)$$

$$2\,NaCl(aq) + 2\,NH_4HCO_3(aq) \rightarrow 2\,NaHCO_3(s) + 2\,NH_4Cl(aq)$$

Very concentrated solutions

$$2\,NaHCO_3(s) \xrightarrow{\text{Heat}} Na_2CO_3(s) + CO_2(g) + H_2O(\ell)$$

$$CaO(s) + H_2O(\ell) \rightarrow Ca(OH)_2(s)$$

$$2\,NH_4Cl(aq) + Ca(OH)_2(s) \rightarrow 2\,NH_3(aq) + 2\,H_2O(\ell) + CaCl_2(aq)$$

If we add all the reactants and all the products in these equations and then delete the compounds that appear on both sides, we get the following overall equation:

$$CaCO_3 + 2\,NaCl \rightarrow Na_2CO_3 + CaCl_2$$

EXAMPLE 8.13

Can industrial chemists simply combine $CaCO_3$ and $NaCl$ to get Na_2CO_3 and $CaCl_2$?

Solution

The proposed reactants are more stable than the desired products because $CaCO_3$ is insoluble in water, and Na_2CO_3 and $CaCl_2$ are both soluble. Thus, this direct reaction is not feasible.

EXAMPLE 8.14

What type of reaction is each of the steps of the Solvay process?

Solution

In the order shown, the six reactions are classed as (1) decomposition, (2) combination, (3) double substitution, (4) decomposition, (5) combination, and (6) double substitution followed by decomposition.

Combustion Reactions

Everyone is familiar with the process called *burning*. Burning, also called **combustion,** is the rapid reaction of a wide variety of materials with oxygen gas. Combustion reactions of elements can also be classified as combination reactions; the *type* of reaction is not as important as the *products*. For example, we can refer to the following reactions as combination reactions or combustion reactions:

$$C(s) + O_2(g) \rightarrow CO_2(g)$$

$$S(s) + O_2(g) \rightarrow SO_2(g)$$

The combustion reactions of **hydrocarbons**—compounds composed of carbon and hydrogen only—are especially important as sources of useful energy. We burn methane, CH_4, called natural gas, in our homes to provide heat, and we combust octane, C_8H_{18}, in our cars to provide mechanical energy:

$$CH_4(g) + 2\,O_2(g) \rightarrow CO_2(g) + 2\,H_2O(g)$$

$$2\,C_8H_{18}(\ell) + 17\,O_2(g) \rightarrow 16\,CO(g) + 18\,H_2O(g)$$

In such reactions, either carbon monoxide or carbon dioxide may be produced, in addition to water. If sufficient oxygen is present, carbon dioxide is produced. If the supply of oxygen is limited, as in a car engine, carbon monoxide is the product. (With very limited oxygen, soot—a form of carbon—and water are produced.) *In any case, water is a product.*

Water is one product of the combustion of hydrocarbons.

EXAMPLE 8.15

Which of the following reactions was carried out in a limited supply of oxygen?

$$2\,C_6H_{14}(\ell) + 19\,O_2(g) \rightarrow 12\,CO_2(g) + 14\,H_2O(g)$$

$$2\,C_6H_{10}(\ell) + 11\,O_2(g) \rightarrow 12\,CO(g) + 10\,H_2O(g)$$

Solution

The reaction of C_6H_{10} produced CO, so that reaction was run in limited oxygen. If the combustion reaction of C_6H_{10} is carried out in excess oxygen, the equation is written as follows:

$$2\,C_6H_{10}(\ell) + 17\,O_2(g) \rightarrow 12\,CO_2(g) + 10\,H_2O(g)$$

Practice Problem 8.15   What will be the effect if between 11 and 17 mol of oxygen is available for the combustion of 2 mol of C_6H_{10}?

EXAMPLE 8.16

Write a balanced equation for the reaction of butyne, C_4H_6, in a limited oxygen supply.

Solution

$$2\,C_4H_6(g) + 7\,O_2(g) \rightarrow 8\,CO(g) + 6\,H_2O(g)$$

The combustion reactions of compounds containing carbon, hydrogen, and oxygen (which include the carbohydrates we use for food) also produce either carbon monoxide or carbon dioxide, depending on the relative quantity of oxygen available.

EXAMPLE 8.17

Write a complete and balanced equation for the reaction of sucrose, table sugar, $C_{12}H_{22}O_{11}$, in a limited supply of oxygen.

Solution

$$C_{12}H_{22}O_{11}(s) + 6\,O_2(g) \rightarrow 12\,CO(g) + 11\,H_2O(g)$$

Practice Problem 8.17   Write a complete and balanced equation for the combustion reaction of sucrose with excess oxygen.

Snapshot Review

ChemSkill Builder
5.1, 5.2, 5.4, 5.5, 5.6

❏ We must classify chemical reactions into types in order to have a chance to predict the products given the reactants. Five simple types are given here, with which it should be fairly easy to make educated guesses as to the correct products. Be sure to practice these problems repeatedly.

A. Complete and balance the following equations:

   (a) $BaO(s) + H_2O(\ell) \rightarrow$

   (b) $Al(s) + H_2SO_4(aq) \rightarrow$

   (c) $HCl(aq, excess) + Na_2CO_3(aq) \rightarrow$

8.4 Acids and Bases

There is another common way to classify chemical reactions: acid-base reactions, oxidation-reduction reactions, and reactions of more complicated types (beyond the scope of this book). Acid-base reactions are considered to involve the reactions of hydrogen ions with hydroxide ions. The reactions of acids and bases will be taken up in this section, and a more sophisticated view of these reactions is presented in Chapter 19. Oxidation-reduction reactions involve the transfer of electrons from one substance to another. Many combination reactions, many decomposition reactions, all single substitution reactions, and all combustion reactions are of this type, but more complex examples are presented in Chapters 16 and 17.

The reactions of acids with active metals fit into the single substitution class discussed in Section 8.3. Reactions of acids with bases are double substitution reactions, also discussed in Section 8.3. However, the reactions of acids and bases are so important that they have a special terminology that we need to know.

According to the most fundamental theory concerning acids and bases—the **Arrhenius theory**—an **acid** is a compound that furnishes hydrogen ions, H^+, to an aqueous solution, and a **base** is a compound that furnishes hydroxide ions, OH^-, to an aqueous solution. The hydrogen ion does not exist alone, as H^+, but is stable in aqueous solution in the form H_3O^+, which is frequently represented as $H^+(aq)$.

In beginning courses, formulas for acids (and no other compounds except water and hydrogen peroxide) are written with the ionizable hydrogen atoms first, as in HCl.

$$HCl(g) \xrightarrow{H_2O} H^+(aq) + Cl^-(aq)$$

Methane, CH_4, ammonia, NH_3, and sucrose (table sugar), $C_{12}H_{22}O_{11}$, are examples of compounds that are not acids because they do not provide hydrogen ions to aqueous solutions. Their hydrogen atoms are therefore not written first in their formulas. For certain acids, such as acetic acid, $HC_2H_3O_2$, and citric acid, $H_3C_6H_5O_7$, only the hydrogen atom(s) written first is (are) capable of being ionized; the other hydrogen atoms do not yield H^+ in solution.

Properties of Acids and Bases

Caution: Do not taste chemicals unless specifically directed to do so by your instructor.

Caution: Never touch concentrated solutions of strong bases, such as liquid Drano, because they are capable of dissolving the fat in the skin.

Acids in general have a sour taste, turn indicators (Section 11.3) certain colors, and react with bases to form salts. For example, the sour taste of lemon is the taste of citric acid, and the sour taste of vinegar is due mainly to acetic acid, its principal acid component. Simple acids have one or more hydrogen atoms per molecule.

Bases feel slippery, turn indicators certain colors that differ from those acids produce, and react with acids to form salts. We may experience the slipperiness of a base by putting our fingertips in some dilute ammonia water. Simple bases contain one or more hydroxide ions or are able to react with water to some extent to form hydroxide ions. For example, ammonia is a base because of the following reaction:

$$NH_3(aq) + H_2O(\ell) \rightarrow NH_4^+(aq) + OH^-(aq) \qquad (0.1\% \text{ to } 2\%)$$

Figure 8.7 Neutralization Reaction

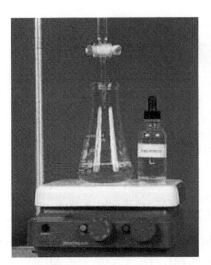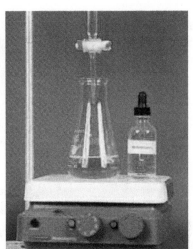

Double Substitution Reactions of Acids and Bases

The most important reactions of acids and bases are their reactions with each other to form salts and water:

$$HNO_3(aq) + NaOH(aq) \rightarrow NaNO_3(aq) + H_2O(\ell)$$

An acid   A base   A salt   Water

A **salt** is any compound of a cation other than H^+ with an anion other than OH^- or O^{2-}. [The word "salt" in everyday conversation means sodium chloride (table salt), which is only one example of a salt under this definition.] Such reactions, actually specific examples of double substitution reactions, are called **neutralization reactions** (Figure 8.7) because they produce products that are more neutral than acids or bases. **Neutral** means "neither acidic nor basic."

● ●

ITEM OF INTEREST

Many individual compounds that are acids have additional properties that make them dangerous. These dangerous compounds give acids a bad name to the general public. For example, LSD (lysergic acid diethylamide) is a mind-affecting hallucinogenic agent, but this property is in addition to any acid properties of the compound. Concentrated sulfuric acid, used in auto batteries, is a powerful oxidizing agent and dehydrating agent. A lump of sugar placed into concentrated sulfuric acid has the elements of water pulled from its molecules, leaving carbon (Figure 8.8):

$$C_{12}H_{22}O_{11}(s) \xrightarrow[H_2SO_4]{\text{Concentrated}} 12\ C(s) + 11\ H_2O(\text{in } H_2SO_4 \text{ solution}) + heat$$

Nitric acid, especially when concentrated but even in dilute solution, is another powerful oxidizing agent. In contrast, boric acid is such a weak acid that it is sometimes used in solution to bathe infected eyes.

Figure 8.8 Dehydration of Sugar by Sulfuric Acid

EXAMPLE 8.18

Which one(s) of the following is (are) acids?

(a) $C_{12}H_{22}O_{11}$ (b) $H_2C_2O_4$ (c) NH_2OH

(d) $HC_4H_7O_2$ (e) H_2SO_3

Solution

(b), (d), and (e) are acids; they are the only ones with hydrogen written first in the formula. The $HC_4H_7O_2$ has additional hydrogen atoms that do not react with bases; that is why they are not included with the H atom at the beginning of the formula.

Common Strong Acids
HCl
HBr
HI
$HClO_3$
$HClO_4$
HNO_3
H_2SO_4

All hydrogen-containing acids are covalent compounds when they are not in solution; they ionize when they react with water:

$$HX(\ell \text{ or } g) + H_2O(\ell) \rightarrow H^+(aq) + X^-(aq)$$

Those that react nearly 100% to form ions are called **strong acids.** Those that react only to a limited extent are called **weak acids.** The common strong acids are HCl, HBr, HI, $HClO_3$, $HClO_4$, HNO_3, and H_2SO_4. Practically all other acids are weak.

Thus double substitution reactions will go to form weak acids or bases—compounds that are mainly covalent even in water solution—but they will not go to form strong acids or bases in water solution.

EXAMPLE 8.19

Which of the following reactions will proceed?

(a) $HF(aq) + NaBr(aq) \rightarrow HBr(aq) + NaF(aq)$

(b) $NaF(aq) + HBr(aq) \rightarrow NaBr(aq) + HF(aq)$

Solution

(b) This reaction takes place because the largely covalent HF is formed from the H^+ and F^- ions in solution. The HBr(aq) is fully ionized—it is a strong acid—and NaF is also ionic, containing Na^+ and F^- ions. Reaction (a) does not go because ions would be formed by reaction of a mainly covalent compound.

Practice Problem 8.19 Predict whether the following reaction will proceed:

$$NaC_2H_3O_2(aq) + HCl(aq) \rightarrow$$

Bases provide hydroxide ions to aqueous solution. Soluble metal hydroxides, including those of the alkali metals and barium, are examples. The soluble metal hydroxides are ionic even when they are pure solids; *they remain ionic in water.* When they are dissolved in water, the hydroxide ions are totally separated from the metal ions. A soluble metal hydroxide is a **strong base. A weak base** is not 100% ionized. Ammonia, the most common weak base, reacts with water to a small extent to provide hydroxide ions:

$$NH_3(aq) + H_2O(\ell) \rightarrow NH_4^+(aq) + OH^-(aq) \quad \text{(Usually from 0.1\% to 2\%)}$$

For example, if 1.00 mol of NH_3 is dissolved in a liter of water, only 0.004 mol of NH_4^+ and 0.004 mol of OH^- will be present. Almost all (0.996 mol) of the NH_3 remains in its molecular form.

Weak acids and weak bases react with water to a small extent but they react with strong bases or acids essentially completely:

$$KOH(aq) + HC_2H_3O_2(aq) \rightarrow KC_2H_3O_2(aq) + H_2O(\ell)$$

$$HBr(aq) + NH_3(aq) \rightarrow NH_4Br(aq)$$

A strong acid and a strong base react with each other completely to form a salt and water:

$$HBr(aq) + KOH(aq) \rightarrow KBr(aq) + H_2O(\ell)$$

The driving force for double substitution reactions is formation of insoluble ionic compounds or covalent compounds from ions in solution. However, if an equation has an insoluble compound on one side and a covalent compound on the other, which way does the reaction go? In many cases like this, the formation of covalent compounds is more important than the formation of insoluble ionic compounds, as shown by the reaction of $Ba(OH)_2$ with HCl. Acids usually react with insoluble bases to produce salts and water:

$$Ba(OH)_2(s) + 2 HCl(aq) \rightarrow BaCl_2(aq) + 2 H_2O(\ell)$$

Single Substitution Reactions of Acids

Acids can react with metals more active than hydrogen (see Table 8.2) to produce a salt and hydrogen gas:

$$Zn(s) + 2 HCl(aq) \rightarrow ZnCl_2(aq) + H_2(g)$$

Extremely active metals, such as the alkali and alkaline earth metals, can even react with water to produce hydrogen gas plus the corresponding metal hydroxide. For example:

$$2 Na(s) + 2 H_2O(\ell) \rightarrow 2 NaOH(aq) + H_2(g) \quad \text{(Caution: Potentially explosive)}$$

Acidic and Basic Anhydrides

Most metal oxides in which the metal ion has a 1+ or 2+ charge are **basic anhydrides,** and most nonmetal oxides are **acidic anhydrides.** In general, an

Anhydrides are like instant coffee; add water to get the acid or base.

anhydride is any compound that can result by loss of water from another compound. If water is added to an acidic anhydride, the anhydride becomes an acid. For example, sulfur dioxide plus water yields sulfurous acid:

$$SO_2(g) + H_2O(\ell) \rightarrow H_2SO_3(aq)$$

If water is added to a basic anhydride, the anhydride becomes a base. For example, barium oxide plus water yields barium hydroxide:

$$BaO(s) + H_2O(\ell) \rightarrow Ba(OH)_2(aq)$$

The first of the previous reactions is responsible for a good portion of the acid rain problem troubling the industrialized world. Sulfur, present in small quantities as an impurity in coal and oil, is converted to sulfur dioxide when the coal or oil is burned; then the sulfur dioxide reacts with the moisture in the air to produce sulfurous acid. Sulfurous acid can react with the oxygen in air to produce sulfuric acid. These acids are washed from the air by rain (or snow), and the solution can cause some corrosion of concrete and metal in buildings. Acids in the air and in the rain or snow also injure trees and other plants, as well as animals, including humans. In high concentrations, acids and acid anhydrides in the air can make breathing difficult, especially for people who are already in poor health.

Acidic anhydrides can react directly with bases, and basic anhydrides can react directly with acids. The same salt is produced as would be produced by the acid and base:

$$SO_2(g) + 2\,NaOH(aq) \rightarrow Na_2SO_3(aq) + H_2O(\ell)$$

$$MgO(s) + 2\,HCl(aq) \rightarrow MgCl_2(aq) + H_2O(\ell)$$

An acidic anhydride and a basic anhydride can even react with each other in a combination reaction:

$$SO_2(g) + MgO(s) \rightarrow MgSO_3(s)$$

EXAMPLE 8.20

Complete and balance an equation for each of the following reactions, and explain the relationships among the four.
(a) $H_2SO_4 + Ca(OH)_2 \rightarrow$
(b) $H_2SO_4 + CaO \rightarrow$
(c) $SO_3 + Ca(OH)_2$
(d) $SO_3 + CaO \rightarrow$

Solution

(a) $H_2SO_4 + Ca(OH)_2 \rightarrow CaSO_4 + 2\,H_2O$
(b) $H_2SO_4 + CaO \rightarrow CaSO_4 + H_2O$
(c) $SO_3 + Ca(OH)_2 \rightarrow CaSO_4 + H_2O$
(d) $SO_3 + CaO \rightarrow CaSO_4$

The reaction of an acid and a base yields a salt and water. The reaction of the acid or base with the anhydride of the other yields the same salt but less water, and the reaction of the two anhydrides yields the same salt but no water.

Practice Problem 8.20   Classify the reactions of parts (a) and (d) of Example 8.20 according to the classes of Section 8.3.

EXAMPLE 8.21

Complete and balance an equation for each of the following reactions:

(a) $N_2O_3 + H_2O \rightarrow$

(b) $Na_2O + H_2O \rightarrow$

Solution

(a) $N_2O_3 + H_2O \rightarrow 2\,HNO_2$

(b) $Na_2O + H_2O \rightarrow 2\,NaOH$

Practice Problem 8.21   Complete and balance an equation for each of the following reactions:

(a) $N_2O_3 + NaOH \rightarrow$

(b) $Na_2O + HNO_3 \rightarrow$

A few nonmetal oxides, including CO and N_2O, are not acidic anhydrides; they do not react with water under ordinary conditions to form acids or with bases to form salts:

$$CO(g) + H_2O(\ell) \xrightarrow[\text{Room temperature}]{} N.R.$$

$$CO(g) + NaOH(aq) \rightarrow N.R.$$

$$N_2O(g) + H_2O(\ell) \rightarrow N.R.$$

Acid Salts

Acids containing more than one ionizable hydrogen atom, such as H_2SO_3 and H_3PO_4, can be *partially* neutralized if less base is used than is needed for complete neutralization. The salt formed contains ionizable hydrogen atoms and therefore is still capable of reacting with bases:

$H_3PO_4(aq) + NaOH(aq) \rightarrow NaH_2PO_4(aq) + H_2O(\ell)$ *(Partial neutralization)*

$H_3PO_4(aq) + 2\,NaOH(aq) \rightarrow Na_2HPO_4(aq) + 2\,H_2O(\ell)$ *(Partial neutralization)*

$H_3PO_4(aq) + 3\,NaOH(aq) \rightarrow Na_3PO_4(aq) + 3\,H_2O(\ell)$ *(Complete neutralization)*

A substance produced by a partial neutralization, such as NaH_2PO_4 or Na_2HPO_4, is partially a salt and partially an acid. As the product of an acid and a base, it is a salt. However, it is capable of neutralizing more base, so it can also act as an acid:

$$NaH_2PO_4(aq) + NaOH(aq) \rightarrow Na_2HPO_4(aq) + H_2O(\ell)$$

$$NaH_2PO_4(aq) + 2\,NaOH(aq) \rightarrow Na_3PO_4(aq) + 2\,H_2O(\ell)$$

or

$$Na_2HPO_4(aq) + NaOH(aq) \rightarrow Na_3PO_4(aq) + H_2O(\ell)$$

Such a substance is called an **acid salt.** The name of the compound includes the word *hydrogen* to denote the fact that one or more ionizable hydrogen atoms remain. The prefix *mono-* or *di-* may be used when it is necessary to indicate how many hydrogen atoms are present:

NaH_2PO_4 Sodium dihydrogen phosphate

Na_2HPO_4 Sodium monohydrogen phosphate (or disodium hydrogen phosphate)

$NaHCO_3$ Sodium hydrogen carbonate

In an older nomenclature system, the word "acid" was used to denote an acid salt. In another old system, the prefix *bi-* was used for a half-neutralized acid that originally contained two ionizable hydrogen atoms. Thus, sodium bicarbonate and sodium acid carbonate are other names that have been used for $NaHCO_3$.

In the anion of an acid salt, the number of hydrogen atoms plus the magnitude of the charge on the ion equals the magnitude of the charge on the oxoanion and also equals the number of hydrogen atoms in the acid:

PO_4^{3-} The zero hydrogen atoms plus 3 negative charges on the phosphate ion equals 3.

HPO_4^{2-} 1 hydrogen atom plus 2 negative charges equals 3.

$H_2PO_4^{-}$ 2 hydrogen atoms plus 1 negative charge equals 3.

H_3PO_4 3 hydrogen atoms plus 0 negative charges equals 3.

EXAMPLE 8.22

What is the charge on the hydrogen sulfite ion?

Solution

The charge is $1-$ in HSO_3^{-}.

Practice Problem 8.22   What is the charge on the monohydrogen phosphate ion?

Carbonates and Acid Carbonates

Carbonates are compounds containing the carbonate ion. **Acid carbonates** are compounds containing the hydrogen carbonate ion. Just as acid-base reactions are an important type of double substitution reaction, the reactions of carbonates and acid carbonates with acids are an important subtype of acid-base reaction.

Carbonates undergo double substitution reactions with acids to form carbon dioxide and water or acid carbonates, depending on the relative quantity of acid added:

$$Na_2CO_3(aq) + 2\,HCl(aq) \rightarrow 2\,NaCl(aq) + CO_2(g) + H_2O(\ell)$$

$$Na_2CO_3(aq) + HCl(aq) \rightarrow NaCl(aq) + NaHCO_3(aq)$$

The acid either totally or partially neutralizes the carbonate.

Figure 8.9 Formation of Caves
(a) Huge underground chambers, such as the Luray Caverns in the Blue Ridge Mountains of Virginia, are formed over eons by the reaction of carbon dioxide dissolved in water with solid limestone, $CaCO_3$. (Note the people near the bottom center of the picture.) (b) Water containing calcium hydrogen carbonate, $Ca(HCO_3)_2$, dripped from the ceiling of the limestone cavern and deposited solid calcium carbonate, $CaCO_3$, when the concentration of carbon dioxide was low. A droplet hanging from the ceiling formed a tiny portion of a stalactite; a droplet that hit the floor formed a tiny portion of a stalagmite.

(a)

(b)

Carbon dioxide, an acidic anhydride, can react with a base to form an acid carbonate or a carbonate:

$$CO_2(g) + NaOH(aq) \rightarrow NaHCO_3(aq)$$

$$CO_2(g) + 2\,NaOH(aq) \rightarrow Na_2CO_3(aq) + H_2O(\ell)$$

The base either partially or totally neutralizes the carbon dioxide.

●●●●●●●●●●●●●●●●●●●●●●●●●

ITEM OF INTEREST

Carbon dioxide present in relatively high concentration in water can dissolve insoluble carbonates to yield soluble acid carbonates:

$$CO_2(g) + H_2O(\ell) + CaCO_3(s) \rightarrow Ca(HCO_3)_2(aq)$$

The reaction of limestone ($CaCO_3$) with water containing carbon dioxide in relatively high concentration can form natural caves, such as Luray Caverns in Virginia (Figure 8.9). If the carbon dioxide concentration is lowered, the reverse reaction can occur:

$$Ca(HCO_3)_2(aq) \rightarrow CO_2(g) + H_2O(\ell) + CaCO_3(s)$$

Thus, water dripping from the ceiling of a cavern can deposit $CaCO_3$ a tiny particle at a time, and over long periods can form stalactites and stalagmites.

Acid carbonates undergo double substitution reactions with either acids or bases, neutralizing them:

$$NaHCO_3(aq) + HCl(aq) \rightarrow NaCl(aq) + H_2O(\ell) + CO_2(g)$$

$$NaHCO_3(aq) + NaOH(aq) \rightarrow Na_2CO_3(aq) + H_2O(\ell)$$

These types of reactions are summarized in Figure 8.10.

Figure 8.10 Acid-Base Reactions Involving Carbonates and Acid Carbonates

Heating an acid carbonate, such as sodium hydrogen carbonate, produces the corresponding carbonate plus carbon dioxide and water. Mixing a carbonate, such as sodium carbonate, with carbon dioxide and water produces the corresponding acid carbonate, such as sodium hydrogen carbonate.

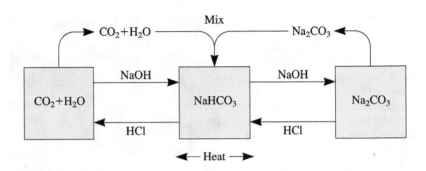

Snapshot Review

❏ Most reactions of acid plus metal or base can be included in the single or double substitution reactions of Section 8.3.
❏ Acids and bases are so important that a special nomenclature has grown up around them.
❏ Carbonates, acid salts, and acid and base anhydrides are similar to acids and bases in some of their chemical properties.

A. Write a balanced chemical equation for the reaction of H_2SO_4 and $Ba(OH)_2$, as well as the acid or base with the anhydride of the other, and of the two anhydrides themselves.

B. Write a balanced chemical equation for the reaction of K_3PO_4 with (a) an equal number of moles of HCl, (b) twice as many moles of HCl, (c) three times as many moles of HCl.

Key Terms

Key terms are defined in the Glossary.

acid (8.4)
acid carbonate (8.4)
acidic anhydride (8.4)
acid salt (8.4)
active (8.3)
anhydride (8.4)
aqueous solution (8.2)
Arrhenius theory (8.4)
balanced equation (8.1)
base (8.4)
basic anhydride (8.4)
carbonate (8.4)
catalyst (8.3)
coefficient (8.1)

combination reaction (8.3)
combustion (8.3)
decomposition reaction (8.3)
double displacement reaction (8.3)
double substitution reaction (8.3)
equation (8.1)
hydrocarbon (8.3)
metathesis reaction (8.3)
molten (8.3)
neutral (8.4)
neutralization reaction (8.4)
precipitate (8.3)
product (8.1)
reactant (8.1)

reactive (8.3)
reagent (8.1)
salt (8.4)
single displacement reaction (8.3)
single substitution reaction (8.3)
solubility (8.3)
stability (8.3)
state (8.2)
strong acid (8.4)
strong base (8.4)
ternary compound (8.3)
weak acid (8.4)
weak base (8.4)

Symbols/Abbreviations

(aq) (aqueous solution) (8.2)

(g) (gas) (8.2)

(ℓ) (liquid) (8.2)

N.R. (no reaction) (8.3)

(s) (solid) (8.2)

Summary

The balanced equation represents a chemical reaction. It not only identifies the reactants and the products, but also gives quantitative information on the ratios of all substances involved in the reaction (Section 8.1).

To balance an equation—that is, to make the numbers of atoms of each of the elements the same on both sides of the equation—we place coefficients in front of each formula in the equation. The state of each substance may be indicated as gas (g), liquid (ℓ), solid (s), or solute in aqueous solution (aq) (Section 8.2).

With a little experience, we can predict the products of simple reactions from the nature of the reactants. In writing formulas for the products, always use the rules given in Chapter 5; do not write incorrect formulas to make balancing an equation easier. Simple reactions can be divided into five types: combination reactions, decomposition reactions, single substitution reactions, double substitution reactions, and combustion reactions. Identifying the type of reaction can help greatly in deducing the product(s). If two free elements are given, they can either combine or do nothing; they cannot be broken down into simpler substances. If only one compound is given, it probably will decompose, especially if energy is provided. An element and a compound can react to give a new compound and another free element. The relative reactivity of the elements (Table 8.2) determines whether a single substitution reaction can occur. Two ionic compounds can swap ions to produce two new compounds. Solubility in water (Table 8.3) often determines whether a double substitution reaction can occur. Rapid reaction with oxygen is combustion. Carbon-containing compounds react with limited oxygen to produce carbon monoxide or react with excess oxygen to give carbon dioxide (Section 8.3).

Acids and bases react according to the rules in Section 8.3, but their reactions are so common that further details need to be learned. The double substitution reaction of an acid with a base is called a neutralization reaction. The products are water and a salt. Strong acids react with water completely to form ions, and weak acids react with water only slightly, but both kinds of acids react with bases to form salts. Substances that react with water to form acids or bases are called anhydrides. Acids containing more than one ionizable hydrogen atom can be partially neutralized, forming acid salts. Carbonates and acid carbonates react similarly to bases (Section 8.4).

Items for Special Attention

■ *Never* treat spilled acid or base with strong base or strong acid. Excess of the reagent might do more harm than the original acid or base, and the heat of the neutralization reaction might also cause problems. Instead, flood with water, and later treat with sodium hydrogen carbonate, $NaHCO_3$, which is almost neutral and produces safe reaction products. Called baking soda in everyday life, sodium hydrogen carbonate is as effective at home as it is in the laboratory.

■ Note the difference between the words "acidic" and "acetic," which sound alike.

■ We can often apply a generality to answer a specific question. For example, you can tell that Na_2MoO_4 is soluble in water even if we have never seen this formula before. According to Table 8.3, all alkali metal compounds are soluble, and this compound is an alkali metal salt.

■ There are no basic salts (corresponding to acid salts) resulting from partial neutralization of bases with more than one hydroxide ion per formula unit.

Answers to Snapshot Reviews

8.1 A. (a) 15 molecules of HCl   (b) 15 mol of HCl
    B. There is no difference.
8.2 A. (a) $P_4O_6(s) + 6 H_2O(\ell) \rightarrow 4 H_3PO_3(\ell)$
    (b) $TiCl_4(\ell) + 2 H_2O(\ell) \rightarrow TiO_2(s) + 4 HCl(g)$
    (c) $2 CoCl_3(aq) + Co(s) \rightarrow 3 CoCl_2(aq)$
8.3 A. (a) $BaO(s) + H_2O(\ell) \rightarrow Ba(OH)_2(s)$
    (b) $2 Al(s) + 3 H_2SO_4(aq) \rightarrow$
                        $Al_2(SO_4)_3(aq) + 3 H_2(g)$
    (c) $2 HCl(aq) + Na_2CO_3(aq) \rightarrow$
                        $2 NaCl(aq) + CO_2(g) + H_2O(\ell)$

8.4 A. $H_2SO_4(aq) + Ba(OH)_2(s) \rightarrow BaSO_4(s) + 2 H_2O(\ell)$
    $H_2SO_4(aq) + BaO(s) \rightarrow BaSO_4(s) + H_2O(\ell)$
    $SO_3(g) + Ba(OH)_2(s) \rightarrow BaSO_4(s) + H_2O(\ell)$
    $SO_3(g) + BaO(s) \rightarrow BaSO_4(s)$
    B. $K_3PO_4(aq) + HCl(aq) \rightarrow KCl(aq) + K_2HPO_4(aq)$
    $K_3PO_4(aq) + 2 HCl(aq) \rightarrow$
                        $2 KCl(aq) + KH_2PO_4(aq)$
    $K_3PO_4(aq) + 3 HCl(aq) \rightarrow$
                        $3 KCl(aq) + H_3PO_4(aq)$

Self-Tutorial Problems

8.1 Assign each of the following types to one of the five classes of reactions presented in Section 8.3:

Reactants	Products
(a) 2 elements	1 compound
(b) 1 compound	2 elements
(c) 2 compounds	2 different compounds
(d) 1 element + 1 compound	1 element + 1 compound
(e) 1 compound	1 element + 1 compound
(f) 1 compound + O_2	2 or more compounds
(g) 1 element + 1 compound	1 compound

8.2 Explain how to recognize that O_2 and MgO will not react with each other in a single substitution reaction.

8.3 Rewrite the following equations with integral coefficients:

(a) $CrF_2(s) + \frac{1}{2}F_2(g) \rightarrow CrF_3(s)$

(b) $CoCl_3(s) + \frac{1}{2}Co(s) \rightarrow \frac{3}{2}CoCl_2(s)$

(c) $CuCl(s) + \frac{1}{2}Cl_2(g) \rightarrow CuCl_2(s)$

(d) $\frac{2}{3}H_3PO_4(aq) + CaCO_3(s) \rightarrow$
$\frac{1}{3}Ca_3(PO_4)_2(s) + H_2O(\ell) + CO_2(g)$

(e) $NH_3(g) + \frac{5}{4}O_2(g) \rightarrow NO(g) + \frac{3}{2}H_2O(g)$

8.4 Write a balanced chemical equation for each of the following reactions:

(a) $SO_2(g) + PCl_5(s) \rightarrow SOCl_2(\ell) + POCl_3(\ell)$

(b) $SO_2(g) + Cl_2(g) \rightarrow SO_2Cl_2(\ell)$

8.5 What is the difference, if any, among (a) the reaction of sodium with chlorine, (b) the combination of sodium and chlorine, and (c) the formation of sodium chloride from its elements?

8.6 Consider the reaction of aqueous chlorine with aqueous zinc iodide.

(a) Identify the reaction type.

(b) Write correct formulas for all reactants and products.

(c) Write a balanced equation.

8.7 Explain how a catalyst resembles a marriage broker.

8.8 A certain double substitution reaction produced silver chloride and potassium acetate. What were the reactants?

8.9 Can a single substitution reaction occur between an element and a compound of that same element?

8.10 Can a double substitution reaction occur between two compounds containing one ion in common?

8.11 Are oxides of reactive metals or oxides of unreactive metals more likely to decompose into their two elements when heated?

8.12 What type of reaction is the following? What are the products?

$$C_2H_6(g) + O_2(g, \text{excess}) \rightarrow$$

8.13 In a certain double substitution reaction, $CrCl_3$ is a reactant. Is $Cr(NO_3)_3$ or $Cr(NO_3)_2$ more likely to be a product?

8.14 Do the classes of reactions described in Section 8.3 include all possible types of chemical reactions?

8.15 Which table in this chapter should be used when working with single substitution reactions, and which ones with double substitution reactions?

8.16 Which of the following compounds are acids?

H_2O	NH_3	C_4H_8	$HClO_3$
AsH_3	LiH	H_2O_2	H_3PO_4

8.17 Classify each of the following as an acidic anhydride, a basic anhydride, or neither:

N_2O_5	CaO	K_2O	SO_3
Cl_2O_7	N_2O		

8.18 Which, if any, of the common acids exist completely in the form of ions (a) as a pure compound and (b) in aqueous solution?

8.19 What products are expected in each of the following cases?

(a) $KClO_3$ is heated in the presence of MnO_2 as a catalyst.

(b) $KClO_3$ is heated in the presence of MnO_2.

(c) $KClO_3$ and MnO_2 are heated together.

(d) $KClO_3$ is heated.

8.20 What type of substance can act as an acid but does not have hydrogen written first in its formula?

8.21 What is the difference between "acidic" and "acetic"?

8.22 Give two reasons why the following reaction produces products:

$Ba(HCO_3)_2(aq) + H_2SO_4(aq) \rightarrow$
$BaSO_4(s) + 2 H_2O(\ell) + 2 CO_2(g)$

Problems

8.1 The Chemical Equation

8.23 How many moles of phosphorus are present in

(a) 4.0 mol of tetraphosphorus hexoxide?

(b) 5.0 mol of phosphoric acid?

(c) 6.0 mol of diphosphorus pentasulfide?

8.24 List the number of atoms of each element in the given number of formula units:

(a) $3 KClO_3$ (b) $4 H_2O_2$

(c) $2 Ca(ClO_3)_2$ (d) $3 CuSO_4 \cdot 5H_2O$

(e) $6 (NH_4)_3PO_4$

8.25 How many atoms of oxygen are present in

(a) Three molecules of ozone, O_3?

(b) Four formula units of $Mg(HCO_3)_2$?

(c) Two formula units of $Mn(C_2H_3O_2)_2$?

8.26 (a) If two molecules of H_2O react with sodium metal according to the following equation, how many molecules of H_2 will be produced?

$$2 Na(s) + 2 H_2O(\ell) \rightarrow 2 NaOH(aq) + H_2(g)$$

(b) If 2.00 mol of H_2O reacts with sodium metal according to the equation, how many moles of H_2 will be produced?

8.27 (a) If one molecule of P_4 reacts with chlorine gas according to the following equation, how many molecules of PCl_5 will be produced?

$$P_4(s) + 10 Cl_2(g) \rightarrow 4 PCl_5(s)$$

(b) If 1.00 mol of P_4 reacts with chlorine gas according to the equation, how many moles of PCl_5 will be produced?

8.2 Balancing Equations

8.28 Write a balanced chemical equation for each of the following reactions:

(a) Aqueous potassium hydroxide plus phosphoric acid yields potassium phosphate plus water.

(b) Aqueous sodium sulfate plus barium bromate yields barium sulfate plus sodium bromate.

(c) Aqueous calcium hydrogen carbonate plus hydrochloric acid yields calcium chloride plus carbon dioxide plus water.

(d) Solid sulfur plus fluorine gas yields liquid sulfur hexafluoride.

8.29 Write a balanced equation for the reaction of oxygen gas and nitrogen monoxide gas to form gaseous N_2O_3.

8.30 Balance the equation for each of the following reactions:

(a) $Cu_2S(s) + O_2(g) \rightarrow Cu(s) + SO_2(g)$

(b) $CO_2(g) + H_2(g) \xrightarrow{\text{Heat}} CO(g) + H_2O(g)$

(c) $ZnS(s) + O_2(g) \rightarrow ZnO(s) + SO_2(g)$

(d) $H_2O(\ell) + SCl_4(\ell) \rightarrow HCl(aq) + H_2SO_3(aq)$

(e) $O_2(g) + MnO(s) \rightarrow Mn_3O_4(s)$

(f) $C_7H_{14}O(\ell) + O_2(g) \rightarrow CO_2(g) + H_2O(g)$

8.31 Balance the equation for each of the following reactions:

(a) $AlCl_3(aq) + NaOH(aq) \rightarrow$
$$NaAl(OH)_4(aq) + NaCl(aq)$$

(b) $H_3PO_4(aq) + NaOH(aq) \rightarrow$
$$Na_3PO_4(aq) + H_2O(\ell)$$

(c) $C_2H_6(g) + O_2(g) \rightarrow CO_2(g) + H_2O(\ell)$

(d) $MnO_2(s) + H_2C_2O_4(aq) \rightarrow$
$$CO_2(g) + MnO(s) + H_2O(\ell)$$

(e) $As_2S_3(s) + O_2(g) \rightarrow As_2O_3(s) + SO_2(g)$

(f) $C_2H_4O(\ell) + O_2(g) \rightarrow CO_2(g) + H_2O(g)$

(g) $CuSO_4 \cdot 5H_2O(s) + NH_3(aq) \rightarrow$
$$CuSO_4 \cdot 4NH_3(aq) + H_2O(\ell)$$

(h) $Na_2SO_3(aq) + S(s) \rightarrow Na_2S_2O_3(aq)$

(i) $Zn(s) + NaOH(aq) + H_2O(\ell) \rightarrow$
$$Na_2Zn(OH)_4(aq) + H_2(g)$$

(j) $BiCl_3(aq) + H_2O(\ell) \rightarrow Bi(O)Cl(s) + HCl(aq)$

(k) $NaAl(OH)_4(aq) + HCl(aq) \rightarrow$
$$AlCl_3(aq) + H_2O(\ell) + NaCl(aq)$$

(l) $C_6H_{12}(\ell) + O_2(g) \rightarrow CO(g) + H_2O(g)$

(m) $Mn_3O_4(s) + O_2(g) \rightarrow Mn_2O_3(s)$

8.32 Write a balanced equation for the reaction of aqueous copper(II) nitrate with aqueous sodium iodide to produce solid copper(I) iodide plus aqueous iodine plus aqueous sodium nitrate.

8.33 Balance the equation for each of the following reactions:

(a) $Al_2O_3(\text{in solution}) + C(s) \xrightarrow[\text{Heat}]{\text{Electricity}} Al(\ell) + CO(g)$

(b) $N_2(g) + O_2(g) \xrightarrow{\text{Lightning}} NO(g)$

(c) $C_3O_2(s) + O_2(g) \rightarrow CO_2(g)$

(d) $B_2H_6(g) + O_2(g) \rightarrow B_2O_3(s) + H_2O(\ell)$

(e) $C(s) + O_2(g) \rightarrow CO_2(g)$

(f) $NO_2(g) \xrightarrow{\text{Cool}} N_2O_4(\ell)$

(g) $Ba(s) + O_2(g) \xrightarrow{\text{Heat}} BaO(s)$

(h) $Na(s) + Cl_2(g) \rightarrow NaCl(s)$

(i) $P(s) + O_2(g) \rightarrow P_2O_5(s)$

8.34 Write a balanced chemical equation for each of the following reactions:

(a) Aqueous lithium hydroxide reacts with gaseous carbon dioxide to produce aqueous lithium hydrogen carbonate.

(b) Solid calcium sulfite decomposes on heating to produce solid calcium oxide and sulfur dioxide gas.

(c) Pentene gas (C_5H_{10}) burns in excess oxygen to produce carbon dioxide and water.

(d) Water reacts with sodium metal to produce aqueous sodium hydroxide and hydrogen gas. *(Caution: This reaction is potentially explosive.)*

(e) Lithium metal when heated with nitrogen gas reacts to produce solid lithium nitride.

8.35 Balance the equation for each of the following reactions:

(a) $Li(s) + O_2(g) \rightarrow Li_2O(s)$

Oxide

(b) $Na(s) + O_2(g) \rightarrow Na_2O_2(s)$

Peroxide

(c) $K(s) + O_2(g) \rightarrow KO_2(s)$

Superoxide

8.3 Predicting the Products of Chemical Reactions

8.36 Write two balanced equations for the reaction of $(NH_4)_2CO_3$ with HCl.

8.37 The following reagents in aqueous solution produce the indicated product. What conclusions can you reach about the barium carbonate?

$$Ba(NO_3)_2 + Na_2CO_3 \rightarrow BaCO_3 + 2\ NaNO_3$$

8.38 Write a balanced equation for the reaction of (a) iron with HCl(aq) to form an iron(II) compound and (b) iron with chlorine to form an iron(III) compound.

8.39 Complete and balance each of the following equations:

(a) $NaCl(\ell) \xrightarrow{\text{Electricity}}$

(b) $H_2O(\ell) \xrightarrow[\text{Na}_2\text{SO}_4]{\text{Electricity}}$

(c) $HCl(aq) \xrightarrow{\text{Electricity}}$

8.40 Write two balanced equations for the possible reactions of H_2SO_3 with NaOH.

8.41 In which of the following systems is a reaction expected? Complete the equation for any reaction that occurs.

(a) $FeCl_2 + Cl_2 \rightarrow$

(b) $FeCl_3 + Cl_2 \rightarrow$

8.42 Complete and balance each of the following equations:

(a) $Al(s) + FeCl_2(s) \xrightarrow{\text{Heat}}$

(b) $Cl_2(g) + AlI_3(aq) \rightarrow$

(c) $Ba(C_2H_3O_2)_2(aq) + Na_2CO_3(aq) \rightarrow$

(d) $BaCl_2(aq) + (NH_4)_2SO_4(aq) \rightarrow$

(e) $Ba(ClO_4)_2(aq) + Na_2SO_4(aq) \rightarrow$

(f) $NH_3(g) + HCl(aq) \rightarrow$

8.43 Complete and balance an equation for each of the following reactions. If no reaction occurs, write N.R.

(a) $Zn(s) + HCl(aq) \rightarrow$

(b) $Ag(s) + HCl(aq) \rightarrow$

(c) $Au(s) + HCl(aq) \rightarrow$

8.44 Table 8.3 states that most sulfides are insoluble in water. Which sulfides are soluble?

8.45 Complete and balance chemical equations for the combustion of propane and butane:

(a) $C_3H_8(g) + O_2(g, \text{limited supply}) \rightarrow$

(b) $C_3H_8(g) + O_2(g, \text{excess}) \rightarrow$

(c) $C_4H_{10}(g) + O_2(g, \text{limited supply}) \rightarrow$

(d) $C_4H_{10}(g) + O_2(g, \text{excess}) \rightarrow$

8.46 Write two balanced equations for the possible reactions of toluene, C_7H_8, with oxygen.

8.47 Complete and balance each of the following equations:

(a) $C_7H_{16}O_2(\ell) + O_2(g, \text{excess}) \rightarrow$

(b) $C_8H_{16}O_2(\ell) + O_2(g, \text{limited}) \rightarrow$

8.48 Which type of reaction involving ionic compounds is most likely to occur without any change in the charges on the ions?

8.49 Complete and balance an equation for each of the following chemical reactions:

(a) Production of copper(I) bromide from its elements

(b) Production of copper(I) sulfide from its elements

(c) Methane (CH_4) plus limited oxygen

(d) Zinc chloride plus silver nitrate

(e) Perchloric acid plus barium hydroxide

8.50 Complete and balance each of the following equations:

(a) $Ba(s) + H_2O(\ell) \rightarrow$

(b) $F_2(g) + H_2O(\ell) \rightarrow$

8.51 In which, if any, of the following systems is a reaction expected?

(a) $MgCl_2(aq) + Pb(s) \rightarrow$

(b) $Au(s) + HCl(aq) \rightarrow$

(c) $ZnCl_2(aq) + Cl_2(g) \rightarrow$

(d) $Ne(g) + O_2(g) \rightarrow$

8.52 Consider the following pair of reactants:

$$Cr + CrCl_3 \rightarrow$$

(a) Adding chromium metal to the compound is equivalent to doing what with the chlorine?

(b) What other compound of chromium and chlorine exists?

(c) Complete and balance the preceding equation.

(d) Write the symbol for chromium surrounded by the symbols for three chlorine atoms, and write a second such set to the right of the first set. Add another chromium atom between two of the chlorine atoms, and encircle three sets of atoms to make the compound in part (b).

8.53 If a compound decomposes without any external energy being added in some form, do you expect the compound to be very long-lasting? Explain.

8.54 Complete and balance each of the following equations:

(a) $C_5H_{10}O(\ell) + O_2(g, \text{limited}) \rightarrow$

(b) $C_5H_{12}O_2(\ell) + O_2(g, \text{excess}) \rightarrow$

8.55 Complete and balance each of the following equations:

(a) $CrO(s) + O_2(g) \rightarrow$

(b) $AsCl_5(\ell) + H_2O(\ell) \rightarrow H_3AsO_4(aq) +$

(c) $PCl_3(\ell) + Cl_2(g) \rightarrow$

(d) $Mg(s) + N_2(g) \rightarrow$

8.56 Complete and balance each of the following equations:

(a) $Fe_2(SO_4)_3(aq) + BaCl_2(aq) \rightarrow$

(b) $FeSO_4(aq) + BaCl_2(aq) \rightarrow$

(c) $(NH_4)_2SO_4(aq) + BaCl_2(aq) \rightarrow$

8.57 Write a balanced equation for the reaction of chlorine with (a) an alkali metal and (b) an alkaline earth metal.

8.4 Acids and Bases

8.58 Complete and balance each of the following equations:

(a) $H_3PO_4(aq) + KOH(aq, \text{excess}) \rightarrow$

(b) $Ba(OH)_2(aq) + HNO_3(aq) \rightarrow$

(c) $Na_2HPO_4(aq) + NaOH(aq) \rightarrow$

(d) $Ba(OH)_2(aq) + H_3PO_4(aq, \text{limited}) \rightarrow$

8.59 Solid $MgCO_3$ "dissolves" in excess HCl(aq). Write an equation for the reaction. Describe what we would expect to see during this reaction.

8.60 Complete and balance each of the following equations:

(a) $K_2CO_3(aq) + HCl(aq, \text{limited}) \rightarrow$

(b) $K_2CO_3(aq) + HCl(aq, \text{excess}) \rightarrow$

(c) $Na_2O(s) + CO_2(g) \rightarrow$

(d) $NaOH(aq) + CO_2(g) \rightarrow$

8.61 Complete and balance each of the following equations:

(a) $NH_4Cl(aq) + KOH(aq) \rightarrow$

(b) $NaC_2H_3O_2(aq) + HClO_3(aq) \rightarrow$

8.62 Write an equation for the reaction of carbon dioxide and water with calcium carbonate to produce a soluble product.

8.63 Write balanced equations for two possible reactions of oxalic acid ($H_2C_2O_4$) with sodium hydroxide (limited and excess).

8.64 State four different ways that $CaCl_2$ can be prepared, starting with HCl(aq) plus other reagents.

8.65 Complete and balance each of the following equations:

(a) $HClO_3(aq) + ZnO(s) \rightarrow$

(b) $N_2O_3(g) + H_2O(\ell) \rightarrow$

(c) $SO_3(g) + LiOH(aq) \rightarrow$

8.66 Complete and balance the following equations:

(a) $Cl_2O_7 + H_2O \rightarrow$ (b) $Cl_2O_5 + H_2O \rightarrow$

(c) $Cl_2O_3 + H_2O \rightarrow$ (d) $Cl_2O + H_2O \rightarrow$

8.67 Complete and balance each of the following equations:

(a) $SO_3(g) + K_2O(s) \rightarrow$

(b) $SO_2(g) + KOH(aq) \rightarrow$

(c) $SO_2(g) + K_2O(s) \rightarrow$

8.68 Complete and balance the following equations:

(a) $KOH + KHCO_3 \rightarrow$

(b) $HCl + KHCO_3 \rightarrow$

(c) $K_2O + CO_2 \rightarrow$

(d) $KOH + CO_2 \rightarrow$

8.69 Complete and balance each of the following equations, assuming that an excess of the second reactant is present. Comment on why each reaction proceeds.

(a) $NaH_2BO_3(aq) + HCl(aq) \rightarrow$

(b) $MgCO_3(s) + HCl(aq) \rightarrow$

(c) $Zn(C_2H_3O_2)_2(aq) + HCl(aq) \rightarrow$

(d) $Na_2O(s) + HClO_3(aq) \rightarrow$

(e) $Ba(OH)_2(aq) + HClO_3(aq) \rightarrow$

(f) $Mg(OH)_2(s) + HNO_3(aq) \rightarrow$

8.70 Complete and balance each of the following equations:

(a) $H_3PO_4(aq) + NaOH(aq, \text{limited quantity}) \rightarrow$

(b) $HClO_3(aq, \text{excess}) + BaCO_3(s) \rightarrow$

(c) $HCl(aq) + Mg(HCO_3)_2(aq) \rightarrow$

8.71 What are the products of the reaction of

(a) An acid and a base?

(b) An acid and a metal oxide?

(c) An acid and a carbonate?

(d) What is the major difference among these?

General Problems

8.72 Explain the difference among the following questions:

What is the product of the electrolysis of water containing dilute NaCl to carry the current?

What is the product of the electrolysis of water containing dilute NaCl?

What is the product of the electrolysis of dilute aqueous NaCl?

8.73 Consider the following pairs of reactants. For each, determine the possible reaction type, and write correct formulas for the products that could be produced. If the reaction can proceed, write a balanced equation.

(a) $CO(g)$ and $O_2(g)$

(b) $HCl(aq)$ and $Al(s)$

(c) $KNO_3(aq)$ and $AgCl(s)$

8.74 Give one example of each type of reaction in Problem 8.1.

8.75 (a) Which class of reaction requires only one reactant?

(b) Does the addition of a catalyst change the answer to part (a)?

(c) How can we recognize a substance as a catalyst?

8.76 Is each of the following equations balanced? Is each correct?

(a) $AgCl(s) + HNO_3(aq) \rightarrow HCl(aq) + AgNO_3(aq)$

(b) $ZnCl_2(aq) + Fe(s) \rightarrow FeCl_2(aq) + Zn(s)$

(c) $KCl(aq) + NaNO_3(aq) \rightarrow NaCl(aq) + KNO_3(aq)$

8.77 What is unusual about the following decomposition reactions?

(a) $NH_4HCO_3(s) \xrightarrow{\text{Heat}}$ (b) $Ca(HCO_3)_2(s) \xrightarrow{\text{Heat}}$

8.78 Complete and balance each of the following equations:

(a) $HCl(aq) + NaHCO_3(aq) \rightarrow$

(b) $NaOH(aq) + NaHSO_3(aq) \rightarrow$

(c) $HNO_3(aq) + Ba(OH)_2(aq) \rightarrow$

(d) $KF(aq) + HCl(aq) \rightarrow$

8.79 Balance the following equation:

$Cu(NO_3)_2(aq) + KI(aq) \rightarrow$
$$I_2(aq) + KNO_3(aq) + CuI(s)$$

8.80 How can we distinguish a combustion reaction from a displacement reaction, considering that each may involve an element and a compound?

8.81 Addition of aqueous ammonia to a solution of $Ca(HCO_3)_2(aq)$ causes a white solid to form. What is the formula of the solid? Write an equation for the reaction.

8.82 Neither N_2O nor CO reacts with water under normal conditions. What is unusual about that lack of reactivity?

8.83 Complete and balance each of the following equations:

(a) $C_5H_{10}O_2(\ell) + O_2(g, \text{excess}) \rightarrow$

(b) $C_3H_8(g) + O_2(g, \text{excess}) \rightarrow$

(c) $C_{12}H_{26}(\ell) + O_2(g, \text{limited}) \rightarrow$
      Kerosene

(d) $C_{12}H_{26}(\ell) + O_2(g, \text{excess}) \rightarrow$
      Kerosene

8.84 Explain why the Solvay process is used instead of the following reaction:

$$CaCO_3 + 2\,NaCl \rightarrow CaCl_2 + Na_2CO_3$$

8.85 Complete and balance each of the following equations:

(a) $CrCl_2(aq) + AgNO_3(aq) \rightarrow$

(b) $CrCl_3(aq) + AgNO_3(aq) \rightarrow$

8.86 Inexpensive metal forks corrode rapidly if used in a delicatessen to remove pickles from the juice in which they are shipped. Explain the probable cause.

8.87 Assuming that water containing $Ca(HCO_3)_2$ deposits 1 mg of $CaCO_3$ per minute on the ceiling of a limestone cavern, how long will it take to produce a stalactite with a mass of 75 metric tons (1 metric ton = 1×10^6 g)?

8.88 What products are expected from the reaction of ammonium chloride and potassium hydroxide? Write an equation for the reaction.

8.89 Complete and balance each of the following equations:

(a) $CrBr_3(s) + Cl_2(g) \rightarrow$

(b) $CrCl_2(s) + Cl_2(g) \rightarrow$

(c) $CrBr_2(s) + Cl_2(g, \text{excess}) \rightarrow$

8.90 Balance the following equation:

$NaI(aq) + Cr(NO_3)_3(aq) \rightarrow$
$$CrI_2(aq) + NaNO_3(aq) + I_2(aq)$$

8.91 A certain double substitution reaction produced sodium sulfate, carbon dioxide, and water. Write four balanced chemical equations that could have occurred.

8.92 Balance the equation for each of the following reactions:

(a) Lithium metal plus oxygen produces lithium oxide.

(b) Sodium metal plus oxygen gas produces sodium peroxide.

(c) Potassium metal plus oxygen produces potassium superoxide.

8.93 A student bubbled an excess of fluorine gas into aqueous sodium iodide, producing sodium fluoride and sodium periodate. What additional products did she obtain?

9

Net Ionic Equations

- **9.1** Properties of Ionic Compounds in Aqueous Solution
- **9.2** Writing Net Ionic Equations

Conversion of Cu^{2+} to a more complex ion by the addition of ammonia is evidenced by the color change

Review Clues

Section 9.1	Sections 5.2, 5.4, 8.3, 8.4
Section 9.2	Chapter 8

Objectives

9.1 To recognize that each type of ion in an aqueous solution of an ionic compound is not affected by the properties of the other type(s) of ion(s) in the solution

To write formulas for the ions present in solution when an ionic compound or a strong acid is dissolved in water

9.2 To write net ionic equations for reactions in aqueous solution and to interpret such equations

Section 9.1 describes the properties of ionic compounds in aqueous solution. Section 9.2 then explains how to write net ionic equations for many reactions in aqueous solution. These equations show the actual reactions that occur; ions that do not change at all during the reaction are not included. Each net ionic equation can summarize many equations involving complete compounds.

Net ionic equations are used in discussions of limiting quantities problems (Chapter 10), molarities of ions (Chapter 11), balancing oxidation-reduction equations (Chapter 16), acid-base theory (Chapter 19), and many other areas beyond the scope of this book. They make possible writing equations for half-reactions at the electrodes in electrochemical experiments (Chapter 17), which have electrons included explicitly in them. They make understandable the heat effects of many reactions such as those of strong acids with strong bases.

9.1 Properties of Ionic Compounds in Aqueous Solution

The properties of ionic compounds in solution are actually the properties of the individual ions themselves (Figure 9.1). These compounds are called **strong electrolytes** because their solutions conduct electricity well. For example, an aqueous solution of sodium chloride consists essentially of sodium ions and chloride ions in water. A similar solution of calcium chloride consists of calcium ions and chloride ions in water. If either solution is treated with a solution containing silver ions, the chloride ions will form silver chloride, which is insoluble. The chloride ions act independently of the cation that is also present, regardless of whether it is sodium ion, calcium ion, or any other ion. Because the properties of the compound are the properties of the component ions, we need to learn to write equations for only the ions that react, omitting the ions that remain unchanged throughout the reaction (Section 9.2).

Strong acids, strong bases (Table 9.1), and salts all provide ions in solution. They are all strong electrolytes, but the process by which these types of compounds form ions in solution differs. When they are pure, strong acids are covalent compounds, but they undergo a chemical reaction with water to form ions in solution. This process, called *ionization,* will be discussed in more detail

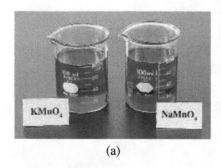
(a)

(b)

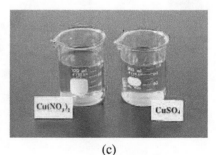
(c)

Figure 9.1 Properties of Ions

(a) The purple color of these two solutions is due to the permanganate ion. (b) Solutions of potassium and sodium ions with different anions than the permanganate ion show that these cations are colorless. (c) The blue color of these solutions is characteristic of the copper(II) ion; the nitrate ion and the sulfate ion are colorless, as shown in part (b).

Table 9.1 Strong Acids and Bases

Strong Acids	Strong Bases
HCl	All soluble metal
HBr	hydroxides,
HI	such as NaOH,
HClO$_3$	KOH, and
HClO$_4$	Ba(OH)$_2$*
HNO$_3$	
H$_2$SO$_4$	

*Note that Ba(OH)$_2$ has limited solubility.

Table 9.2 Electrolytic Properties of Various Types of Compounds

Electrolytes
  Strong electrolytes
    Salts
    Strong acids
    Strong bases
  Weak electrolytes
    Weak acids
    Weak bases
Nonelectrolytes
  Covalent compounds other than acids or bases

Compounds must be both soluble and ionic to be written in the form of their separate ions.

in Chapter 19. Salts and strong bases are ionic even when they are pure, and their interaction with water is more a physical process than a chemical reaction. The solution process for them is called *dissociation* because the ions dissociate from each other; that is, they get out of each other's sphere of influence and are able to move relatively independently of ions of the opposite charge.

Weak acids and bases ionize only slightly in aqueous solution. Because their solutions conduct electricity poorly, they are called **weak electrolytes.** Compounds whose solutions do not conduct electricity at all are called **non-electrolytes.** An outline of the electrolytic properties of compounds is presented in Table 9.2.

A strong electrolyte *in aqueous solution* may be represented as separate ions because the ions of each type are free to move about independently of the ions of the other type. However, an ionic solid that is not dissolved in water is not written as separate ions; the oppositely charged ions in the solid lattice of an ionic compound are not independent of each other (Figure 9.2).

Thus, compounds must be both soluble and ionic to be written in the form of their separate ions. A listing of water-soluble compounds was given in Table 8.3. In addition to the compounds listed there, all strong acids are water soluble. In summary strong electrolytes—compounds that dissociate or ionize extensively in aqueous solution—include the following:

1. All soluble metal hydroxides

2. All salts (other compounds containing metal or ammonium ions) that are soluble

3. Strong acids (HCl, HClO$_3$, HClO$_4$, HBr, HI, HNO$_3$, H$_2$SO$_4$)

All other compounds (for example, gases, other covalent compounds, and all solids) either contain no ions or have ions that are affected by the presence of the other ions. These weak electrolytes, nonelectrolytes, or solids (ionic or not) are written using their regular formulas.

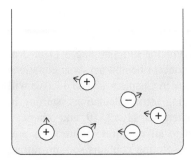

(a) Solution of ions

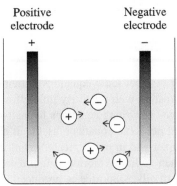

(b) Effect of charged electrodes

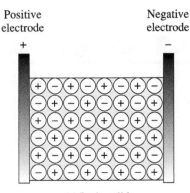

(c) Ionic solid

Figure 9.2 Mobility of Ions

(a) Ions in dilute solutions are free to move independently of other ions. In the absence of electrodes, they move in random directions. (b) Under the influence of the charges on electrodes, the ions move toward the electrode of opposite charge. (c) In contrast, even if charged electrodes are present, ions in solids cannot move because of the surrounding ions of opposite charge.

EXAMPLE 9.1

Write each of the following compounds to represent best how it acts in the presence of water:

(a) $NH_4Cl(aq)$ (b) $AgCl(s)$ (c) $HNO_3(aq)$ (d) $CoCl_2(aq)$

(e) $CH_3OH(aq)$ (f) $H_2O(\ell)$

Solution

(a) $NH_4^+(aq) + Cl^-(aq)$ (b) $AgCl(s)$ (c) $H^+(aq) + NO_3^-(aq)$

(d) $Co^{2+}(aq) + 2\,Cl^-(aq)$ (e) $CH_3OH(aq)$ (f) $H_2O(\ell)$

Practice Problem 9.1 Write each of the following compounds to represent best how it acts in the presence of water:

(a) $BaSO_4$ (b) HNO_2 (c) $NaOH$

 Snapshot Review

❏ Strong and weak electrolytes conduct electricity only in the liquid state. Strong and weak acids and weak bases conduct in solution only; ionic compounds conduct in solution or in the molten state.

❏ Compounds that are ionic in solution are written as separate ions because they behave almost independently of the other ion(s) present. Such compounds include (a) metal-containing compounds, (b) ammonium compounds, (c) strong acids and bases.

A. Write each of the following compounds to best represent it in the presence of water: (a) $C_{12}H_{22}O_{11}$ (table sugar), (b) NH_4Cl, and (c) Na_2SO_4.

B. Which of the following conduct electricity well?

(a) $HClO_2(aq)$ (b) $HClO_3(aq)$ (c) $C_6H_{12}O_6(aq)$ (glucose)

(d) $KCl(aq)$ (e) $KCl(\ell)$ (f) $KCl(s)$

9.2 Writing Net Ionic Equations

We will find net ionic equations extremely useful for summarizing a great deal of information with relatively little effort. The concept behind net ionic equations is essential in writing equations for half-reactions in Chapters 16 and 17. We will also find net ionic equations useful in simplifying some calculations, starting in this chapter and in much greater detail in Chapters 10, 11, 17, 19, and others.

When sodium chloride solution is added to silver nitrate solution, a precipitate of silver chloride is produced, and the solution contains sodium nitrate (Figure 9.3):

$$AgNO_3(aq) + NaCl(aq) \rightarrow AgCl(s) + NaNO_3(aq)$$

This type of equation can be called the **total equation.** (A total equation is sometimes referred to as a *molecular equation* because the compounds in it are written "as if they were molecules.")

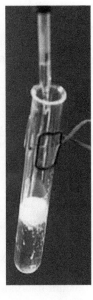

Figure 9.3 Reaction of Silver Nitrate and Sodium Chloride

NaCl solution in the medicine dropper; AgNO$_3$ in the test tube.

Even more informative than a total equation is an **ionic equation.** An ionic compound *in aqueous solution* may be represented as separate ions, but an ionic solid that is not dissolved in water is written as a complete compound. We can write an ionic equation for the reaction of sodium chloride with silver nitrate in aqueous solution (see Figure 9.3) as follows:

$$Ag^+(aq) + NO_3^-(aq) + Na^+(aq) + Cl^-(aq) \rightarrow$$
$$AgCl(s) + Na^+(aq) + NO_3^-(aq)$$

Because the Na$^+$ and NO$_3^-$ ions appear on both sides of this equation (unchanged by the reaction), they are called **spectator ions.** They may be eliminated from the equation:

$$Ag^+(aq) + Cl^-(aq) \rightarrow AgCl(s)$$

This equation is an example of a **net ionic equation.** All the spectator ions are omitted from a net ionic equation.

While we are learning to write net ionic equations, we will use the following procedure. After we get used to working with them, we will be able to write them directly and save even more effort with their use.

1. Start with a total equation for the reaction, making sure that it is balanced.
2. Write all compounds that are both soluble and ionic in the form of their separate ions, making sure to have the correct number of ions of each type. Write all other compounds (for example, gases, other covalent compounds, and all solids) as complete compounds.
3. Eliminate the ions that are unchanged on both sides of the equation to obtain the net ionic equation.

EXAMPLE 9.2

Write a net ionic equation for the reaction of silver chlorate and potassium chloride.

Solution

1. The total equation for the reaction is

$$AgClO_3(aq) + KCl(aq) \rightarrow AgCl(s) + KClO_3(aq)$$

2. The ionic equation is

$$Ag^+(aq) + ClO_3^-(aq) + K^+(aq) + Cl^-(aq) \rightarrow$$
$$AgCl(s) + K^+(aq) + ClO_3^-(aq)$$

3. Eliminating the K$^+$ and ClO$_3^-$ spectator ions produces the net ionic equation:

$$Ag^+(aq) + Cl^-(aq) \rightarrow AgCl(s)$$

This is the same as the net ionic equation given previously for the reaction of sodium chloride with silver nitrate because essentially the same reaction has taken place. Whether it was the sodium ions or the potassium ions or the nitrate ions or the chlorate ions that *did not react* is not important to us. In general, we can say that soluble ionic chlorides react with soluble silver salts to produce silver chloride. This statement does not mention the other ions present in the reactant solutions and may be represented by the net ionic equation, which similarly does not mention any other ions that may be present.

Practice Problem 9.2   Write a net ionic equation for the reaction of $AgC_2H_3O_2$ with $CuCl_2$.

Be careful not to misinterpret the name *net ionic equation*. It is not necessarily true that all the substances appearing in such an equation are ionic. Covalent compounds often occur in net ionic equations. Also, just because the formula for a complete compound is written in such an equation does not mean that the compound is not ionic; it might simply be insoluble.

An important type of reaction is the reaction of a strong acid with a strong base (see Table 9.1) to produce a salt and water. In solution, strong acids and bases exist completely in the form of their ions. All salts, the products of reactions of acids with bases, may also be regarded as completely ionic (but not all are water soluble). We may therefore write net ionic equations for this type of reaction. The reaction of chloric acid and potassium hydroxide is typical:

1. $$HClO_3(aq) + KOH(aq) \rightarrow KClO_3(aq) + H_2O(\ell)$$

In solution, both of the reactants and the potassium chlorate are ionic, but the water is covalent, of course.

2. The ionic equation for the reaction is

$$H^+(aq) + ClO_3^-(aq) + K^+(aq) + OH^-(aq) \rightarrow$$
$$K^+(aq) + ClO_3^-(aq) + H_2O(\ell)$$

3. Eliminating the spectator ions from both sides of this equation yields the net ionic equation:

$$H^+(aq) + OH^-(aq) \rightarrow H_2O(\ell)$$

Note that water, which is molecular, not ionic, is included in this net ionic equation.

EXAMPLE 9.3

Write a net ionic equation for the reaction of aqueous $Ba(OH)_2$ with aqueous HNO_3.

Solution

1. The total equation is

$$Ba(OH)_2(aq) + 2\,HNO_3(aq) \rightarrow Ba(NO_3)_2(aq) + 2\,H_2O(\ell)$$

2. The ionic equation is

$$Ba^{2+}(aq) + 2\,OH^-(aq) + 2\,H^+(aq) + 2\,NO_3^-(aq) \rightarrow$$
$$Ba^{2+}(aq) + 2\,NO_3^-(aq) + 2\,H_2O(\ell)$$

3. Eliminating the spectator ions yields

$$2\,OH^-(aq) + 2\,H^+(aq) \rightarrow 2\,H_2O(\ell)$$

Be careful with the coefficients of the ions in the ionic equation.

Figure 9.4 Silver Ion Test Solution

A solution that can be used to test whether another solution contains silver ions can contain any soluble ionic chloride. A bottle containing such a solution may be labeled "Cl⁻ solution" or "Ag⁺ Test Reagent." That this solution also contains Na⁺ ions or K⁺ ions does not matter, since these cations would not react with the ions in a solution containing silver ions.

This equation can be simplified by dividing each coefficient by 2:

$$OH^-(aq) + H^+(aq) \rightarrow H_2O(\ell)$$

Again, this is the same net ionic equation as that for the reaction of KOH with HClO₃. In fact, the reaction of *any* aqueous strong acid with *any* aqueous strong base yields this net ionic equation (unless some precipitation occurs).

Practice Problem 9.3 Write a net ionic equation for the reaction of NaOH(aq) with aqueous solutions of each of the following:

(a) HCl   (b) HBr   (c) HNO₃   (d) HClO₄

Net ionic equations can also be written for reactions in which gases are produced. For example, sodium hydrogen carbonate reacts with nitric acid to produce sodium nitrate, carbon dioxide, and water:

$$NaHCO_3(aq) + HNO_3(aq) \rightarrow NaNO_3(aq) + CO_2(g) + H_2O(\ell)$$

The net ionic equation is

$$HCO_3^-(aq) + H^+(aq) \rightarrow CO_2(g) + H_2O(\ell)$$

What does a net ionic equation actually tell us? As an example, the net ionic equation of Example 9.3 indicates that any strong acid in water reacts with any soluble strong hydroxide to yield water as a product. The ions that do not react are not of immediate concern. However, no aqueous solution contains only H⁺ ions or only OH⁻ ions. The net ionic equation does not state that these ions occur without ions of the opposite charge, only that the identities of the oppositely charged ions are not important because they do not react (Figure 9.4).

Weak acids—any acids not listed in Table 9.1—are essentially covalent in solution and should be written as complete compounds.

EXAMPLE 9.4

Write a net ionic equation for the reaction of acetic acid, HC₂H₃O₂, with aqueous barium hydroxide, Ba(OH)₂.

Solution

1. The total equation for the reaction is

$$2\, HC_2H_3O_2(aq) + Ba(OH)_2(aq) \rightarrow Ba(C_2H_3O_2)_2(aq) + 2\, H_2O(\ell)$$

2. To write the ionic equation, we must remember that acetic acid is a weak acid; that is, it does not ionize completely in water. It is written as a covalent compound. The ionic equation is

$$2\, HC_2H_3O_2(aq) + Ba^{2+}(aq) + 2\, OH^-(aq) \rightarrow$$
$$Ba^{2+}(aq) + 2\, C_2H_3O_2^-(aq) + 2\, H_2O(\ell)$$

3. The net ionic equation is written without the barium ions or the four "2" coefficients:

$$HC_2H_3O_2(aq) + OH^-(aq) \rightarrow C_2H_3O_2^-(aq) + H_2O(\ell)$$

Note that this net ionic equation is *not* the same as the one for the reaction of a strong acid and a strong base!

Practice Problem 9.4　Write a net ionic equation for the reaction of aqueous NH_3 with aqueous HNO_3.

EXAMPLE 9.5

Reaction of excess $HClO_4(aq)$ with 1 mol of $NaOH(aq)$ produces 55.2 kJ of heat. How much heat is liberated when 1 mol of $Ba(OH)_2(aq)$ is treated with excess $HClO_4(aq)$? How can we tell?

Solution

The same net ionic equation describes both reactions:

$$H^+ + OH^- \rightarrow H_2O$$

Because 55.2 kJ of heat is liberated per mole of water formed, as shown by the NaOH reaction, the same quantity of heat is produced *per mole* of water formed by the $Ba(OH)_2$. Thus 2 mol $\times$ 55.2 kJ/mol = 110 kJ is produced.

Practice Problem 9.5　Explain why 1 mol of NaOH plus excess $HC_2H_3O_2$ does *not* produce 55.2 kJ of heat.

EXAMPLE 9.6

Write seven total equations corresponding to the following net ionic equation:

$$HF(aq) + OH^-(aq) \rightarrow F^-(aq) + H_2O(\ell)$$

Solution

Any soluble, ionic hydroxide may be used. We know that barium hydroxide (to a limited extent) and the six alkali metal hydroxides are soluble:

$$HF(aq) + LiOH(aq) \rightarrow LiF(aq) + H_2O(\ell)$$
$$HF(aq) + NaOH(aq) \rightarrow NaF(aq) + H_2O(\ell)$$
$$HF(aq) + KOH(aq) \rightarrow KF(aq) + H_2O(\ell)$$
$$HF(aq) + RbOH(aq) \rightarrow RbF(aq) + H_2O(\ell)$$
$$HF(aq) + CsOH(aq) \rightarrow CsF(aq) + H_2O(\ell)$$
$$HF(aq) + FrOH(aq) \rightarrow FrF(aq) + H_2O(\ell)$$
$$2\,HF(aq) + Ba(OH)_2(aq) \rightarrow BaF_2(aq) + 2\,H_2O(\ell)$$

EXAMPLE 9.7

Explain how we can write 90 or more complete equations for which the net ionic equation is

$$Cl^-(aq) + Ag^+(aq) \rightarrow AgCl(s)$$

That is, which chlorides should we select? Which silver salts?

Solution

We should choose reagents that we know are both ionic and soluble. The chlorides that we know have these properties are HCl and NH_4Cl, the 12 alkali metal and alkaline earth metal chlorides, about 16 transition metal chlorides (for example, $FeCl_2$, $FeCl_3$, and $CdCl_2$), and chlorides of some other main group metals like $AlCl_3$ and $SnCl_2$. Each of these chlorides can react with silver nitrate, silver acetate, or silver chlorate (which we know are ionic and soluble), producing the required number of complete equations.

Practice Problem 9.7 Why can we not use $PbCl_2$ as an answer in Example 9.7? Comment on one important reason to learn to use net ionic equations.

For a net ionic equation to be balanced, both the numbers of each type of atom and the net charge must be the same on the two sides of the equation. For example, we know that zinc is more active than silver is (Table 8.2) and will replace silver from its compounds. We could start to write the net ionic equation for the reaction in solution as follows:

$$Zn(s) + Ag^+(aq) \rightarrow Zn^{2+}(aq) + Ag(s) \qquad \textit{(Not balanced)}$$

This net ionic equation is balanced only with regard to the numbers of zinc and silver atoms. Because the charge is not balanced, however, the equation is not balanced. We can balance it by doubling the charge on the left side (with a 2 before the Ag^+) and keeping the number of silver atoms balanced (with a 2 before the Ag):

$$Zn(s) + 2\,Ag^+(aq) \rightarrow Zn^{2+}(aq) + 2\,Ag(s) \qquad \textit{(Balanced)}$$

EXAMPLE 9.8

Write a total equation corresponding to the net ionic equation for the reaction of silver ions and zinc, using nitrate ions as the spectator ions. Explain why the charges in the net ionic equation have to be balanced.

Solution

$$Zn(s) + 2\,AgNO_3(aq) \rightarrow Zn(NO_3)_2(aq) + 2\,Ag(s)$$

Each positive charge in the net ionic equation represents one nitrate ion in this total equation. The charges must be balanced in the net ionic equation because the nitrate ions must be balanced in the total equation.

Practice Problem 9.8   Write a balanced total equation that is represented by the following net ionic equation:

$$Cl_2(aq) + 2\,I^-(aq) \rightarrow I_2(aq) + 2\,Cl^-(aq)$$

EXAMPLE 9.9

Write a net ionic equation for the reaction of iron metal with aqueous iron(III) nitrate to produce aqueous iron(II) nitrate.

Solution

1. The total equation is

$$Fe(s) + 2\,Fe(NO_3)_3(aq) \rightarrow 3\,Fe(NO_3)_2(aq)$$

2. The ionic equation is

$$Fe(s) + 2\,Fe^{3+}(aq) + 6\,NO_3^-(aq) \rightarrow 3\,Fe^{2+}(aq) + 6\,NO_3^-(aq)$$

3. Eliminating the nitrate ions from each side yields the net ionic equation:

$$Fe(s) + 2\,Fe^{3+}(aq) \rightarrow 3\,Fe^{2+}(aq)$$

> Be sure the total equation is balanced before attempting to write the ionic equation.

Note that the cations are *not* eliminated because they are not the same on each side. There has been a change from iron(III) to iron(II). The uncharged metal atom has also changed and cannot be eliminated as a spectator ion. The net ionic equation indicates that iron metal will react with *any* soluble iron(III) compound as long as the corresponding iron(II) compound is soluble.

Practice Problem 9.9   Write a net ionic equation for the following reaction:

$$Cu(s) + CuCl_2(aq) \rightarrow 2\,CuCl(s)$$

The advantage of using net ionic equations becomes even greater when we become familiar enough with the process to avoid having to write out total equations at all. We know that alkali metal ions are almost always spectator ions. Such ions as nitrate ions are spectator ions almost as often. Thus when confronted with a reaction such as RbCl plus $AgNO_3$, we can just ignore the probable spectator ions and write the net ionic equation directly:

$$Ag^+(aq) + Cl^-(aq) \rightarrow AgCl(s)$$

Similarly, when we see a strong acid and a strong base, we can write directly

$$H^+(aq) + OH^-(aq) \rightarrow H_2O(\ell)$$

In some cases, the net ionic equation is significantly simpler than the full equation. For example, consider the reaction of solid calcium carbonate with a limited quantity of hydrochloric acid. (In this case, these substances react in a 1:1 ratio.) Assuming that the chloride ion is a spectator ion allows us to write the net ionic equation directly:

$$CaCO_3(s) + H^+(aq) \rightarrow Ca^{2+}(aq) + HCO_3^-(aq)$$

The full equation is

$$2\,CaCO_3(s) + 2\,HCl(aq) \rightarrow CaCl_2(aq) + Ca(HCO_3)_2(aq)$$

The net ionic equation is obviously much simpler.

Net ionic equations are also useful in quantitative calculations, as will be introduced here and used extensively in Chapters 11, 17, and 19. For example, we can calculate the numbers of moles of individual ions in solution using net ionic equations.

EXAMPLE 9.10

Calculate the number of moles of sodium ion present in a solution containing 1 mol of sodium sulfate.

Solution

$$1\,mol\,Na_2SO_4\left(\frac{2\,mol\,Na^+}{1\,mol\,Na_2SO_4}\right) = 2\,mol\,Na^+$$

There is 2 mol of sodium ion in this solution.

Practice Problem 9.10   Calculate the number of moles of nitrate ion in a solution containing 1 mol of aluminum nitrate.

EXAMPLE 9.11

Calculate the number of moles of sodium ion in a solution containing 1 mol of sodium sulfate to which some barium nitrate is added.

Solution

The net ionic equation for the reaction that takes place is

$$Ba^{2+}(aq) + SO_4^{2-}(aq) \rightarrow BaSO_4(s)$$

This equation shows that the sodium ion is a spectator ion, and does not react. Since there is 2 mol of sodium ion present initially (Example 9.10), and the sodium does not react, there will always be 2 mol of sodium ion present no matter how much barium nitrate is added.

Net ionic equations are also very useful for the ions that do react, as will be shown in Chapter 11 and in later chapters.

Net ionic equations are used extensively in chemistry. For example, equilibrium expressions for acid-base reactions, as well as for the ionization of water itself, are conventionally written in the form of net ionic equations. Many complex oxidation-reduction equations are balanced using net ionic equations. These topics are introduced in Chapters 16 and 19.

Snapshot Review

ChemSkill Builder 5.3

❐ Only spectator ions—ions that are identical and in solution before and after the reaction—are omitted from a net ionic equation.

A. Write a net ionic equation for each of the following:
   (a) $(NH_4)_2SO_4(aq) + Ba(NO_3)_2(aq) \rightarrow BaSO_4(s) + 2\,NH_4NO_3(aq)$
   (b) $2\,HClO_2(aq) + Ba(OH)_2(aq) \rightarrow Ba(ClO_2)_2(aq) + 2\,H_2O(\ell)$
   (c) $2\,HClO_2(aq) + Ba(OH)_2(s) \rightarrow Ba(ClO_2)_2(aq) + 2\,H_2O(\ell)$

B. Complete and balance a net ionic equation for each of the following reactions: (a) aqueous chromium(III) nitrate plus chromium metal and, (b) zinc metal plus hydrochloric acid.

Key Terms

Key terms are defined in the Glossary.

ionic equation (9.2)   spectator ion (9.2)   total equation (9.2)
net ionic equation (9.2)   strong electrolyte (9.1)   weak electrolyte (9.1)
nonelectrolyte (9.1)

Summary

In aqueous solutions of ionic compounds, the ions act independently of each other. Soluble ionic compounds are written as their separate ions. We must be familiar with the solubility rules presented in Chapter 8 and recognize that the following types of compounds are strong electrolytes: strong acids in solution, soluble metallic hydroxides, and salts. (Salts, which can be formed as the products of reactions of acids with bases, include all ionic compounds except strong acids and bases and metallic oxides and hydroxides.) Compounds must be *both ionic and soluble* to be written in the form of their separate ions. (Section 9.1)

A net ionic equation describes the actual reaction between ions of compounds in aqueous solution. Ions that do not change at all during the reaction are omitted from

the equation; these ions are called spectator ions. One net ionic equation may describe the reactions of many compounds. For example, the net ionic equation

$$Ag^+(aq) + Cl^-(aq) \rightarrow AgCl(s)$$

summarizes all the reactions described by the statement: "Any soluble silver salt reacts with any soluble ionic chloride to produce (the insoluble) silver chloride." The equation also gives the mole ratios, which the statement does not.

Net ionic equations are balanced only if the numbers of atoms of each element and the net charge on each side of the equation are all balanced.

Net ionic equations also make many quantitative examples easier to solve. (Section 9.2)

Items for Special Attention

■ Strong acids react completely with water to form ions in solution. Metal hydroxides and salts are ionic in the solid state, as well as in solution; however, in the solid state, such compounds are written as complete compounds because the ions are not independent of each other.

■ Pure HCl is classified as a strong electrolyte (even though it does not conduct electricity) because its aqueous solution conducts well.

■ Most ionic compounds are composed of only one type of positive ion and one type of negative ion. (Of course, more than one of each type of ion may be present in each formula unit.)

■ Don't be confused about what should be included in net ionic equations. It is easier to remember what should be left out: *Only ions in solution that remain unchanged in solution* should be left out to produce net ionic equations; all other species must be included. Thus, insoluble compounds (ionic or not), covalent compounds, elements, and ions that change in any way between reactants and products are all included. Remembering what to omit—the spectator ions—is much easier!

Answers to Snapshot Reviews

9.1 A. (a) $C_{12}H_{22}O_{11}$ (b) $NH_4^+ + Cl^-$
       (c) $2\ Na^+ + SO_4^{2-}$
     B. (b) $HClO_3(aq)$, (d) $KCl(aq)$, and (e) $KCl(\ell)$
9.2 A. (a) $SO_4^{2-}(aq) + Ba^{2+}(aq) \rightarrow BaSO_4(s)$
       (b) $HClO_2(aq) + OH^-(aq) \rightarrow$
                                 $ClO_2^-(aq) + H_2O(\ell)$

     (c) $2\ HClO_2(aq) + Ba(OH)_2(s) \rightarrow$
                       $2\ ClO_2^-(aq) + Ba^{2+}(aq) + 2\ H_2O(\ell)$
     B. (a) $2\ Cr^{3+}(aq) + Cr(s) \rightarrow 3\ Cr^{2+}(aq)$
       (b) $Zn(s) + 2\ H^+(aq) \rightarrow H_2(g) + Zn^{2+}(aq)$

Self-Tutorial Problems

9.1 What is the difference in the nature of the bonding of the chlorine in the following species?

PCl_3 $FeCl_3$ $Fe(ClO_3)_3$ Cl_2

9.2 Write formulas for the ions that constitute each of the following compounds:

(a) $Mg(NO_2)_2$ (b) CrF_2 (c) $(NH_4)_3PO_4$

(d) K_2SO_4 (e) $KMnO_4$ (f) BaO_2

9.3 For each of the following compounds, determine whether it is soluble in water, whether it is ionic in the pure state or in solution, and whether it should be written as a compound or as separate ions in an ionic equation. Then write the compound as it should be written in an ionic equation.

(a) H_2O_2 (b) Hg_2Cl_2 (c) $HgCl_2$

(d) HI   (e) $HClO_4$ (f) C_4H_9OH
                                    (butyl alcohol)

9.4 Write each of the following species (in aqueous solution, if soluble) as it should appear in an ionic equation:

(a) H_3PO_4 (b) $BaSO_4$

(c) $AgC_2H_3O_2$ (d) $Pb(ClO_3)_2$

(e) NH_4IO_3 (f) $PbCl_2$

(g) $KMnO_4$ (h) $K_2Cr_2O_7$

(i) HNO_3 (j) $C_3H_6O(aq)$ (acetone)

9.5 Write each of the following species (in aqueous solution, if soluble) as it should appear in an ionic equation:

(a) HClO   (b) $Cd(C_2H_3O_2)_2$

(c) NH_4Cl (d) NH_3

(e) AgCl   (f) Al_2O_3

(g) $Fe(ClO_3)_3$ (h) KH_2PO_4

(i) $Co(ClO_3)_2$ (j) CO_2

(k) $PbCl_2$ (l) $HClO_4$

(m) $Ba(OH)_2(s)$ (n) $KC_2H_3O_2$

(o) CuCl   (p) $C_2H_5OH(aq)$ (ethyl alcohol)

9.6 Which, if any, of the common acids exist as ions (a) in the pure state and (b) in aqueous solution?

9.7 Assuming that each of the following acids is in aqueous solution, write its formula to best represent it:

(a) HCl   (b) HClO   (c) $HClO_2$

(d) $HClO_3$ (e) $HClO_4$

9.8 Assuming that each of the following compounds is in aqueous solution, write its formula to best represent it:

(a) KCl   (b) KClO   (c) $KClO_2$

(d) $KClO_3$ (e) $KClO_4$

9.9   Write a net ionic equation for the reaction of (a) Zn with HCl, (b) Zn with any strong acid, and (c) Zn with a strong acid.

9.10 Assuming that each of the following compounds is in aqueous solution, write its formula to best represent it:

(a) NH_4ClO_3 (b) $HC_2H_3O_2$ (c) CO_2

(d) $AlCl_3$ (e) CH_2O (formaldehyde)

9.11 Which ones of the following are strong electrolytes? Which conduct electricity?

(a) $HCl(g)$ (b) $KCl(s)$ (c) $H_2SO_3(\ell)$

9.12 Write a net ionic equation for each of the following reactions:

(a) $Ba(OH)_2(aq) + 2\,HCl(aq) \rightarrow$
$$BaCl_2(aq) + 2\,H_2O(\ell)$$

(b) $Ba(OH)_2(s) + 2\,HCl(aq) \rightarrow$
$$BaCl_2(aq) + 2\,H_2O(\ell)$$

(c) Is the same quantity of heat expected in each reaction?

9.13 A bottle labeled "Ag^+ Test Reagent" in a chemistry lab is used to test for the presence of silver ion. What does the bottle contain?

Problems

9.1 Properties of Ionic Compounds in Aqueous Solution

9.14 Assuming that each of the following compounds is in aqueous solution, write its formula to best represent it:

(a) $CuSO_4$ (b) H_2S (c) HNO_2

(d) $UO_2(NO_3)_2$ (e) $(NH_4)_2Cr_2O_7$

9.15 Write the formula for each of the following compounds to best represent it in the presence of water:

(a) $HClO_4$ (b) $CuCl_2$ (c) $HClO_2$

(d) Cu_2S (e) $AgCl$ (f) $(NH_4)_2SO_3$

9.16 Write the formula for each of the following compounds to best represent it in the presence of water:

(a) $ZnCl_2$ (b) $(NH_4)_2S_2O_3$ (c) Hg_2O

(d) $BaCO_3(s)$ (e) Li_2SO_4 (f) H_3PO_4

9.17 (a) Would HF or NaF be better for making a solution containing fluoride ion, or doesn't it make any difference?

(b) Would HCl or NaCl be better for making a solution containing chloride ion, or doesn't it make any difference?

9.18 Would an alkali metal phosphate or a transition metal phosphate be better for making a solution containing phosphate ion?

9.2 Writing Net Ionic Equations

9.19 Balance each of the following net ionic equations:

(a) $Pb(s) + Cr^{3+}(aq) \rightarrow Cr^{2+}(aq) + Pb^{2+}(aq)$

(b) $Br^-(aq) + Ce^{4+}(aq) \rightarrow Ce^{3+}(aq) + Br_2(aq)$

(c) $Ag^+(aq) + Cu(s) \rightarrow Cu^{2+}(aq) + Ag(s)$

(d) $Cu_2O(s) + H^+(aq) \rightarrow Cu(s) + Cu^{2+}(aq) + H_2O(\ell)$

(e) $Co^{3+}(aq) + Co(s) \rightarrow Co^{2+}(aq)$

9.20 Write a net ionic equation for the reaction of an insoluble metal oxide, represented as M_2O_3, with a strong acid, H_2X.

9.21 Balance each of the following net ionic equations:

(a) $Mn(s) + Co^{3+}(aq) \rightarrow Co^{2+}(aq) + Mn^{2+}(aq)$

(b) $NH_3(aq) + Cu^{2+}(aq) \rightarrow Cu(NH_3)_4{}^{2+}(aq)$

(c) $Ce^{4+}(aq) + Pd^{2+}(aq) \rightarrow Pd^{4+}(aq) + Ce^{3+}(aq)$

(d) $PbSO_4(s) + H_2O(\ell) \rightarrow$
$$PbO_2(s) + SO_4{}^{2-}(aq) + H^+(aq) + Pb(s)$$

9.22 Write a net ionic equation for each of the following reactions:

(a) $BaI_2(aq) + K_2CO_3(aq) \rightarrow 2\,KI(aq) + BaCO_3(s)$

(b) $2\,HNO_3(aq) + Ba(OH_2)(s) \rightarrow$
$$Ba(NO_3)_2(aq) + 2\,H_2O(\ell)$$

(c) $NaHCO_3(aq) + NaOH(aq) \rightarrow$
$$Na_2CO_3(aq) + H_2O(\ell)$$

(d) $NaHCO_3(aq) + HCl(aq) \rightarrow$
$$NaCl(aq) + H_2O(\ell) + CO_2(g)$$

(e) $NaBr(aq) + AgNO_3(aq) \rightarrow NaNO_3(aq) + AgBr(s)$

(f) $Pb(C_2H_3O_2)_2(aq) + 2\,KI(aq) \rightarrow$
$$PbI_2(s) + 2\,KC_2H_3O_2(aq)$$

9.23 Do either part (a) or part (b).

(a) Write a total equation for the reaction of 15 different soluble metal chlorides with each of the following: lead(II) nitrate, lead(II) acetate, and lead(II) chlorate.

(b) Write one net ionic equation representing all 45 equations of part (a).

9.24 Write six total equations that correspond to the following net ionic equation and have an alkali metal ion and nitrate ion as spectator ions:

$$Pb^{2+}(aq) + S^{2-}(aq) \rightarrow PbS(s)$$

9.25 Write a net ionic equation for the reaction of silver acetate with each of the following in aqueous solution:

(a) Aluminum chloride

(b) Vanadium(II) chloride

(c) Cadmium chloride

(d) Hydrochloric acid

(e) Chromium(III) chloride

(f) Nickel(II) chloride

(g) Cobalt(III) chloride

9.26 Write six total equations that are represented by the following net ionic equation and have spectator ions chosen from Na^+, NH_4^+, ClO_3^-, NO_3^-, and $C_2H_3O_2^-$:

$$Ca^{2+}(aq) + CO_3^{2-}(aq) \rightarrow CaCO_3(s)$$

9.27 Write a net ionic equation for the reaction of aqueous barium chlorate with aqueous sodium carbonate to yield solid barium carbonate and aqueous sodium chloride.

9.28 Write a net ionic equation for the reaction of aqueous silver acetate with aqueous sodium carbonate to yield solid silver carbonate and aqueous sodium acetate.

9.29 Write a net ionic equation for each of the following reactions:

(a) $HClO_3(aq) + NaOH(aq) \rightarrow NaClO_3(aq) + H_2O(\ell)$

(b) $HClO_2(aq) + NaOH(aq) \rightarrow NaClO_2(aq) + H_2O(\ell)$

9.30 Complete and balance the following equations:

(a) $NH_4^+(aq) + OH^-(aq) \rightarrow$

(b) $NH_3(aq) + H^+(aq) \rightarrow$

9.31 (a) Write six total equations that correspond to the following net ionic equation and have an alkali metal ion and nitrate ion as spectator ions:

$$Ag^+(aq) + I^-(aq) \rightarrow AgI(s)$$

(b) If any of three anions—acetate ion, chlorate ion, or nitrate ion—were used as a spectator ion, how many total equations could be written?

9.32 Balance the following equations. Then write a net ionic equation for each.

(a) $Sn(s) + HCl(aq) \rightarrow H_2(g) + SnCl_2(aq)$

(b) $Sn(s) + H_2SO_4(aq) \rightarrow H_2(g) + SnSO_4(aq)$

(c) $Sn(s) + HClO_3(aq) \rightarrow H_2(g) + Sn(ClO_3)_2(aq)$

9.33 Balance the following net ionic equations:

(a) $Ce^{4+}(aq) + Pt^{2+}(aq) \rightarrow Pt^{4+}(aq) + Ce^{3+}(aq)$

(b) $H_2(g) + Ag^+(aq) \rightarrow Ag(s) + H^+(aq)$

(c) $I^-(aq) + Cu^{2+}(aq) \rightarrow CuI(s) + I_2(aq)$

9.34 Write a net ionic equation for the reaction of aqueous barium nitrate with aqueous sodium hydrogen carbonate to yield solid barium carbonate, aqueous sodium nitrate, carbon dioxide, and water.

9.35 Write five total equations that are represented by the following net ionic equation:

$$2\,H^+(aq) + CO_3^{2-}(aq) \rightarrow H_2O(\ell) + CO_2(g)$$

9.36 Write a net ionic equation for the reaction of aqueous $Ba(OH)_2$ with aqueous H_2SO_4.

9.37 Name one compound which could be used to provide each ion in Problem 9.30.

9.38 Write a net ionic equation for the reaction of

(a) A strong acid with a strong base

(b) A strong acid with ammonia (a weak base)

(c) A weak acid, represented as HA, with a strong base

9.39 Write a net ionic equation for the reaction of ammonium sulfide with each of the following in aqueous solution. An insoluble sulfide is formed in each case.

(a) Manganese(II) sulfate   (b) Iron(II) sulfate

(c) Copper(II) sulfate   (d) Zinc sulfate

(e) Cobalt(II) sulfate   (f) Nickel(II) sulfate

9.40 Barium hydroxide, $Ba(OH)_2$, has limited water solubility. If a small quantity of barium hydroxide is added to a given volume of water, it might dissolve. If a large quantity of barium hydroxide is added to the same volume of water, most of it will not dissolve. Thus, barium hydroxide might appear in an equation as either solid or aqueous. Write a net ionic equation for the reaction of barium hydroxide with $HClO_4$ for each of these cases.

General Problems

9.41 Complete and balance the following net ionic equations. There is a reaction in each case.

(a) $Pb^{2+}(aq) + SO_4^{2-}(aq) \rightarrow$

(b) $Ag^+(aq) + CN^-(aq) \rightarrow$

(c) $H^+(aq) + NH_3(aq) \rightarrow$

(d) $H^+(aq) + CO_3^{2-}(aq,\ excess) \rightarrow$

(e) $HCO_3^-(aq) + H^+(aq) \rightarrow$

(f) $HCO_3^-(aq) + OH^-(aq) \rightarrow$

9.42 Write a balanced total equation and a balanced net ionic equation for each of the following reactions (there is a reaction in each case):

(a) $BaCO_3(s) + HNO_3(aq) \rightarrow$

(b) $H_2SO_4(aq) + BaCO_3(s) \rightarrow$

(c) $MgCO_3(s) + CO_2(g) + H_2O(\ell) \rightarrow$

(d) $Ca(HCO_3)_2(aq) + H_2SO_4(aq) \rightarrow$

(e) $BaO(s) + HCl(aq) \rightarrow$

■ General Problems

9.43 Write a balanced total equation and a balanced net ionic equation for each of the following reactions (there is a reaction in each case):

(a) $NH_4NO_3(aq) + Ba(OH)_2(aq) \rightarrow$

(b) $NH_4C_2H_3O_2(aq) + HCl(aq) \rightarrow$

(c) $Na_2HPO_4(aq) + HNO_3(aq, excess)$

9.44 Write a balanced total equation and a balanced net ionic equation for each of the following reactions (there is a reaction in each case):

(a) $KC_2H_3O_2(aq) + HClO_3(aq) \rightarrow$

(b) $NH_4Cl(aq) + NaOH(aq) \rightarrow$

(c) $NaH_2PO_4(aq) + HClO_4(aq) \rightarrow$

(d) $(NH_4)_2CO_3(aq) + HNO_3(aq, excess) \rightarrow$

9.45 Write a balanced net ionic equation for each of the following reactions (there is a reaction in each case):

(a) $Ba(NO_3)_2(aq) + K_3PO_4(aq) \rightarrow$

(b) $Hg_2(NO_3)_2(aq) + NaCl(aq) \rightarrow$

(c) $CuCl_2(aq) + (NH_4)_2S(aq) \rightarrow$

(d) $ZnCl_2(aq) + (NH_4)_2S(aq) \rightarrow$

(e) $Hg(C_2H_3O_2)_2(aq) + K_3PO_4(aq) \rightarrow$

(f) $CaCl_2(aq) + K_2CO_3(aq) \rightarrow$

9.46 Write a net ionic equation for the reaction of (a) a soluble carbonate with excess strong acid, (b) a soluble acid carbonate with a strong acid, (c) a soluble acid carbonate with a strong base, and (d) CO_2 with excess strong aqueous base.

9.47 When $CHCl_3(\ell)$ (chloroform) is treated with $AgNO_3(aq)$, no reaction occurs. Explain why.

9.48 Write net ionic equations for the reactions required in Problem 8.91.

9.49 Write a net ionic equation for the reaction of sodium metal with water. What is unusual about this equation?

9.50 Write a total equation corresponding to the following net ionic equation:

$$CaC_2O_4(s) + H^+(aq) \rightarrow Ca^{2+}(aq) + HC_2O_4^-(aq)$$

9.51 Write a net ionic equation corresponding to the following total equation:

$$2\,MgC_2O_4(s) + 2\,HCl(aq) \rightarrow$$
$$MgCl_2(aq) + Mg(HC_2O_4)_2(aq)$$

9.52 Write a net ionic equation and a full equation for each of the following reactions:

(a) Oxalic acid $(H_2C_2O_4)$ with a limited quantity of aqueous KOH

(b) MgO with HCl

(c) Solid $Ca(H_2PO_4)_2$ with a limited quantity of NaOH to give solid $CaHPO_4$

(d) Aqueous $Mg(H_2PO_4)_2$ with a limited quantity of NaOH to give aqueous $MgHPO_4$

9.53 Explain why the reaction of HCl with NaOH and the reaction of HNO_3 with aqueous $Ba(OH)_2$ yield the same quantity of heat per mole of water produced.

9.54 When two equations are added to yield a third equation, the heats of reaction of the two may be added to obtain the heat of reaction of the third. The following reactions were carried out at 25°C under the same conditions of concentration, pressure, etc. The first two yielded 59.4 kilojoules (kJ) and 2.5 kJ of heat per mole of the first reactant, respectively. What was the heat liberated per mole of the first reactant for the third reaction? How can we tell?

$$Na_2S(aq) + HCl(aq) \rightarrow$$
$$NaHS(aq) + NaCl(aq) + 59.4\,kJ$$

$$KHS(aq) + HClO_3(aq) \rightarrow$$
$$KClO_3(aq) + H_2S(g) + 2.5\,kJ$$

$$Li_2S(aq) + 2\,HClO_4(aq) \rightarrow 2\,LiClO_4(aq) + H_2S(g)$$

10

Stoichiometry

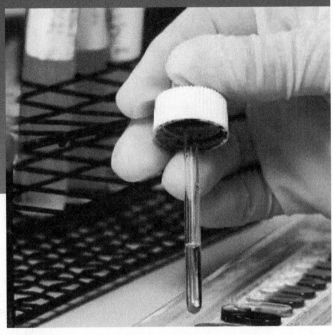

Color testing to analyze a sample

Review Clues

Objectives

10.1   To calculate the number of moles of any other substance in a chemical reaction from the number of moles of any one of the substances

10.2   To use the mass of one substance to determine masses of other substances involved in a chemical reaction

10.3   To determine how much of any substance is involved in a chemical reaction, given any quantity of another substance, no matter what units are involved

10.4   To calculate the quantities of substances produced in a reaction when quantities of more than one reactant are specified

10.5   To express the quantity of product obtained from a reaction as a percentage of what the reaction is theoretically capable of producing

10.6   To calculate the numbers of moles involved in net ionic equations, to calculate the masses of complete compounds involved in such equations, and to recognize the limitations of net ionic equations in calculating masses of individual ions

In Chapter 7, we learned to interpret chemical formulas in terms of the quantities of the elements involved. In Chapters 8 and 9, we learned to complete and balance chemical equations. This chapter shows how to interpret the quantities of substances involved in a chemical reaction, using the balanced chemical equation almost as the formula was used in Chapter 7.

Just as compounds have definite ratios of elements, chemical reactions have definite ratios of reactants and products. Those ratios are used in Section 10.1 to calculate the number of moles of other substances in a reaction from the number of moles of any one of the substances. Section 10.2 combines information from Section 10.1, Chapter 7, and elsewhere to explain how to calculate the mass of any substance involved in a reaction from the mass of another. Section 10.3 demonstrates how to work with quantities in units other than moles or masses when finding quantities of reactants or products. Section 10.4 shows how to calculate the quantities of substances involved in a reaction even if the quantities of reactants present are not in the mole ratio of the balanced equation. Section 10.5 covers the calculation of the percentage yield of a product from the actual yield and the theoretical yield, based on the amount(s) of reactant(s). Section 10.6 explains which of these types of calculations can and cannot be done with net ionic equations.

10.1   Mole Calculations for Chemical Reactions

Stoichiometry involves the calculation of quantities of any substances involved in a chemical reaction from the quantities of the other substances. The balanced equation gives the ratios of formula units of all the substances in a chemical reaction. It also gives the corresponding ratios of moles of the substances. These relationships are shown in Figure 10.1. For example, one reaction of phosphorus with chlorine gas is governed by the equation

$$2\,P(s) + 3\,Cl_2(g) \rightarrow 2\,PCl_3(\ell)$$

Figure 10.1 Mole Conversions for Stoichiometry Problems

The double-headed arrows indicate that the conversions can be made in either direction.

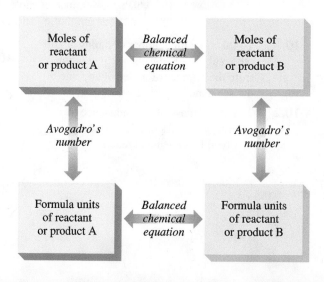

This equation can be interpreted, as shown in Chapter 8, in two ways:

1. Two atoms of phosphorus react with three molecules of Cl_2 to produce two molecules of PCl_3.
2. Two moles of phosphorus react with 3 mol of Cl_2 to produce 2 mol of PCl_3.

Using Factors to Solve Mole-Mole Problems

Consider the reaction of phosphorus with chlorine as shown in the previous equation. Of course, the chemist is not required to place exactly 2 mol of P and 3 mol of Cl_2 in a reaction flask. The equation gives the **reacting ratio.** Ratios of coefficients from balanced chemical equations can be used as conversion factors for solving problems.

EXAMPLE 10.1

Write all the possible factors from the coefficients in the following balanced equation:

$$2\,P(s) + 3\,Cl_2(g) \rightarrow 2\,PCl_3(\ell)$$

Solution

$$\frac{3\ \text{mol}\ Cl_2}{2\ \text{mol}\ P} \qquad \frac{3\ \text{mol}\ Cl_2}{2\ \text{mol}\ PCl_3} \qquad \frac{2\ \text{mol}\ P}{2\ \text{mol}\ PCl_3} \qquad \frac{2\ \text{mol}\ P}{3\ \text{mol}\ Cl_2} \qquad \frac{2\ \text{mol}\ PCl_3}{3\ \text{mol}\ Cl_2} \qquad \frac{2\ \text{mol}\ PCl_3}{2\ \text{mol}\ P}$$

Practice Problem 10.1   Write all the possible factors from the coefficients in the following balanced equation, a reaction used to make smoke-screens in World War I:

$$TiCl_4(\ell) + 2\,H_2O(\ell) \rightarrow TiO_2(s) + 4\,HCl(g)$$

The ratio that should be used in a particular problem will have the substance for which the number of moles is given in the denominator and the substance for which the number of moles is desired in the numerator, as introduced in Section 2.1.

EXAMPLE 10.2

Calculate the number of moles of aluminum atoms that will react with 3.18 mol of oxygen molecules to form aluminum oxide. The balanced equation is

$$4\,Al(s) + 3\,O_2(g) \rightarrow 2\,Al_2O_3(s)$$

Solution

$$3.18\ \text{mol}\ O_2\left(\frac{4\ \text{mol}\ Al}{3\ \text{mol}\ O_2}\right) = 4.24\ \text{mol}\ Al$$

Moles of O_2 → Balanced chemical equation → Moles of Al

Practice Problem 10.2   Calculate the number of moles of Al_2O_3 that will be produced by the reaction in Example 10.2.

Essentially, most problems involving mole calculations are as simple as the one in Example 10.2. A problem may seem more difficult if we have to write and balance an equation, but we learned how to do that in Chapter 8.

EXAMPLE 10.3

Calculate the number of moles of hydrogen gas that can be produced by reaction of 0.750 mol of hydrochloric acid, HCl, with calcium metal.

Solution

The first step, as in most stoichiometry problems, is to write a balanced equation for the reaction:

$$2\,HCl(aq) + Ca(s) \rightarrow H_2(g) + CaCl_2(aq)$$

Now the stoichiometry problem can be solved, as in Example 10.2:

$$0.750 \text{ mol HCl}\left(\frac{1 \text{ mol } H_2}{2 \text{ mol HCl}}\right) = 0.375 \text{ mol } H_2$$

Moles of HCl → Balanced chemical equation → Moles of H_2

Practice Problem 10.3   Calculate the number of moles of aqueous NaOH that must react completely with aqueous H_2SO_4 to produce 1.24 mol of Na_2SO_4.

Remember that the quantities involved in mole calculations are the quantities that *react*, not necessarily the quantities that are *present*.

EXAMPLE 10.4

A sample of 0.1712 mol of solid $KClO_3$ is heated gently for a time, and 0.1146 mol of the compound decomposes. Calculate the number of moles of oxygen gas produced.

Solution

The equation (Section 8.3) is

$$2\,KClO_3(s) \xrightarrow{\text{Heat}} 3\,O_2(g) + 2\,KCl(s)$$

In this experiment, even though 0.1712 mol of potassium chlorate is present, only 0.1146 mol reacts. The number of moles of oxygen gas produced depends on the number of moles of potassium chlorate that reacts:

Moles of $KClO_3$ → Balanced chemical equation → Moles of O_2

$$0.1146 \text{ mol KClO}_3\left(\frac{3 \text{ mol } O_2}{2 \text{ mol KClO}_3}\right) = 0.1719 \text{ mol } O_2$$

Practice Problem 10.4 In a certain reaction, 0.225 mol of H_2 gas reacts partially with N_2 gas to yield gaseous NH_3. If 0.033 mol of H_2 remains after the reaction is stopped, how many moles of N_2 is used up?

Tabulation Method

Many times (Section 10.4, Chapters 18 and 19) we will find it useful to tabulate the numbers of moles (or related quantities to be introduced later) of the substances undergoing reaction. For example, the data of Example 10.2 can be tabulated as follows:

> Quantities must be in moles.

	4 Al(s)	+	3 O_2(g)	→	2 Al_2O_3(s)
Initial quantities	Excess		3.18 mol		0.00 mol
Change due to reaction	−4.24 mol		−3.18 mol		+2.12 mol

It must be noted that the magnitudes of the quantities in the "change due to reaction" line are *always* in the ratio of the coefficients in the balanced chemical equation. It will also become apparent that the numbers of moles of reactants in the "change" line are *subtracted* from the initial quantities present and the numbers of moles of products are *added* to any initial quantities present.

	4 Al(s)	+	3 O_2(g)	→	2 Al_2O_3(s)
Initial quantities	Excess		3.18 mol		0.00 mol
Change due to reaction	−4.24 mol		−3.18 mol		+2.12 mol
Final quantities	Some excess		0.00 mol		2.12 mol

EXAMPLE 10.5

Calculate the quantities of the salt and water in solution after the reaction of 1.33 mol of HCl and excess NaOH in 15.17 mol of water.

Solution

	HCl(aq)	+	NaOH(aq)	→	H_2O(ℓ)	+	NaCl(aq)
Initial quantities	1.33 mol		Excess		15.17 mol		0.00 mol
Change due to reaction	−1.33 mol		−1.33 mol		+1.33 mol		+1.33 mol
Final quantities	0.00 mol		Some excess		16.50 mol		1.33 mol

Snapshot Review

❑ The balanced chemical equation gives the mole ratios of all the substances in the reaction, just as an empirical formula gives the ratios of atoms of the elements in a compound. As with chemical formulas, these ratios can be used as factors in calculations involving any two of the substances.

A. How many moles of hydrochloric acid does it take to prepare 1.50 mol of calcium chloride by reaction with calcium carbonate?

$$CaCO_3(s) + 2\,HCl(aq) \rightarrow CaCl_2(aq) + CO_2(g) + H_2O(\ell)$$

B. If the equation were not given in problem A, what sections of the text would have to be reviewed to answer?

10.2 Mass Calculations for Chemical Reactions

In Section 10.1, we learned to calculate the number of moles of any substances involved in a chemical reaction from the number of moles of any other substance. We can solve problems that include mass calculations by simply changing the masses to moles or the moles to masses, as discussed in Chapter 7. In Figure 10.2, these conversions have been added to those shown in Figure 10.1.

If necessary, review Chapter 6 to solve stoichiometry problems that give the names of compounds, rather than their formulas.

EXAMPLE 10.6

Calculate the mass of chlorine gas that will react with 2.88 g of phosphorus to form phosphorus pentachloride.

Solution

First, write the balanced chemical equation:

$$5\,Cl_2(g) + 2\,P(s) \rightarrow 2\,PCl_5(s)$$

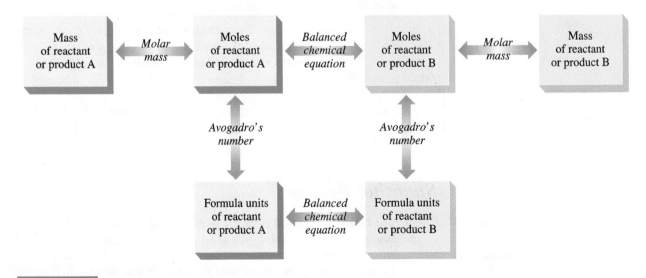

Figure 10.2 Mass and Mole Conversions for Stoichiometry Problems

The equation gives the *mole ratios,* so we need to convert the mass of phosphorus to the number of moles of phosphorus, and then we can proceed as in Section 10.1:

$$2.88 \text{ g P}\left(\frac{1 \text{ mol P}}{31.0 \text{ g P}}\right) = 0.0929 \text{ mol P}$$

$$0.0929 \text{ mol P}\left(\frac{5 \text{ mol Cl}_2}{2 \text{ mol P}}\right) = 0.2323 \text{ mol Cl}_2$$

Finally, convert the number of moles of chlorine to the mass of chlorine:

$$0.2323 \text{ mol Cl}_2\left(\frac{70.9 \text{ g Cl}_2}{1 \text{ mol Cl}_2}\right) = 16.5 \text{ g Cl}_2$$

As usual, we could combine all these steps into a single calculation:

$$2.88 \text{ g P}\left(\frac{1 \text{ mol P}}{31.0 \text{ g P}}\right)\left(\frac{5 \text{ mol Cl}_2}{2 \text{ mol P}}\right)\left(\frac{70.9 \text{ g Cl}_2}{1 \text{ mol Cl}_2}\right) = 16.5 \text{ g Cl}_2$$

Practice Problem 10.6 Calculate the mass of phosphorus pentachloride that will be produced by the reaction in Example 10.6.

> Note that the coefficient in the balanced equation has nothing to do with the molar mass.

> The coefficients in the equation relate the number of moles of one substance to the number of any other substance.

EXAMPLE 10.7

Electrolysis of concentrated aqueous sodium chloride solution (called brine) yields aqueous sodium hydroxide, hydrogen gas, and chlorine gas—three important industrial chemicals. Calculate the mass of chlorine that can be produced by electrolysis of 50.0 kg of sodium chloride in concentrated aqueous solution:

$$2 \text{ NaCl(aq)} + 2 \text{ H}_2\text{O}(\ell) \xrightarrow{\text{Electricity}} 2 \text{ NaOH(aq)} + \text{Cl}_2\text{(g)} + \text{H}_2\text{(g)}$$

Solution

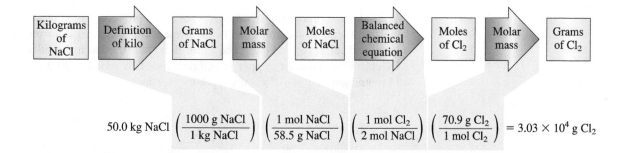

$$50.0 \text{ kg NaCl}\left(\frac{1000 \text{ g NaCl}}{1 \text{ kg NaCl}}\right)\left(\frac{1 \text{ mol NaCl}}{58.5 \text{ g NaCl}}\right)\left(\frac{1 \text{ mol Cl}_2}{2 \text{ mol NaCl}}\right)\left(\frac{70.9 \text{ g Cl}_2}{1 \text{ mol Cl}_2}\right) = 3.03 \times 10^4 \text{ g Cl}_2$$

Practice Problem 10.7 The industrial process for the production of sodium metal and chlorine gas involves electrolysis of molten (melted) sodium chloride (in the absence of water). Calculate the mass of sodium that can be prepared by electrolysis of 207 kg of sodium chloride. The balanced equation is

$$2\,NaCl(\ell) \xrightarrow{\text{Electricity}} 2\,Na(\ell) + Cl_2(g)$$

EXAMPLE 10.8

Sulfuric acid, H_2SO_4, is the chemical produced in the greatest tonnage worldwide. Calculate the number of metric tons of SO_2 gas required to prepare 50.0 metric tons of liquid H_2SO_4 (1 metric ton = 1×10^6 g). The balanced equation for the overall reaction (which is actually carried out in steps) is

$$2\,SO_2(g) + O_2(g) + 2\,H_2O(\ell) \rightarrow 2\,H_2SO_4(\ell)$$

Solution

The balanced equation can be used to calculate the quantity of a reactant from the quantity of any product, as well as vice versa. The same type of calculation is performed:

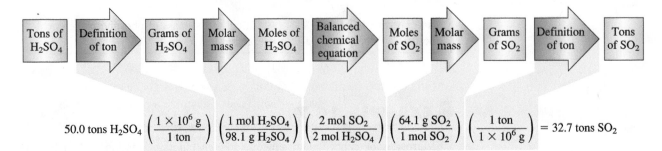

$$50.0 \text{ tons } H_2SO_4 \left(\frac{1 \times 10^6 \text{ g}}{1 \text{ ton}} \right) \left(\frac{1 \text{ mol } H_2SO_4}{98.1 \text{ g } H_2SO_4} \right) \left(\frac{2 \text{ mol } SO_2}{2 \text{ mol } H_2SO_4} \right) \left(\frac{64.1 \text{ g } SO_2}{1 \text{ mol } SO_2} \right) \left(\frac{1 \text{ ton}}{1 \times 10^6 \text{ g}} \right) = 32.7 \text{ tons } SO_2$$

Note that the two factors for the number of grams per metric ton cancel out.

Practice Problem 10.8 Calculate the mass of chlorine gas that must be treated with chromium metal to prepare 17.6 g of solid chromium(III) chloride.

EXAMPLE 10.9

The industrial processing of copper(I) sulfide to produce copper metal involves roasting (heating) the solid ore in the presence of oxygen gas to produce the metal and sulfur dioxide gas. (The sulfur dioxide is used to make sulfuric acid.) Calculate the mass of copper(I) sulfide needed to produce 70.0 metric tons (1 metric ton = 1×10^6 g) of copper by roasting.

Solution

$$Cu_2S(s) + O_2(g) \xrightarrow{\text{Heat}} 2\,Cu(s) + SO_2(g)$$

$$70.0 \times 10^6 \text{ g Cu}\left(\frac{1 \text{ mol Cu}}{63.5 \text{ g Cu}}\right)\left(\frac{1 \text{ mol Cu}_2\text{S}}{2 \text{ mol Cu}}\right)\left(\frac{159 \text{ g Cu}_2\text{S}}{1 \text{ mol Cu}_2\text{S}}\right)$$
$$= 8.76 \times 10^7 \text{ g Cu}_2\text{S} = 87.6 \text{ metric tons Cu}_2\text{S}$$

Practice Problem 10.9 Copper(II) sulfide can also be roasted in the same way as copper(I) sulfide. Calculate the mass of copper(II) sulfide needed to produce 70.0 metric tons of copper by roasting.

▌ EXAMPLE 10.10

Excess hydrochloric acid was added to an aqueous solution of calcium hydrogen carbonate, and the resulting solution was evaporated to dryness, which produced 2.29 g of solid product. Calculate the mass of calcium hydrogen carbonate in the original solution.

Solution

The equation is

$$\text{Ca(HCO}_3)_2(\text{aq}) + 2 \text{ HCl(aq)} \rightarrow \text{CaCl}_2(\text{aq}) + 2 \text{ CO}_2(\text{g}) + 2 \text{ H}_2\text{O}(\ell)$$

After evaporation to dryness, the only solid remaining is calcium chloride. The carbon dioxide bubbled off during the reaction. The water produced by the reaction and the excess hydrochloric acid were evaporated, along with the water present to make the aqueous solution. Thus, the 2.29 g of solid is calcium chloride.

$$2.29 \text{ g CaCl}_2\left(\frac{1 \text{ mol CaCl}_2}{111 \text{ g CaCl}_2}\right)\left(\frac{1 \text{ mol Ca(HCO}_3)_2}{1 \text{ mol CaCl}_2}\right)\left(\frac{162 \text{ g Ca(HCO}_3)_2}{1 \text{ mol Ca(HCO}_3)_2}\right)$$
$$= 3.34 \text{ g Ca(HCO}_3)_2$$

Practice Problem 10.10 Excess hydrochloric acid was added to 1.47 g of solid barium carbonate, and the resulting solution was evaporated to dryness. What mass of solid remained?

Snapshot Review

ChemSkill Builder 4.2

❏ This section is totally review, mostly of Sections 7.3 and 10.1. It gives some students trouble because it involves multiple steps to each problem.

A. List the steps necessary to calculate the mass of $(\text{NH}_4)_2\text{SO}_4$ that can be prepared by reaction of 13.5 g of H_2SO_4 in water solution with excess ammonia.

B. Which one of the following is true concerning the reaction

$$2 \, K(s) + Cl_2(g) \rightarrow 2 \, KCl(s)$$

(a) 2 g K will react with 1 g Cl_2 or (b) 2 mol K will react with 1 mol Cl_2?

10.3   Calculations Involving Other Quantities

Not only masses but quantities of substances in any units can be used for stoichiometry purposes. The quantities given must be changed to moles. Just as a mass is a measure of the number of moles of a reactant or product, the number of individual atoms, ions, or molecules involved in a chemical reaction may be converted to moles of reactant or product and used to solve problems. The number of moles of individual atoms or ions of a given element within a compound may also be used to determine the number of moles of reactant or product. The density of a substance may be used to determine the mass of a given volume of it and the mass may be used to determine the number of moles present. Some of these additional relationships are illustrated in Figure 10.3.

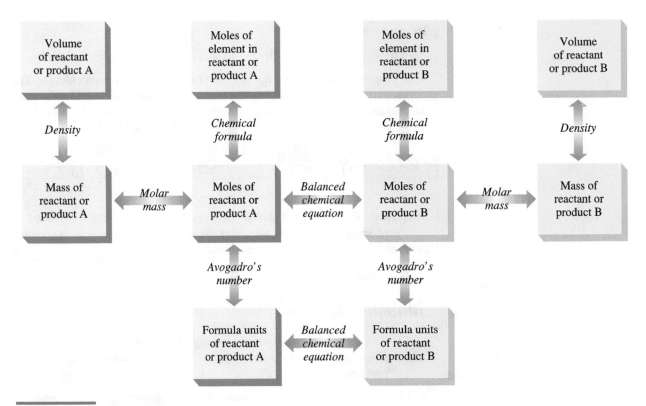

Figure 10.3 Mass, Mole, and Other Conversions

EXAMPLE 10.11

Calculate the number of moles of solid mercury(I) oxide that can be produced by the reaction of oxygen gas with 25.0 mL of liquid mercury (density = 13.6 g/mL). Also, calculate the number of molecules of oxygen required.

Solution

$$4\,\text{Hg}(\ell) + \text{O}_2(g) \rightarrow 2\,\text{Hg}_2\text{O}(s)$$

$$25.0 \text{ mL Hg}\left(\frac{13.6 \text{ g Hg}}{1 \text{ mL Hg}}\right)\left(\frac{1 \text{ mol Hg}}{200.6 \text{ g Hg}}\right)\left(\frac{2 \text{ mol Hg}_2\text{O}}{4 \text{ mol Hg}}\right) = 0.847 \text{ mol Hg}_2\text{O}$$

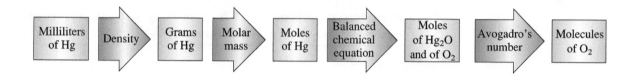

$$25.0 \text{ mL Hg}\left(\frac{13.6 \text{ g Hg}}{1 \text{ mL Hg}}\right)\left(\frac{1 \text{ mol Hg}}{200.6 \text{ g Hg}}\right)\left(\frac{1 \text{ mol O}_2}{4 \text{ mol Hg}}\right)\left(\frac{6.02 \times 10^{23} \text{ molecules O}_2}{1 \text{ mol O}_2}\right)$$
$$= 2.55 \times 10^{23} \text{ molecules O}_2$$

Practice Problem 10.11 Calculate the volume of liquid water (density = 1.00 g/mL) produced by burning 48.4 g of propane gas, C_3H_8, and condensing the gaseous water produced.

EXAMPLE 10.12

(a) A girl takes 444 pennies from her piggy bank to buy jelly beans, which cost \$3.30 per pound. If there are 110 jelly beans per pound, how many jelly beans can she buy?

(b) How many O_2 molecules does it take to produce 425 mmol of H_2O by a combination reaction with sufficient H_2 gas?

Solution

(a)

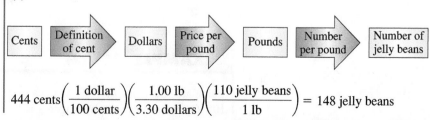

$$444 \text{ cents}\left(\frac{1 \text{ dollar}}{100 \text{ cents}}\right)\left(\frac{1.00 \text{ lb}}{3.30 \text{ dollars}}\right)\left(\frac{110 \text{ jelly beans}}{1 \text{ lb}}\right) = 148 \text{ jelly beans}$$

(b) $$2\,H_2(g) + O_2(g) \rightarrow 2\,H_2O(\ell)$$

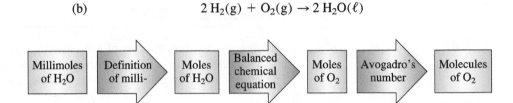

$$425\,\text{mmol}\,H_2O\left(\frac{1\,\text{mol}\,H_2O}{1000\,\text{mmol}\,H_2O}\right)\left(\frac{1\,\text{mol}\,O_2}{2\,\text{mol}\,H_2O}\right)\left(\frac{6.02\times10^{23}\,\text{molecules}\,O_2}{1\,\text{mol}\,O_2}\right)$$
$$= 1.28 \times 10^{23}\,\text{molecules}\,O_2$$

The main difference between parts (a) and (b) is that the values of more factors have to be stated in the problem in part (a) than in part (b).

Practice Problem 10.12 How many SO_2 molecules does it take to combine with O_2 to produce 0.751 mol of SO_3?

EXAMPLE 10.13

Calculate the number of molecules of CO_2 that can be produced by complete combustion of 12.5 g of gaseous C_4H_{10}.

Solution

The balanced equation for the reaction is

$$2\,C_4H_{10}(g) + 13\,O_2(g) \rightarrow 8\,CO_2(g) + 10\,H_2O(g)$$

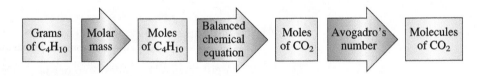

$$12.5\,\text{g}\,C_4H_{10}\left(\frac{1\,\text{mol}\,C_4H_{10}}{58.1\,\text{g}\,C_4H_{10}}\right)\left(\frac{8\,\text{mol}\,CO_2}{2\,\text{mol}\,C_4H_{10}}\right)\left(\frac{6.02\times10^{23}\,\text{molecules}\,CO_2}{1\,\text{mol}\,CO_2}\right)$$
$$= 5.18 \times 10^{23}\,\text{molecules}\,CO_2$$

Practice Problem 10.13 Calculate the mass of H_2O produced by the complete combustion of 4.57×10^{22} molecules of C_4H_{10}.

EXAMPLE 10.14

Calculate the mass of H_2O that can be prepared by the reaction of 4.51×10^{22} O_2 molecules with hydrogen gas.

Solution

$$2\,H_2(g) + O_2(g) \rightarrow 2\,H_2O(\ell)$$

Because the equation gives the mole ratio, the number of molecules is changed to moles of O_2, then to moles of H_2O, which can then be converted to grams (mass) of H_2O:

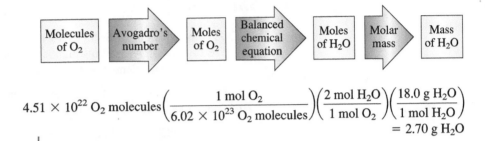

$$4.51 \times 10^{22}\ O_2\ \text{molecules} \left(\frac{1\ \text{mol}\ O_2}{6.02 \times 10^{23}\ O_2\ \text{molecules}} \right) \left(\frac{2\ \text{mol}\ H_2O}{1\ \text{mol}\ O_2} \right) \left(\frac{18.0\ \text{g}\ H_2O}{1\ \text{mol}\ H_2O} \right)$$
$$= 2.70\ \text{g}\ H_2O$$

Practice Problem 10.14   Calculate the number of individual atoms of barium metal that can react when heated with aluminum oxide to form solid barium oxide and 7.33 g of aluminum.

The number of moles of an element in a mole of compound can also be used to calculate the number of moles of the compound involved in a reaction. The ratio of the number of moles of an element within a compound to the number of moles of the compound is determined by the compound's chemical formula (Section 7.3). Thus, the subscripts of the formula may be used to form conversion factors.

EXAMPLE 10.15

The quantities of nitrogen, phosphorus, and potassium in a fertilizer are critical to the fertilizer's function in helping crops grow. Calculate the number of moles of nitrogen atoms in the ammonium phosphate, $(NH_4)_3PO_4$, produced by the reaction of excess aqueous ammonia with 227 mol of phosphoric acid.

Solution

The reaction is

$$3\,NH_3(aq) + H_3PO_4(aq) \rightarrow (NH_4)_3PO_4(aq)$$

$$227\ \text{mol}\ H_3PO_4 \left(\frac{1\ \text{mol}\ (NH_4)_3PO_4}{1\ \text{mol}\ H_3PO_4} \right) \left(\frac{3\ \text{mol}\ N}{1\ \text{mol}\ (NH_4)_3PO_4} \right) = 681\ \text{mol}\ N$$

From the
chemical formula

Practice Problem 10.15   Calculate the mass of nitrogen in the ammonium phosphate, $(NH_4)_3PO_4$, prepared by treating 6.15×10^6 g of phosphoric acid with excess aqueous ammonia.

Snapshot Review

❑ The conversions of Sections 10.1 and 10.2 are extended in this section, using Avogadro's number, density, and chemical formulas (moles of one element per mole of any other substance).

A. Calculate the mass of PCl_3 required to prepare the quantity of HCl that contains 4.55×10^{23} chlorine atoms by the following reaction:

$$PCl_3(\ell) + 3\,H_2O(\ell) \rightarrow H_3PO_3(\ell) + 3\,HCl(g)$$

10.4   Problems Involving Limiting Quantities

In problems in the preceding sections, a quantity of one reactant was given, and it was assumed that enough of any other reactants was present. In Example 10.3, for instance, 0.750 mol of hydrochloric acid reacted with calcium. If no calcium is present, however, no reaction is possible—no matter how many moles of hydrochloric acid there are. In Example 10.3, we assumed that sufficient calcium was present because nothing was stated about the quantity of calcium used. In contrast, problems involving limiting quantities have the quantities of at least two reactants given. The reactant used up first limits the quantities of the products and is referred to as being present in **limiting quantity.** Any other reactant may be present in an amount that represents a number of moles equal to or greater than is required for the reaction and is said to be present in sufficient or **excess** quantity. The reaction is said to have gone to **completion** when the limiting quantity has been used up. An example from everyday life illustrates this principle.

> The reactant that is present in limiting quantity determines the extent of reaction that can take place.

EXAMPLE 10.16

(a) If cashew nuts cost $8.00 per pound, how many pounds of these nuts can be purchased with $108.00?

(b) How many pounds of cashew nuts can be purchased with $108.00 if the store has 12.5 lb in stock?

Solution

(a) Assuming that the store has sufficient nuts,

$$108.00 \text{ dollars}\left(\frac{1 \text{ lb}}{8.00 \text{ dollars}}\right) = 13.5 \text{ lb}$$

Dollars → Price per pound → Pounds

(b) Even though the amount of money is sufficient to purchase 13.5 lb of nuts, the store does not have that much. The maximum quantity that can be purchased is the 12.5 lb on hand. The nuts are said to be available in limited quantity. No matter how much more money is available, the quantity of nuts limits the purchase.

Practice Problem 10.16 How many pounds of cashew nuts, at $8.00 per pound, can be purchased with $150.00 if the store has 20.0 pounds of the nuts?

EXAMPLE 10.17

(a) Calculate the quantity of calcium metal required to react with 1.50 mol of aqueous hydrochloric acid.

(b) Calculate the quantity of calcium that will react with 1.50 mol of HCl if 1.00 mol of calcium is present.

(c) Calculate the quantity of calcium that will react with 1.50 mol of HCl if 0.500 mol of calcium is present.

Solution

(a) The quantity of calcium is determined in the same way as the quantity of hydrogen was in Example 10.3:

$$Ca(s) + 2\,HCl(aq) \rightarrow CaCl_2(aq) + H_2(g)$$

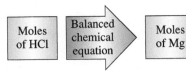

$$1.50\text{ mol HCl}\left(\frac{1\text{ mol Ca}}{2\text{ mol HCl}}\right) = 0.750\text{ mol Ca}$$

(b) In part (a), we determined that 0.750 mol of Ca will react with 1.50 mol of HCl. Because more calcium is present in this case, 0.750 mol will be used up, and the remaining 0.25 mol will not react. Ca is *in excess*.

(c) In part (a), we showed that 0.750 mol of Ca is required to react with 1.50 mol of HCl, but in this case, not that much calcium is present. Calcium is *in limiting quantity*, and the entire 0.500 mol of Ca will react with 1.00 mol of HCl:

$$0.500\text{ mol Ca}\left(\frac{2\text{ mol HCl}}{1\text{ mol Ca}}\right) = 1.00\text{ mol HCl}$$

The hydrochloric acid is in excess. The number of moles of HCl that will be left unreacted is the difference:

$$
\begin{array}{r}
1.50\text{ mol HCl present} \\
-1.00\text{ mol HCl reacts} \\
\hline
0.50\text{ mol HCl unreacted}
\end{array}
$$

Practice Problem 10.17 Calculate the number of moles of hydrogen gas that will be produced in each part of Example 10.17.

> Limiting quantities problems have the quantities of two (or more) reactants given.

The first task in doing a problem involving a limiting quantity is to recognize that it is such a problem. Fortunately, that is fairly easy: The quantities of two different reactants are given. Then, use the tabulation method outlined in Section 10.1. Do the steps given in the left column to solve the following example in the right column:

Calculate the number of moles of each of the products and of the excess reactant when 1.500 mol of A and 0.500 mol of B are allowed to react according to the following general equation:

$$3\,A + 2\,B \rightarrow C + 3\,D$$

Steps

Step 1:   Write the balanced chemical equation for the reaction.

Step 2:   Write the initial number of moles of each reactant (and product) under its formula.

Step 3:   Determine which reactant is limiting by dividing the number of moles of each reactant given in the problem by the coefficient of that reactant in the balanced chemical equation. The smallest quotient indicates the limiting reagent. Then draw a line through the results so as not to use them later. Rewrite the number of moles present of the limiting quantity with a minus sign in a row corresponding to the change due to reaction.

Step 4:   Complete the "change" row by writing the number of moles of each substance that would react with or be produced from the quantity in step 3. Use a minus sign with each quantity of reactant. The magnitudes in the "change" row are in the same ratio as the coefficients in the balanced chemical equation.

Step 5:   Subtract the quantity of each reactant in the "change" row from the initial quantity and add the quantity of each product in the change row to any initial quantity to get a final quantity.

Example

$$3\,A \quad + \quad 2\,B \quad \rightarrow \quad C \quad + \quad 3\,D$$

All quantities are in moles.

| *Present initially* | 1.500 | 0.500 | 0 | 0 |

$$\frac{1.500 \text{ mol A}}{3 \text{ mol A}} = \cancel{0.500} \qquad \frac{0.500 \text{ mol B}}{2 \text{ mol B}} = \cancel{0.250}$$

B is limiting.

| *Change due to reaction* | | −0.500 | | |

| *Change due to reaction* | −0.750 | −0.500 | +0.250 | +0.750 |

| *Present finally* | 0.750 | 0.00 | 0.250 | 0.750 |

Using this method, we calculate the quantity of each product produced and the quantity of any excess reactant all in one calculation. Note that the quantities in the "initial" and "final" rows are *not* in the ratio of the balanced chemical equation; only the magnitudes of the ratios in the "change" row are in the same ratio as those in the balanced equation.

EXAMPLE 10.18

Calculate the number of moles of each of the products and of the excess reactant when 0.250 mol of PCl_5 and 1.50 mol of H_2O are allowed to react, yielding H_3PO_4 and HCl.

Solution

$$PCl_5 \;+\; 4\,H_2O \rightarrow H_3PO_4 \;+\; 5\,HCl$$

	PCl_5	H_2O	H_3PO_4	HCl
Step 1:				
Step 2: *Present initially*	0.250	1.50	0.00	0.00
Steps 3 and 4: *Change due to reaction*	−0.250	−1.00	+0.250	+1.25
Step 5: *Present finally*	0.000	0.50	0.250	1.25

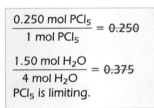

$$\dfrac{0.250 \text{ mol } PCl_5}{1 \text{ mol } PCl_5} = \cancel{0.250}$$

$$\dfrac{1.50 \text{ mol } H_2O}{4 \text{ mol } H_2O} = \cancel{0.375}$$

PCl_5 is limiting.

Note that the ratio of the magnitudes of PCl_5 to H_2O to H_3PO_4 to HCl in the "change" row is 1 : 4 : 1 : 5, just as in the balanced chemical equation.

Practice Problem 10.18 Calculate the number of moles of each product produced and the number of moles of excess reagent when 0.100 mol of HCl and 0.0250 mol of $Ba(OH)_2(aq)$ are allowed to react.

EXAMPLE 10.19

If 0.600 mol of chlorine gas is treated with 0.500 mol of aluminum metal to produce solid aluminum chloride, which reactant is in excess? How many moles of aluminum chloride can be produced?

Solution

Step 1: The balanced chemical equation is

$$2\,Al(s) + 3\,Cl_2(g) \rightarrow 2\,AlCl_3(s)$$

Step 2: We tabulate these quantities, all in moles, as follows:

$$\dfrac{0.500 \text{ mol } Al}{2 \text{ mol } Al} = \cancel{0.250}$$

$$\dfrac{0.600 \text{ mol } Cl_2}{3 \text{ mol } Cl_2} = \cancel{0.200}$$

Cl_2 is limiting.

Moles of Cl_2 (limiting)	Balanced chemical equation	Moles of Al and $AlCl_3$

	$2\,Al(s) + $	$3\,Cl_2(g) \rightarrow$	$2\,AlCl_3(s)$
Present initially	0.500	0.600	0.000
Steps 3 and 4: *Change due to reaction*	−0.400	−0.600	+0.400
Step 5: *Present finally*	0.100	0.000	0.400

In step 3, the number of moles of Cl_2 present (the limiting quantity) was used to calculate the number of moles of Al used up and $AlCl_3$ produced:

$$0.600 \text{ mol } Cl_2 \left(\dfrac{2 \text{ mol Al}}{3 \text{ mol } Cl_2} \right) = 0.400 \text{ mol Al}$$

$$0.600 \text{ mol } Cl_2 \left(\dfrac{2 \text{ mol } AlCl_3}{3 \text{ mol } Cl_2} \right) = 0.400 \text{ mol } AlCl_3$$

Remember, in such a tabulation, the magnitudes of the numbers of moles in the row showing the changes due to the reaction will always be in the same ratio as the coefficients in the balanced equation.

Practice Problem 10.19 If 1.00 mol of aluminum metal is treated with 1.75 mol of solid sulfur to produce solid aluminum sulfide, which reactant is in excess? How many moles of aluminum sulfide can be produced?

EXAMPLE 10.20

Calculate the number of moles of $BaCl_2(aq)$ that will be produced by the reaction of 1.95 mol of $Ba(OH)_2(s)$ and 4.25 mol of $HCl(aq)$.

Solution

We recognize this as a problem involving a limiting quantity because the quantities of *two* reactants are given. Because this reaction takes place in aqueous solution, the number of moles of water present before and after the reaction is unknown.

$$\frac{4.25 \text{ mol HCl}}{2 \text{ mol HCl}} = \cancel{2.125}$$

$$\frac{1.95 \text{ mol Ba(OH)}_2}{1 \text{ mol Ba(OH)}_2} = \cancel{1.95}$$

$Ba(OH)_2$ is limiting.

		$2 HCl(aq)$ +	$Ba(OH)_2(s) \rightarrow$	$BaCl_2(aq)$ +	$2 H_2O(\ell)$
Step 1:					
Step 2:	*Present initially*	4.25	1.95	0.00	
Steps 3 and 4:	*Change due to reaction*	−3.90	−1.95	+1.95	+3.90
Step 5:	*Present finally*	0.35	0.00	1.95	

Note the difference between the water *present* and the water *produced*.

Practice Problem 10.20 Calculate the number of moles of water that will be produced by the reaction of 1.95 mol of $Ba(OH)_2(s)$ and 4.25 mol of $HCl(aq)$.

If the number of moles present for each reactant is exactly the number required, then *both* reactants are in limiting quantity. *Either* quantity of reactant may be used to calculate the quantity of product.

EXAMPLE 10.21

Calculate the number of moles of $BaCl_2$ that will be produced by the reaction of 0.250 mol of $Ba(OH)_2$ and 0.500 mol of HCl.

$$\frac{0.250 \text{ mol Ba(OH)}_2}{1 \text{ mol Ba(OH)}_2} = \cancel{0.250}$$

$$\frac{0.500 \text{ mol HCl}}{2 \text{ mol HCl}} = \cancel{0.250}$$

Both reactants are limiting.

Solution

		$2 HCl(aq)$ +	$Ba(OH)_2(s) \rightarrow$	$BaCl_2(aq)$ +	$2 H_2O(\ell)$
Step 1:					
Step 2:	*Present initially*	0.500	0.250	0.000	
Steps 3 and 4:	*Change due to reaction*	−0.500	−0.250	+0.250	+0.500
Step 5:	*Present finally*	0.000	0.000	0.250	

Practice Problem 10.21 (a) Calculate the number of millimoles of PbI_2 that can be produced by treating 2.50 mmol of $Pb(NO_3)_2$ with 5.00 mmol of NaI. (b) Calculate the number of millimoles of PbI_2 that can be produced by treating 2.00 mmol of $Pb(NO_3)_2$ with 1.00 mmol of NaI.

Some quantity of a product of a reaction might be present in a reaction mixture before the reaction occurs. The tabular method of solving makes this type of problem as easy as the others. The only difference is a nonzero value for the initial number of moles of a product.

EXAMPLE 10.22

Calculate the final number of moles of HF, NaF, and NaOH present after 0.750 mol of HF, 0.250 mol of NaF, and 0.400 mol of NaOH are placed in enough water to make 1.00 L of solution.

Solution

HF reacts with NaOH, but NaF does not react with either of the others. The equation for the reaction involves the acid reacting with the base, yielding the salt and water. Tabulating the values given, all in moles, yields:

	HF	+	NaOH	→	NaF	+	H_2O
Present initially	0.750		0.250		0.400		
Change due to reaction	−0.250		−0.250		+0.250		
Present finally	0.500		0.000		0.650		

Practice Problem 10.22 Calculate the final number of moles of each reactant and product present after 0.250 mol of HF, 0.150 mol of NaF, and 0.0550 mol of NaOH are placed in 1.000 mol of water.

Problems involving limiting quantities may be stated in terms of masses, rather than moles, and a mass of product might be required. To solve, convert the masses of reactants to moles, perform the steps given earlier in this section, and convert the final number of moles of product to a mass, if required. Figure 10.4 summarizes the conversions and procedure.

EXAMPLE 10.23

What mass of Na_2SO_4 will be formed by addition of 14.4 g of $NaHCO_3$ in aqueous solution to an aqueous solution containing 4.90 g of H_2SO_4?

Solution

Change the given masses to moles:

$$14.4 \text{ g NaHCO}_3\left(\frac{1 \text{ mol NaHCO}_3}{84.0 \text{ g NaHCO}_3}\right) = 0.1714 \text{ mol NaHCO}_3 \text{ present}$$

$$4.90 \text{ g H}_2\text{SO}_4\left(\frac{1 \text{ mol H}_2\text{SO}_4}{98.1 \text{ g H}_2\text{SO}_4}\right) = 0.04995 \text{ mol H}_2\text{SO}_4 \text{ present}$$

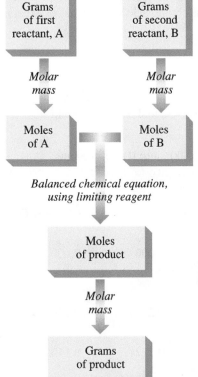

Figure 10.4 Procedure for Solving Problems Involving Limiting Quantities When Masses Are Given and Required

Then proceed as before:

Step 1:	$2\,NaHCO_3$ +	$H_2SO_4 \rightarrow$	Na_2SO_4 +	$2\,CO_2 + 2\,H_2O$

Step 2:
Present initially   0.1714   0.04995   0.000   0.000

Steps 3 and 4:
Change due to
reaction   0.0999   −0.04995   +0.04995   +0.0999

Step 5:
Present finally   0.0715   0.000   0.04995   0.0999

Change the number of moles of Na_2SO_4 to grams:

$$0.04995\ \text{mol Na}_2\text{SO}_4\left(\frac{142\ \text{g Na}_2\text{SO}_4}{1\ \text{mol Na}_2\text{SO}_4}\right) = 7.09\ \text{g Na}_2\text{SO}_4$$

Practice Problem 10.23   What mass of NaBr will be formed by addition of 12.3 g of $NaHCO_3$ to 25.0 g of HBr, both in aqueous solution?

EXAMPLE 10.24

What mass of sodium chlorate will result from the reaction of 15.5 g of aqueous sodium carbonate with 42.3 g of aqueous chloric acid? What mass of excess reagent will remain unreacted?

Solution

First convert the masses to moles:

$$15.5\ \text{g Na}_2\text{CO}_3\left(\frac{1\ \text{mol Na}_2\text{CO}_3}{106\ \text{g Na}_2\text{CO}_3}\right) = 0.1462\ \text{mol Na}_2\text{CO}_3\ \text{present}$$

$$42.3\ \text{g HClO}_3\left(\frac{1\ \text{mol HClO}_3}{84.5\ \text{g HClO}_3}\right) = 0.5006\ \text{mol HClO}_3\ \text{present}$$

Then proceed as before:

Step 1:	$2\,HClO_3$ +	$Na_2CO_3 \rightarrow$	$2\,NaClO_3$ +	$CO_2 + H_2O$

Step 2:
Present initially   0.5006   0.1462   0.000   0.000

Steps 3 and 4:
Change due to
reaction   −0.2924   −0.1462   +0.2924   +0.1462

Step 5:
Present finally   0.2082   0.000   0.2824   0.1462

Converting to mass:

$$0.2924\ \text{mol NaClO}_3\left(\frac{106.5\ \text{g NaClO}_3}{1\ \text{mol NaClO}_3}\right) = 31.1\ \text{g NaClO}_3$$

$$0.2802\ \text{mol HClO}_3\left(\frac{84.5\ \text{g HClO}_3}{1\ \text{mol HClO}_3}\right) = 23.7\ \text{g HClO}_3$$

> **Practice Problem 10.24**   What mass of $Na_2SO_4(aq)$ will result from the reaction of 22.7 g of $NaOH(aq)$ and 10.0 g of $H_2SO_4(aq)$?

EXAMPLE 10.25

Calculate the quantity of H_2O present after the reaction of 0.425 mol HCl and 0.100 mol $Al(OH)_3(s)$ in 12.00 mol of water.

Solution

Step 1:	$3\,HCl(aq) + Al(OH)_3(s) \rightarrow AlCl_3(aq) + 3\,H_2O(\ell)$		

Step 2: *Present initially*	0.425 mol	0.100 mol	0.00 mol	12.00 mol
Steps 3 and 4: *Change due* *to reaction*	−0.300 mol	−0.100 mol	+0.100 mol	+0.300 mol
Step 5: *Present finally*	0.125 mol	0.000 mol	0.100 mol	12.30 mol

$$\frac{0.425 \text{ mol HCl}}{3 \text{ mol HCl}} = 0.1417$$

$$\frac{0.100 \text{ mol Al}}{1 \text{ mol Al}} = 0.100$$

Al is limiting.

The fact that some water was present initially does not affect the solution method.

> **Practice Problem 10.25**   Calculate the number of moles of sodium acetate present after a solution containing 0.400 mol of acetic acid, $HC_2H_3O_2$, and 0.100 mol of sodium acetate, $NaC_2H_3O_2$, in 10.00 mol of water, is treated with 0.300 mol of NaOH.

Snapshot Review

ChemSkill Builder 4.4

❏ When a reaction of two or more substances has proceeded until one of the reactants has been used up, the reaction stops. To determine which reactant is limiting, divide the number of moles of each by its coefficient in the balanced equation. The lowest quotient is that of the limiting quantity. Do not use these quotients for any further calculations.

A. For each part determine which reactant in the following equation is limiting:

$$2\,Ag(s) + S(s) \rightarrow Ag_2S(s)$$

(a) 2 mol Ag and 1.5 mol S
(b) 4 mol Ag and 1 mol S
(c) 2 mol Ag and 2 mol S

B. (a) How much Ag would react with 2.5 mol S?
(b) How much S would react with 4.0 mol Ag?
(c) How much Ag and how much S react when 2.5 mol S and 4.0 mol Ag are heated together?

10.5   Theoretical Yield and Percent Yield

When a quantity of product is calculated from a quantity or quantities of reactants, as was done in Sections 10.1 through 10.4 of this chapter, that quantity of product is called the **theoretical yield.** When a reaction is run, however, less product than the calculated amount is often obtained: Some of the product may stay in the solution in which the reaction was run; some side reaction may use up some of the reactants; or the reaction may be stopped before it is completed. No matter why, the fact is that many reactions produce less product than the calculated quantity; that is, the actual yield is less than the theoretical yield. No reaction can produce more than the theoretical yield. The **percent yield** is defined as 100% times the ratio of the actual yield to the theoretical yield:

$$\text{Percent yield} = \left(\frac{\text{Actual yield}}{\text{Theoretical yield}}\right) \times 100\%$$

Example 10.26

Calculate the percent yield of a reaction if calculations indicated that 7.44 g of product could be obtained, but only 7.02 g of product was actually obtained.

Solution

$$\text{Percent yield} = \left(\frac{\text{Actual yield}}{\text{Theoretical yield}}\right) \times 100\% = \left(\frac{7.02 \text{ g}}{7.44 \text{ g}}\right) \times 100\% = 94.4\%$$

Example 10.27

Calculate the percent yield if 14.1 g of solid PCl_5 is obtained in a certain experiment in which 10.0 g of liquid PCl_3 is treated with excess gaseous Cl_2.

Solution

The theoretical yield in grams is calculated as discussed in Section 10.2:

$$PCl_3(\ell) + Cl_2(g) \rightarrow PCl_5(s)$$

$$10.0 \text{ g PCl}_3\left(\frac{1 \text{ mol PCl}_3}{138 \text{ g PCl}_3}\right)\left(\frac{1 \text{ mol PCl}_5}{1 \text{ mol PCl}_3}\right)\left(\frac{209 \text{ g PCl}_5}{1 \text{ mol PCl}_5}\right) = 15.14 \text{ g PCl}_5$$

The percent yield is

$$\left(\frac{\text{Actual yield}}{\text{Theoretical yield}}\right) \times 100\% = \left(\frac{14.1 \text{ g}}{15.14 \text{ g}}\right) \times 100\% = 93.1\%$$

Practice Problem 10.27   Calculate the percent yield if 14.1 g of PCl_5 is obtained from treatment of 10.0 g of PCl_3 with 6.00 g of gaseous Cl_2.

EXAMPLE 10.28

Ozone, O_3, is produced when O_2 molecules are subjected to electrical discharge or the action of cosmic rays in the upper atmosphere.

(a) Calculate the mass of ozone that could theoretically be produced by conversion of 1.47 g of O_2.

(b) If 0.111 g of O_3 is actually produced, what is the percent yield?

Solution

(a) $$3\,O_2(g) \rightarrow 2\,O_3(g)$$

$$1.47 \text{ g } O_2 \left(\frac{1 \text{ mol } O_2}{32.0 \text{ g } O_2} \right)\left(\frac{2 \text{ mol } O_3}{3 \text{ mol } O_2} \right)\left(\frac{48.0 \text{ g } O_3}{1 \text{ mol } O_3} \right) = 1.47 \text{ g } O_3$$

This part of the problem could have been solved by simply applying the law of conservation of mass.

(b) The percent yield is

$$\left(\frac{0.111 \text{ g}}{1.47 \text{ g}} \right) \times 100\% = 7.55\% \text{ yield}$$

 Snapshot Review

ChemSkill Builder 4.4

❏ The calculated quantity of product (Sections 10.1–10.4) is the largest possible quantity that can ever be expected, but many factors may reduce the actual yield of product. Competing reactions, solute remaining in solution, and reactions not going to completion (Chapters 18 and 19) all lead to less product than calculated. The percent yield is 100% times the ratio of the actual yield divided by the theoretical yield.

A. If 12.1 g of a certain reactant is calculated to yield 15.5 g of a product, but only 10.9 g of product is obtained, what is (a) the theoretical yield? (b) the actual yield? (c) the percent yield?

10.6   Calculations with Net Ionic Equations

Net ionic equations (Chapter 9), like all other balanced chemical equations, give the mole ratios of reactants and products. Therefore, any calculations that require mole ratios may be done with net ionic equations as well as with total equations. However, a net ionic equation does not yield mass data directly because part of each soluble ionic compound is not given. For example, we can tell how many moles of silver ion are required to produce a certain number of moles of a product, but it is impossible to weigh out just the silver ions. The compound must contain some anions, too. The net ionic equation indicates that we are not interested in the anions because they do not react. However, the anions have some mass. We cannot tell how much of the mass of the compound is composed of silver ions and how much is composed of anions if we do not specify which anions are present. Thus, net ionic equations are often not directly useful for mass computations.

EXAMPLE 10.29

How many moles of barium ions is required to produce 175 g of barium sulfate?

Solution

$$Ba^{2+}(aq) + SO_4^{2-}(aq) \rightarrow BaSO_4(s)$$

Grams of $BaSO_4$ → Molar mass → Moles of $BaSO_4$ → Formula → Moles of Ba^{2+}

$$175 \text{ g } BaSO_4 \left(\frac{1 \text{ mol } BaSO_4}{233 \text{ g } BaSO_4} \right) \left(\frac{1 \text{ mol } Ba^{2+}}{1 \text{ mol } BaSO_4} \right) = 0.751 \text{ mol } Ba^{2+}$$

We cannot weigh out 0.751 mol of Ba^{2+} if we do not know what anion is included in the compound. Even though the anion does not react, it still has some mass.

EXAMPLE 10.30

To provide 0.751 mol of Ba^{2+} takes how many grams of (a) $Ba(NO_3)_2$? (b) $Ba(ClO_3)_2$?

(a)

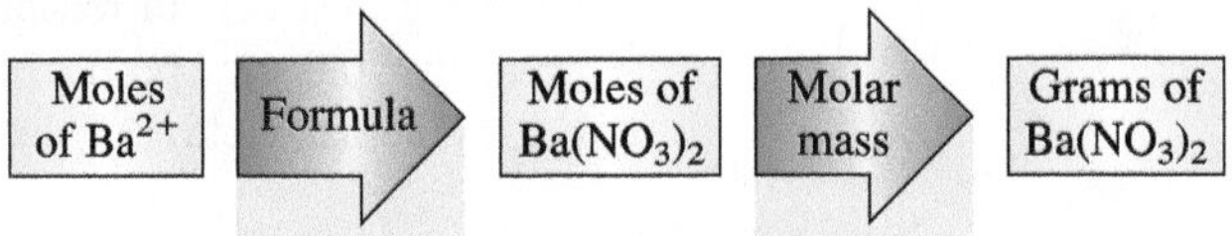

Moles of Ba^{2+} → Formula → Moles of $Ba(NO_3)_2$ → Molar mass → Grams of $Ba(NO_3)_2$

$$0.751 \text{ mol } Ba^{2+} \left(\frac{1 \text{ mol } Ba(NO_3)_2}{1 \text{ mol } Ba^{2+}} \right) \left(\frac{261 \text{ g } Ba(NO_3)_2}{1 \text{ mol } Ba(NO_3)_2} \right) = 196 \text{ g } Ba(NO_3)_2$$

(b) $$0.751 \text{ mol } Ba^{2+} \left(\frac{1 \text{ mol } Ba(ClO_3)_2}{1 \text{ mol } Ba^{2+}} \right) \left(\frac{304 \text{ g } Ba(ClO_3)_2}{1 \text{ mol } Ba(ClO_3)_2} \right)$$
$$= 228 \text{ g } Ba(ClO_3)_2$$

Practice Problem 10.30 How many moles of barium ions and how many grams of barium chloride would be required to produce 6.11 g of barium sulfate?

●●●●●●●●●●●●●●●●●●●●●●●●
ITEM OF INTEREST

The masses of individual ions are important in food chemistry. For example, too much sodium in the diet may be harmful to our health. Since it doesn't matter much what anion is present, the quantity of sodium is given on package labels. The general public, however, is not familiar with moles, so the mass of sodium is stated as part of the nutritional information on packaged foods.

The mass of a metal ion is essentially that of the atom, since the electrons have such a small fraction of the mass of the atom.

EXAMPLE 10.31

(a) Calculate the percent difference between the mass of a sodium atom and a sodium ion.

(b) Compare this percentage to those for a lithium atom and ion as well as for a beryllium atom and ion.

Solution

(a) The difference is the mass of an electron, 0.000549 amu.

$$\frac{0.000549 \text{ amu}}{23.0 \text{ amu}} \times 100\% = 0.00239\%$$

(b) For lithium:

$$\frac{0.000549 \text{ amu}}{6.94 \text{ amu}} \times 100\% = 0.00791\%$$

For beryllium, which has lost two electrons:

$$\frac{2 \times 0.000549 \text{ amu}}{9.01 \text{ amu}} \times 100\% = 0.0122\%$$

The difference is very small indeed.

Snapshot Review

ChemSkill Builder 5.3

❏ The mass of only the cations or only the anions in a compound cannot be measured on a balance.

❏ The mass of an ionic compound cannot be calculated from its number of moles unless the identity of both ions is known.

A. A solution is treated with 0.400 mol of Ag^+, whereupon AgCl precipitates and 0.013 mol of Ag^+ remains unprecipitated. (a) What fraction of a mole of chloride ion was present in the original solution? (b) What fraction of a mole of AgCl precipitated? (c) What mass of AgCl was produced? (d) Is it possible to tell what mass of the original compound chloride was present? (e) If the original solution contained $MgCl_2$, could its mass be calculated?

Key Terms

Key terms are defined in the Glossary.

completion (10.4)	percent yield (10.5)	stoichiometry (10.1)
excess (10.4)	reacting ratio (10.1)	theoretical yield (10.5)
limiting quantity (10.4)		

Summary

The ratios of the numbers of moles of reactants and products involved in any chemical reaction are given by the coefficients in the balanced equation for the reaction. Each ratio of moles may be used as a factor to convert the number of moles of one reactant or product to the number of moles of any other (Section 10.1).

If the quantity of any substance is given in terms of mass instead of in moles, the mass must be changed to moles before calculating the number of moles of another substance in the reaction. If the mass of a substance is required as an answer to a problem, its number of moles must be converted to a mass. (Conversions between mass and moles are presented in Chapter 7.) (Section 10.2) If some other measure of the quantity of a substance is given or required (for example, the number of molecules of a substance), an appropriate conversion factor is needed to convert to or from moles (Section 10.3).

For problems in which the quantities of two (or more) reactants are given, we must determine if one of the reactants is present in a quantity less than, equal to, or greater than that required to react with *all* the other reactants. Determine which reactant is in limiting quantity and use that quantity to calculate the quantities of the substances that will be used up and produced. A table of reactant and product quantities is useful. If masses are given, rather than moles, they must be converted to moles first (Section 10.4).

The theoretical yield is the quantity of product calculated from the quantity of reactant used (or the limiting quantity if more than one quantity is given). In some reactions, not all of the calculated product can be collected. The percent yield is the ratio of the actual yield to the theoretical yield, converted to a percentage:

$$\text{Percent yield} = \left(\frac{\text{Actual yield}}{\text{Theoretical yield}} \right) \times 100\%$$

(Section 10.5)

Net ionic equations can be used to calculate mole ratios but often cannot be used directly with masses. Although spectator ions do not react, they do have mass, and the molar mass of the compound cannot be determined if all the ions are not specified (Section 10.6).

The small number of key terms for this chapter suggests that this chapter does not introduce many new concepts. However, this chapter may seem difficult because it draws extensively on background material from earlier chapters. The concepts presented in this chapter are extremely important because they are applied in later chapters on gas laws, electrochemistry, and equilibrium, among others.

Items for Special Attention

■ The balanced chemical equation gives the *mole ratios* of reactants and products *involved in the reaction,* not the mass ratios and not the numbers of moles *present.*

■ Include the formulas of the substances involved with the units when applying the factor label method to solve stoichiometry problems. For example, write "g NaCl" or "mol NaCl," rather than just "g" or "mol."

■ The coefficient in the balanced chemical equation is *not* used in conversions between grams and moles of a substance.

■ The substance present in limiting quantity may be present in a greater number of moles than the substance in excess (but always less than would be required to react with all of the substance in excess).

Answers to Snapshot Review

10.1 A. $1.50 \text{ mol } CaCl_2 \left(\dfrac{2 \text{ mol HCl}}{1 \text{ mol } CaCl_2} \right) = 3.00 \text{ mol HCl}$

   B. Sections 6.2 and 6.3 for writing formulas from names and Sections 8.2 and 8.4 to complete and balance the equation.

10.2 A. Write a balanced chemical equation.
   Convert the 13.5 g of H_2SO_4 to moles, using the molar mass.
   Convert the moles of H_2SO_4 to moles of $(NH_4)_2SO_4$, using the ratio from the balanced chemical equation.
   Convert the moles of $(NH_4)_2SO_4$ to mass of $(NH_4)_2SO_4$, using its molar mass.

   B. Only (b) is true. The equation is a mole ratio, not a mass ratio.

10.3 A. $4.55 \times 10^{23} \text{ Cl} \left(\dfrac{1 \text{ mol Cl}}{6.02 \times 10^{23} \text{ Cl}} \right) \left(\dfrac{1 \text{ mol HCl}}{1 \text{ mol Cl}} \right) \times$
   $\left(\dfrac{1 \text{ mol } PCl_3}{3 \text{ mol HCl}} \right) \left(\dfrac{137 \text{ g } PCl_3}{1 \text{ mol } PCl_3} \right) = 34.5 \text{ g } PCl_3$

10.4 A. (a) Ag   (b) S   (c) Ag
   B. (a) 5.0 mol Ag reacts with 2.5 mol S.
      (b) 2.0 mol S reacts with 4.0 mol Ag.
      (c) 2.0 mol S reacts with 4.0 mol Ag.
      (It takes 5.0 mol of Ag to react with all the S.)

10.5 A. (a) 15.5 g   (b) 10.9 g   (c) 70.3%

10.6 A. (a) 0.387 mol   (b) 0.387 mol   (c) 55.5 g
   (d) We cannot tell, because we have no way of knowing the molar mass of the metal chloride or its number of chloride ions per formula unit.   (e) Yes

Self-Tutorial Problems

10.1 Write all the possible conversion factors using the coefficients from the following equation:

$$2 \text{ Al(s)} + 3 \text{ Cl}_2(g) \rightarrow 2 \text{ AlCl}_3(s)$$

10.2 Write all of the possible conversion factors using the coefficients from each of the following equations:

   (a) $P_2O_5(s) + 3 H_2O(\ell) \rightarrow 2 H_3PO_4(\ell)$

   (b) $2 NO(g) + Cl_2(g) \rightarrow 2 NOCl(g)$

10.3 Consider the following reaction:

$$2 \text{ Al(s)} + 6 \text{ HCl(aq)} \rightarrow 3 H_2(g) + 2 \text{ AlCl}_3(aq)$$

   Because 2 Al atoms react with 6 molecules of HCl, how many HCl molecules will react with each of the following?

   (a) 12 atoms of Al

   (b) 24 atoms of Al

   (c) 100 atoms of Al

   (d) 1 dozen atoms of Al

   (e) 1 mol of Al

   (f) 3 mol of Al

10.4 Consider the following reaction:

$$4 NH_3(g) + 5 O_2(g) \rightarrow 4 NO(g) + 6 H_2O(\ell)$$

   Because 4 NH_3 molecules react with 5 O_2 molecules, how many O_2 molecules will react with each of the following quantities of NH_3?

   (a) 12 NH_3 molecules

   (b) 1 dozen NH_3 molecules

   (c) 4 dozen NH_3 molecules

   (d) 4 mol NH_3

   (e) 1 mol NH_3

10.5 For the reaction

$$2 KClO_3(s) \xrightarrow{\text{Heat}} 2 KCl(s) + 3 O_2(g)$$

one student placed 2.00 mol of $KClO_3$ in a flask, a second student placed 0.750 mol of $KClO_3$ in a flask, and a third student placed 0.250 mol of $KClO_3$ in a flask. Which student(s) could carry out the reaction specified in the equation?

10.6 For the reaction

$$Sn(s) + 2 HCl(aq) \rightarrow H_2(g) + SnCl_2(aq)$$

one student placed 1.00 mol of tin plus excess HCl in a flask, a second student placed 2.50 mol of tin plus excess HCl in a flask, and a third student placed 5.00 mol of tin plus excess HCl in a flask. Which student(s) could carry out the reaction specified in the equation?

10.7 Consider the following balanced equation:

$$14 HCl(aq) + K_2Cr_2O_7(aq) + 6 FeCl_2(aq) \rightarrow$$
$$2 KCl(aq) + 2 CrCl_3(aq) + 6 FeCl_3(aq) + 7 H_2O(\ell)$$

   What is the ratio of moles of HCl to moles of $CrCl_3$?

10.8 Calculate the number of moles of each of the following that is necessary to produce 2.20 mol of AgCl by reaction with $AgC_2H_3O_2$:

   (a) $CoCl_2$ (b) $CrCl_2$ (c) $CaCl_2$

10.9 Calculate the number of moles of each of the following that is necessary to produce 0.700 mol of AgCl by reaction with $AgC_2H_3O_2$:

   (a) NH_4Cl (b) $ZnCl_2$ (c) $AlCl_3$

10.10 (a) How many (two-slice) sandwiches can you make with 24 slices of bread?

   (b) How many sandwiches can you make with 24 slices of bread and 14 hamburger patties?

   (c) How many sandwiches can you make with 24 slices of bread and 11 hamburger patties?

   (d) How can you recognize when a problem involves a limiting quantity?

10.11 How many moles of NaBr will be produced by the following reaction in each case?

$$2\,Na(s) + Br_2(\ell) \rightarrow 2\,NaBr(s)$$

(a) 1 mol Na and 0 mol Br_2

(b) 2 mol Na and 1 mol Br_2

(c) 3 mol Na and 1 mol Br_2

10.12 Consider the following reaction:

$$Ba(OH)_2(aq) + 2\,HNO_3(aq) \rightarrow$$
$$Ba(NO_3)_2(aq) + 2\,H_2O(\ell)$$

(a) How many moles of $Ba(NO_3)_2$ can be made with 2.50 mol of HNO_3?

(b) How many moles of $Ba(NO_3)_2$ can be made with 2.50 mol of HNO_3 and 1.10 mol of $Ba(OH)_2$?

(c) How many moles of $Ba(NO_3)_2$ can be made with 2.50 mol of HNO_3 and 2.00 mol of $Ba(OH)_2$?

10.13 Complete the "Change due to reaction" line for each of the following reactions:

(a)	A	+	2 B	→	C	+	2 D
Change due to reaction	−1.00 mol		____		____		____

(b)	A	+	2 B	→	C	+	3 D
Change due to reaction	____		−2.00 mol		____		____

(c)	2 A	+	3 B	→	C	+	2 D
Change due to reaction	____		____		+2.00 mol		____

(d)	A	+	3 B	→	C	+	2 D
Change due to reaction	____		−0.450 mol		____		____

10.14 Complete each table below:

(a)	A	+	B	→	2 C	+	2 D
Present initially	1.00 mol		1.10 mol		0.00 mol		0.00 mol
Change due to reaction	____		____		____		____
Present finally	____		____		____		____

(b)	A	+	2 B	→	C	+	2 D
Present initially	3.00 mol		4.00 mol		0.00 mol		0.00 mol
Change due to reaction	____		____		____		____
Present finally	____		____		____		____

(c)	2 A	+	3 B	→	C	+	2 D
Present initially	1.50 mol		4.00 mol		0.00 mol		0.00 mol
Change due to reaction	____		____		____		____
Present finally	____		____		____		____

(d)	A	+	2 B	→	C	+	2 D
Present initially	0.750 mol		1.25 mol		0.00 mol		0.10 mol
Change due to reaction	____		____		____		____
Present finally	____		____		____		____

10.15 For the reaction

$$Zn + 2\,AgNO_3 \rightarrow Zn(NO_3)_2 + 2\,Ag$$

calculate the number of moles of products as well as the number of moles of excess reagent after the following pairs of reagents are combined:

(a) 0.400 mol Zn + 0.400 mol $AgNO_3$

(b) 0.400 mol Zn + 1.000 mol $AgNO_3$

(c) 0.800 mol Zn + 2.000 mol $AgNO_3$

(d) 0.900 mol Zn + 1.800 mol $AgNO_3$

10.16 Explain why limiting quantities problems do not usually involve decomposition reactions.

10.17 Consider three different experiments involving the reaction of nitrogen and hydrogen:

$$N_2 + 3\,H_2 \rightarrow 2\,NH_3$$

(a) If 6.00 mol of H_2 reacts, how much N_2 reacts?

(b) If 6.00 mol of H_2 is placed in a vessel with N_2, can you tell how much N_2 reacts?

(c) If 3.00 mol of NH_3 is produced, can you tell how much H_2 reacts?

10.18 Consider the following reaction:

$$La(OH)_3(s) + 3\,HCl(aq) \rightarrow LaCl_3(aq) + 3\,H_2O(\ell)$$

(a) How many moles of $LaCl_3$ can be made with 9 mol of HCl?

(b) How many moles of $LaCl_3$ can be made with 9 mol of HCl and 5 mol of $La(OH)_3$?

(c) How many moles of $LaCl_3$ can be made with 9 mol of HCl and 2 mol of $La(OH)_3$?

Problems

10.1 Mole Calculations for Chemical Reactions

10.19 Calculate the number of moles of H_3PO_4 that will react with 1.29 mol of NaOH in aqueous solution to form Na_3PO_4.

10.20 Calculate the number of moles of H_3PO_4 that will react with 0.800 mol of $Ba(OH)_2$ to form solid $Ba_3(PO_4)_2$.

10.21 Calculate the number of moles of $Ba(OH)_2$ that will react with 0.600 mol of H_3PO_4 to form solid $BaHPO_4$.

10.22   Calculate the number of moles of $Ba(OH)_2$ that will react with 0.600 mol of H_3PO_4 to form $Ba(H_2PO_4)_2$.

10.23   Which of the following samples of metal can produce the most hydrogen by reaction with HCl?

0.500 mol Zn   0.500 mol Al   0.500 mol Mg

10.24   How many moles of C_6H_{14} can be produced by the reaction of 4.86 mol of H_2 and sufficient C_6H_{10}? The balanced equation is

$$C_6H_{10}(\ell) + 2\,H_2(g) \rightarrow C_6H_{14}(\ell)$$

10.25   How many moles of oxygen gas are required for the combustion of 7.04 mol of octane, C_8H_{18}, to yield CO_2 and water?

10.26   How many moles of oxygen gas are required for the incomplete combustion of 7.80 mol of octane, C_8H_{18}, yielding CO and H_2O?

10.27   How many moles of oxygen gas are required for the complete combustion of 6.16 mol of butane, C_4H_{10}?

10.28   How many moles of $AlCl_3$ are also produced along with 2.46 mol of H_2O from the reaction of $Al(OH)_3$ and HCl?

10.29   How many moles of $MgCl_2$ are produced along with 0.750 mol of CO_2 from the reaction of $Mg(HCO_3)_2$ and HCl?

10.30   (a) Calculate the number of millimoles of $CrO_4{}^{2-}$ that reacts with 7.00 mmol of Co^{2+} according to the following equation:

$$3\,Co^{2+}(aq) + CrO_4{}^{2-}(aq) + 8\,H^+(aq) \rightarrow$$
$$3\,Co^{3+}(aq) + Cr^{3+}(aq) + 4\,H_2O(\ell)$$

(b) How many millimoles of water are produced?

10.31   Part of an 8.00-mmol sample of HgO was decomposed by heating, and 1.50 mmol of O_2 was produced.

(a) Write the balanced equation for the reaction.

(b) Which of the numbers of millimoles given in the problem is governed by the balanced equation?

(c) Calculate the percentage of HgO that decomposed.

10.2 Mass Calculations for Chemical Reactions

10.32   Calculate the number of moles of H_2 that are produced by the reaction of aqueous HCl with 2.48 g of metallic

(a) Zn.

(b) Cd.

(c) Explain why the numbers of moles of H_2 produced in parts (a) and (b) differ greatly, even though the same number of grams of metal is used in each case.

10.33   (a) Butane, C_4H_{10}, burns in excess oxygen to produce carbon dioxide and water. Write a balanced equation for the reaction.

(b) Calculate the number of moles of carbon dioxide in 14.9 g of carbon dioxide.

(c) Calculate the number of moles of butane required to produce that number of moles of carbon dioxide.

(d) Calculate the mass of butane in that number of moles.

(e) Combine the calculations for parts (b)–(d) into one factor label solution.

10.34   (a) In an internal combustion engine, octane, C_8H_{18}, burns in limited oxygen supply to produce carbon monoxide and water. Write a balanced equation for the reaction.

(b) Calculate the number of moles of carbon monoxide in 75.7 g of carbon monoxide.

(c) Calculate the number of moles of octane required to produce that number of moles of carbon monoxide.

(d) Calculate the mass of octane in that number of moles.

(e) Combine the calculations for parts (b)–(d) into one factor label solution.

10.35   Calculate the mass of each of the following that is necessary to produce 4.00 mol of AgCl by reaction with $AgC_2H_3O_2$. (Compare with Problem 10.9.)

(a) $CoCl_3$ (b) $CaCl_2$ (c) KCl

10.36   Calculate the mass of each of the following reagents that is necessary to produce 1.75 mol of AgCl by reaction with $AgNO_3$.

(a) $PtCl_2$ (b) $SrCl_2$ (c) $NiCl_2$

10.37   Calculate the mass of product produced by each of the following combinations:

(a) 15.0 g of sodium with excess bromine

(b) 25.0 g of magnesium with excess oxygen

(c) 35.0 g of aluminum with excess sulfur

10.38   Excess $AgNO_3(aq)$ was added to a sample of $FeCl_3(aq)$, and 12.1 g of $AgCl(s)$ was produced. What mass of $FeCl_3$ was present initially?

10.39   Aluminum is produced commercially by high-temperature electrolysis of aluminum oxide dissolved in a nonaqueous melt. The electrodes are carbon.

$$Al_2O_3(solution) + 3\,C(s) \rightarrow 2\,Al(\ell) + 3\,CO(g)$$

Calculate the mass of Al_2O_3 used to produce 10.0 metric tons (10.0×10^6 g) of aluminum by this process.

10.40   *Caution: The following reactions can proceed explosively!* Calculate the number of moles of hydrogen that can be produced by reaction with water of (a) 0.600 g of lithium and (b) 0.600 g of barium. (c) Explain the difference.

10.41   Silver can be prepared from aqueous silver nitrate by reaction with zinc metal. Zinc nitrate is formed.

(a) Write a balanced equation for the reaction.

(b) Calculate the number of moles of zinc in 12.10 g of zinc.

(c) Calculate the number of moles of silver that can be produced from that number of moles of zinc.

(d) Calculate the mass of that number of moles of silver.

(e) Combine the calculations for parts (b)–(d) into a factor label solution to determine the mass of silver that can be produced using 12.10 g of zinc.

10.42 How many moles of KOH are required to completely neutralize 71.3 g of $H_2C_2O_4$?

10.43 Consider the following reaction:

$$2\,NaHCO_3(s) \xrightarrow{\text{Heat}} Na_2CO_3(s) + CO_2(g) + H_2O(g)$$

Heating 12.2 g of $NaHCO_3$ until no further reaction takes place can produce

(a) what mass of Na_2CO_3?

(b) what mass of solid product(s)?

(c) What is the difference, if any, in parts (a) and (b)?

10.44 What mass of $CaCO_3$ can be "dissolved" by 82.3 g of $HClO_3$?

$$CaCO_3(s) + 2\,HClO_3(aq) \rightarrow$$
$$Ca(ClO_3)_2(aq) + H_2O(\ell) + CO_2(g)$$

10.45 (a) Calculate the mass of NaCl that can be prepared with 7.11 g of Cl_2 and sufficient Na.

(b) Calculate the mass of NaCl that can be prepared with 7.11 g of HCl and sufficient NaOH.

(c) Which of parts (a) and (b) can be solved without any of the calculations presented in this chapter? Explain why the other part cannot be solved in the same manner.

10.46 The compound $(NH_4)_3PO_4$ is used as a fertilizer. Calculate the mass of $(NH_4)_3PO_4$ that can be produced by the reaction of 2.00 metric tons (2.00×10^6 g) of NH_3 with sufficient H_3PO_4.

$$3\,NH_3(aq) + H_3PO_4(aq) \rightarrow (NH_4)_3PO_4(aq)$$

10.47 The recharge of a lead storage cell in an automobile battery can be represented by the following equation:

$$2\,PbSO_4(s) + 2\,H_2O(\ell) \xrightarrow{\text{Electricity}}$$
$$Pb(s) + PbO_2(s) + 2\,H_2SO_4(aq)$$

Calculate the mass of elemental lead produced when 49.7 g of lead(II) sulfate reacts.

10.48 Calculate the mass of gaseous SO_2 that will be produced along with 1.500 kg of copper from the roasting of copper(II) sulfide. (*Hint:* See Practice Problem 10.9 and Example 10.9, if necessary.)

$$CuS(s) + O_2(g) \xrightarrow{\text{Heat}} Cu(s) + SO_2(g)$$

10.49 Calculate the mass of NO that can be produced by the reaction of 14.0 g of Cu according to the following balanced equation:

$$8\,HNO_3(aq) + 3\,Cu(s) \rightarrow$$
$$2\,NO(g) + 3\,Cu(NO_3)_2(aq) + 4\,H_2O(\ell)$$

10.50 Excess $Ba(NO_3)_2(aq)$ was added to a sample of $NaHCO_3(aq)$, and 7.27 g of $BaCO_3(s)$ was produced (along with CO_2, H_2O, and $NaNO_3$). What mass of $NaHCO_3$ was present initially?

10.51 Sulfur dioxide in the atmosphere contributes to acid rain. One method of controlling sulfur dioxide emission is to absorb the sulfur dioxide into a solution of a base. Calculate the mass of SO_2 that can be absorbed by 125 kg of $Ca(OH)_2$ to make $CaSO_3$.

10.52 Calculate the mass of Cl_2 required to convert 115 g of AuCl to $AuCl_3$.

10.53 Silver bromide can be "dissolved" by the action of aqueous $Na_2S_2O_3$ (called "hypo") after any silver that has been "activated" by exposure to light is reduced to metallic silver by another reagent. This process is the basis for the development of black-and-white film. Calculate the mass of hypo necessary to dissolve 2.66 g of AgBr. The equation for the dissolving process is

$$AgBr(s) + 2\,Na_2S_2O_3(aq) \rightarrow$$
$$Na_3Ag(S_2O_3)_2(aq) + NaBr(aq)$$

10.54 How many grams of steric acid, $C_{17}H_{35}COOH$, a fatty acid, can be produced by the reaction of 1110 g of H_2 and sufficient $C_{17}H_{31}COOH$, a component of an oil? The balanced equation is

$$C_{17}H_{31}COOH(\ell) + 2\,H_2(g) \rightarrow C_{17}H_{35}COOH(s)$$

10.55 What mass of HNO_3 does it take to "dissolve" 14.4 g of aluminum?

$$8\,Al(s) + 30\,HNO_3(aq) \rightarrow$$
$$3\,NH_4NO_3(aq) + 8\,Al(NO_3)_3(aq) + 9\,H_2O(\ell)$$

10.56 Calculate the mass of silver metal that can be produced by the action of 12.2 g of cadmium metal on excess aqueous silver nitrate.

10.57 Calculate the mass of zinc that must be used to produce 7.33 g of NH_4NO_3 according to the equation:

$$10\,HNO_3(aq) + 4\,Zn(s) \rightarrow$$
$$NH_4NO_3(aq) + 4\,Zn(NO_3)_2(aq) + 3\,H_2O(\ell)$$

10.58 Powdered aluminum metal can be used to reduce iron(II) oxide to molten iron, usable for spot welding. Calculate the mass of iron that can be produced by the reaction of 775 g of aluminum.

$$2\,Al(s) + 3\,FeO(s) \xrightarrow{\text{Heat}} 3\,Fe(\ell) + Al_2O_3(s)$$

10.59 What mass of P_4O_{10} results from the combustion of 45.7 g of P_4S_6? SO_2 is the other product.

10.60 In the softening of temporary hard water—water containing magnesium hydrogen carbonate—the acid salt is converted to magnesium carbonate, carbon dioxide, and water by heating.

$$Mg(HCO_3)_2(aq) \xrightarrow{\text{Heat}} MgCO_3(s) + CO_2(g) + H_2O(\ell)$$

Calculate the mass of $MgCO_3$ that can be produced from 175 g of $Mg(HCO_3)_2$.

10.61 HBF_4 is a useful reagent, especially in organic chemistry. Calculate the mass of HF required to make 125 g of HBF_4 by the following reaction:

$$H_3BO_3(aq) + 4\,HF(aq) \rightarrow HBF_4(aq) + 3\,H_2O(\ell)$$

10.62 What mass of P_4O_{10} can be prepared by combustion of 41.7 g of P_4O_6?

10.63 What mass of tin can be prepared by the reaction of 72.9 g of zinc and excess aqueous tin(II) nitrate?

10.64 Iron ore is reduced to iron with coke (impure carbon). Calculate the mass of Fe that can be produced from Fe_2O_3 with 15.00 kg of carbon. The reaction may be represented as follows:

$$Fe_2O_3(s) + 3\,C(s) \xrightarrow{\text{Heat}} 2\,Fe(\ell) + 3\,CO(g)$$

10.65 What mass of silver can be prepared by the reaction of 144 g of copper metal and excess aqueous silver nitrate?

10.66 Calculate the number of moles of oxygen gas required to convert SO_2 to 2.77 g of SO_3.

10.67 Calculate the mass of NH_3 that can be prepared by heating 122 g of solid $(NH_4)_2CO_3$. The balanced equation is

$$(NH_4)_2CO_3(s) \xrightarrow{\text{Heat}} 2\,NH_3(g) + CO_2(g) + H_2O(g)$$

10.68 What mass of $HClO_3$ is required to completely neutralize 12.8 g of $Ca(OH)_2(s)$.

10.69 What mass of P_4S_6 can be prepared by treatment of 6.19 g of sulfur with excess P_4?

10.70 Calculate the number of moles of NH_3 that can be prepared by heating 122 g of solid $(NH_4)_2SO_3$. The balanced equation is

$$(NH_4)_2SO_3(s) \xrightarrow{\text{Heat}} 2\,NH_3(g) + SO_2(g) + H_2O(g)$$

10.71 (a) Calculate the number of moles of H_2 that can be produced by the reaction of aqueous HCl with 2.48 g of metallic indium, In, forming $InCl_3$.

(b) Compare the value with the result of Problem 10.32(b), and explain the difference.

10.72 What are the differences among the following problems?

(a) Calculate the total mass of the acids produced by the reaction of excess water with 20.83 g of phosphorus pentachloride.

(b) Calculate the total mass of the acids produced by the reaction of excess H_2O with 20.83 g of PCl_5.

(c) Calculate the total mass of the HCl and H_3PO_4 produced by the reaction of excess H_2O with 20.83 g of PCl_5.

(d) $PCl_5 + 4\,H_2O \rightarrow 5\,HCl + H_3PO_4$

Calculate the total mass of the acids produced by the reaction of excess water with 20.83 g of phosphorus pentachloride.

(e) $PCl_5 + 4\,H_2O \rightarrow 5\,HCl + H_3PO_4$

Calculate the total mass of the acids produced by the reaction of excess water with 20.83 g of phosphorus pentachloride (MM = 208.3 g/mol).

(f) Calculate the mass of water that reacts with 20.83 g of phosphorus pentachloride. Use this value to calculate the total mass of the acids produced.

10.3 Calculations Involving Other Quantities

10.73 (a) How many moles of chlorine atoms does 2.35×10^{23} chlorine atoms represent?

(b) How many moles of PCl_3 contain that number of chlorine atoms?

(c) How many moles of PCl_5 can be prepared by treatment of that much PCl_3 with Cl_2?

(d) What mass of PCl_5 is that?

10.74 Calculate the number of moles of fluorine atoms in 61.7 mL of $CHClF_2$ (density = 1.49 g/mL).

10.75 What mass of $SOCl_2$ can be prepared by heating SO_2 gas with the quantity of PCl_5 that contains 3.01×10^{23} Cl atoms? The balanced equation for the reaction is

$$SO_2(g) + PCl_5(s) \rightarrow POCl_3(\ell) + SOCl_2(\ell)$$

10.76 How many nitrogen atoms are contained in the $N_2H_6(NO_3)_2$ prepared by treatment of 4.14 g of aqueous hydrazine, N_2H_4, with excess dilute nitric acid?

$$N_2H_4(aq) + 2\,HNO_3(aq) \rightarrow N_2H_6(NO_3)_2(aq)$$

10.77 What mass of diphosphorus trisulfide can be prepared by heating sulfur with the quantity of phosphorus that contains 1.50×10^{23} P atoms?

10.78 What mass of nitrogen is contained in the ammonium nitrate prepared by treatment of 6.69 g of aqueous ammonia with excess dilute nitric acid?

$$NH_3(aq) + HNO_3(aq) \rightarrow NH_4NO_3(aq)$$

10.79 Calculate the number of oxygen atoms in the chromium(III) oxide prepared by treating chromium(II) oxide with 1.72 g of oxygen gas.

10.80 Calculate the number of moles of hydrogen atoms in 45.3 mL of pure H_2O_2 (density = 1.44 g/mL).

10.81 A solid combustible material can sometimes be changed into a more useful fuel if it is converted to a gas before burning. The following reaction, known as the water gas reaction, can be used to provide gaseous fuels:

$$H_2O(g) + C(s) \xrightarrow{1200°C} CO(g) + H_2(g)$$

Water gas

(a) Calculate the number of moles of water required to convert 1.00×10^{26} carbon atoms to carbon monoxide and hydrogen.

(b) What are the products of the complete combustion of water gas?

10.82 Calculate the number of fluorine atoms in the sulfur hexafluoride prepared by treating sulfur difluoride with 6.11 g of fluorine gas.

10.83 The hydrogen used for about 90% of the industrial synthesis of ammonia comes from the following reaction at high temperature:

$$CH_4(g) + H_2O(g) \xrightarrow{\text{Ni}} CO(g) + 3 H_2(g)$$

Calculate the number of molecules of CH_4 required to produce 1.25 metric tons (1.25×10^6 g) of H_2.

10.4 Problems Involving Limiting Quantities

10.84 The director of a summer baseball camp has five home plates and 12 bases. One home plate and three bases are needed for each baseball field.

(a) How many baseball fields can the director equip?

(b) How many extra pieces of equipment will there be?

10.85 (a) Calculate the number of moles of $MgCl_2$ that will react with 5.00 mol of $AgNO_3$.

(b) Calculate the number of moles of $MgCl_2$ that will react if 2.00 mol of $MgCl_2$ is treated with 5.00 mol of $AgNO_3$.

(c) Calculate the number of moles of $MgCl_2$ that will react if 4.00 mol of $MgCl_2$ is treated with 5.00 mol of $AgNO_3$.

10.86 Calculate the number of moles of $AgCl$ that is produced in each part of Problem 10.85.

10.87 Calculate the mass of hydrogen produced when 12.7 g of zinc is treated with 22.7 g of hydrobromic acid.

10.88 For the reaction

$$Cu(s) + 2 AgNO_3(aq) \rightarrow Cu(NO_3)_2(aq) + 2 Ag(s)$$

calculate the number of moles of products as well as the number of moles of excess reagent after 0.272 mol of Cu and 0.576 mol of $AgNO_3$ are combined.

10.89 Calculate the number of moles of H_2O produced and the number of moles of excess reactant when 0.444 mol of $Mg(OH)_2$ is treated with 6.66×10^{23} molecules of HNO_3.

10.90 Calculate the number of moles of unreacted starting material that will be present when 15.50 g of HNO_3 (in aqueous solution) is treated with 5.05 g of solid $CaCO_3$.

10.91 Calculate the number of moles of each solute in the final solution after 1.75 mol of aqueous $BaCl_2$ and 2.70 mol of aqueous $AgNO_3$ are mixed.

10.92 Consider the following equation:

$$C_4H_6(g) + 2 Cl_2(g) \longrightarrow C_4H_6Cl_4(\ell)$$

(a) Calculate the mass of $C_4H_6Cl_4$ that can be prepared from 35.0 g of C_4H_6 and 105.0 g of Cl_2.

(b) Explain why this problem cannot be solved by applying the law of conservation of mass.

10.93 Calculate the number of moles of unreacted starting material that will be present when 41.2 g of HCl is treated with 25.0 g of solid $Mg(HCO_3)_2$.

10.94 Calculate the mass of solid Cu produced when 4.33×10^6 g of Cu_2S is treated with 2.00×10^6 g of O_2. SO_2 is the other product.

10.95 Calculate the mass of unreacted starting material when 17.3 g of H_2SO_4 is treated with 42.7 g of NaOH.

10.96 Calculate the mass of solid Ag_2SO_4 produced when 5.79 g of Na_2SO_4 is treated with 3.48 g of $AgNO_3$.

10.97 Calculate the number of moles of H_2O produced by the reaction of 6.02 g of $HClO_3$ and 4.95×10^{22} formula units of NaOH.

10.98 Calculate the mass of unreacted starting material when 91.1 g of H_3PO_4 is treated with 145 g of NaOH.

10.99 Calculate the number of moles of H_2O that will be produced by the reaction of 40.7 mol of $HClO_3$ and 1.25 kg of $Ca(OH)_2$.

10.100 How many molecules of NO can be produced by the reaction of 65.00 g of NH_3 with 150.0 g of O_2 according to the following balanced equation?

$$4 NH_3(g) + 5 O_2(g) \rightarrow 4 NO(g) + 6 H_2O(g)$$

10.5 Theoretical Yield and Percent Yield

10.101 Calculate (a) the theoretical yield and (b) the percent yield, if 0.151 mol of liquid SO_2Cl_2 is obtained from the reaction of 0.160 mol of gaseous SO_2 and excess gaseous Cl_2.

10.102 Calculate (a) the theoretical yield and (b) the percent yield, if 12.4 g of liquid SO_2Cl_2 is obtained from the reaction of 6.11 g of gaseous SO_2 and excess gaseous Cl_2.

10.103 Calculate the percent yield for an experiment in which 29.8 g of PCl_5 was obtained by treatment of 4.50 g of P with sufficient Cl_2.

10.104 Calculate the percent yield of a reaction which produced 36.0 g of $C_4H_8Br_2$ from 10.0 g of C_4H_8 and excess Br_2.

$$C_4H_8(g) + Br_2(\ell) \longrightarrow C_4H_8Br_2(\ell)$$

10.105 Calculate the percent yield for an experiment in which 46.9 g of SO_3 was obtained by treatment of 51.2 g of SO_2 with 25.0 g of O_2.

10.6 Calculations with Net Ionic Equations

10.106 (a) Calculate the number of moles of Na^+ present in 0.750 mol of NaOH.

(b) How many moles of NaCl will be produced by the reaction of that quantity of NaOH with 0.600 mol of HCl?

(c) How many moles of NaOH will be present after the reaction?

(d) How many moles of Na^+ will be present in the final solution?

(e) Does your answer to part (d) confirm that Na^+ is a spectator ion?

10.107 How many moles of carbonate ion can be converted to carbon dioxide and water with 4.42 mol H^+?

10.108 Calculate the mass of solid Ag_2S that can be produced by the reaction of 0.300 mol of S^{2-} with excess Ag^+.

10.109 How many moles of sulfite ion can be converted to sulfur dioxide and water with 0.650 mol H^+?

10.110 Calculate the number of moles of each ion in the final solution after 1.75 mol of aqueous $BaCl_2$ and 2.70 mol of aqueous $AgNO_3$ are mixed.

10.111 Calculate the number of moles of SO_2 that will be produced by the reaction of 1.00 mol of SO_3^{2-} with 2.76 mol of H^+.

10.112 Calculate the number of moles of CO_2 that will be produced by the reaction of 2.20 mol of HCO_3^- with 1.80 mol of H^+.

10.113 Calculate the mass of CO_2 that will be produced by the reaction of 0.550 mol of CO_3^{2-} with 1.25 mol of H^+.

10.114 Calculate the mass of $BaSO_4$ that can be produced by the reaction of 0.234 mol of SO_4^{2-} with 0.125 mol of Ba^{2+}.

10.115 Calculate the mass of PbI_2 that can be produced by the reaction of 0.105 mol of Pb^{2+} with 0.400 mol of I^-.

General Problems

10.116 List the steps necessary to do each of the following stoichiometry problems:

(a) Calculate the number of moles of aluminum metal required to prepare 6.11 mol of solid Al_2O_3.

(b) Calculate the number of grams of $Ca(OH)_2(s)$ required to prepare 0.885 mol of $Ca(ClO_4)_2(aq)$ by reaction with $HClO_4(aq)$.

(c) Calculate the number of grams of $CO_2(g)$ that can be prepared from 6.16 g of $CO(g)$ and 3.60 g of $O_2(g)$.

10.117 Calculate the number of moles of each substance except water in solution after 3.11 mol of NaOH(aq) is added to 3.82 mol of $HC_2H_3O_2(aq)$. Why was water excluded?

10.118 In each case, calculate the mass of the product other than water:

(a) 75.0 g of sulfuric acid is treated with sufficient aqueous potassium hydroxide so that the acid is completely neutralized

(b) 75.0 g of aqueous sodium hydroxide is treated with excess chloric acid

(c) 75.0 g of solid magnesium oxide is treated with excess hydrochloric acid

(d) 75.0 g of gaseous dinitrogen trioxide is treated with excess aqueous sodium hydroxide

10.119 Rewrite Problem 10.33 as a single-step problem.

10.120 (a) Write three stepwise equations for the reaction of NaOH and H_3PO_4, using only 1 mol of NaOH in each step. (b) If we add 1.50 mol of NaOH to 1.00 mol of NaH_2PO_4, how many moles of Na_2HPO_4 and Na_3PO_4 will be present at the end of all reaction?

10.121 How many moles of H_2 can be prepared using 0.500 mol of silver and excess H_3PO_4?

10.122 What mass of barium carbonate can be produced by treatment in aqueous solution of 31.2 g of sodium hydrogen carbonate with 30.0 g of barium nitrate? (CO_2 is also produced.)

10.123 Heating of solid sodium hydrogen carbonate is one step in the industrial process for production of washing soda—sodium carbonate. Carbon dioxide and water are also produced. Calculate the mass of solid produced when a 2.11-kg sample of sodium hydrogen carbonate is heated.

10.124 (a) After 2.06 g of solid $KClO_3$ is heated for a brief time, 1.18 g of KCl has been produced. What mass of O_2 has been produced?

(b) What mass of $KClO_3$ remained undecomposed?

10.125 (a) A 1.221-g sample of a mixture of $KClO_3(s)$ and $MnO_2(s)$ was heated for a brief time, after which 0.998 g of solid remained. Write the balanced equation for the reaction, indicating which of the substances is the catalyst and including the states of all reactants and products.

(b) How many grams of oxygen were produced?

(c) How many grams of $KClO_3$ decomposed?

(d) How many grams of KCl were produced?

(e) What is the minimum mass of $KClO_3$ that was present originally?

10.126 After 0.0800 mol of solid $KClO_3$ has been heated for a period of time, 0.0188 mol remains. Calculate the mass of each product.

10.127 What mass of nitrogen is contained in the ammonium nitrate that can be prepared by treatment of 20.2 g of aqueous ammonia with 41.6 g of nitric acid?

10.128 A 60.0-mmol sample of solid $KClO_3$ was partially decomposed by heating, and 75.0 mmol of O_2 was produced. Calculate the percentage of $KClO_3$ that decomposed.

10.129 A 2.172-g sample of a mixture of $KClO_3(s)$ and $MnO_2(s)$ was heated for a brief time, after which 1.951 g of solid remained. How many grams of KCl is present in the final mixture?

10.130 What mass of barium sulfate can be produced by treatment in aqueous solution of 11.6 g of ammonium sulfate with 25.5 g of barium fluoride?

10.131 Calculate the number of moles of each substance in solution after 0.150 mol of $Ba(C_2H_3O_2)_2(aq)$ is added to 0.500 mol of HCl(aq). The balanced equation is

$$Ba(C_2H_3O_2)_2(aq) + 2\,HCl(aq) \rightarrow$$
$$BaCl_2(aq) + 2\,HC_2H_3O_2(aq)$$

10.132 For a store's going-out-of business sale, a set consisting of a card table and four chairs is advertised at $233. The store has 31 tables and 98 chairs. An outlet manager arrives with $5000. What is the maximum number of *sets* the outlet manager can buy?

10.133 Determine the number of moles of $MnCl_2$ that can be prepared by the reaction of 0.300 mol $KMnO_4$, 1.08 mol of $FeCl_2$, and 3.10 mol of HCl, according to the following balanced equation:

$$KMnO_4(aq) + 5\,FeCl_2(aq) + 8\,HCl(aq) \rightarrow$$
$$MnCl_2(aq) + KCl(aq) + 5\,FeCl_3(aq) + 4\,H_2O(\ell)$$

11

Molarity

- 11.1 Definition and Uses of Molarity
- 11.2 Molarities of Ions
- 11.3 Titration

Titration

Review Clues

Section 11.1	Sections 1.1, 2.2, 7.3
Section 11.2	Sections 5.1, 5.5, 9.2, 10.3
Section 11.3	Sections 7.3, 10.6

Objectives

11.1 To define molarity—the most often used chemical measure of concentration—and to use molarity to solve problems

11.2 To extend the concept of molarity to the individual ions in solutions of ionic substances

11.3 To determine the concentration, or the number of moles present, of a substance by an experimental technique called titration

Solutions were introduced in Chapter 1, and quantities of substances in moles were presented in Section 7.3. We can easily measure the quantity of a solute in solution by measuring the volume of a solution if we can determine the concentration of the solute. In this chapter, we will limit our discussions to aqueous solutions.

Molarity, the most common measure of concentration used by chemists, is introduced in Section 11.1 and used to solve problems involving numbers of moles and volumes. The concentrations of individual ions in aqueous solutions of ionic substances are discussed in Section 11.2. The technique of titration, used to determine experimentally the unknown concentrations of solutions or unknown numbers of moles of a substance, is presented in Section 11.3.

11.1 Definition and Uses of Molarity

A **solute** is the substance dissolved in a **solvent,** the substance doing the dissolving. Most often, the solvent is the component present in greatest quantity, and the solutes are present in lower quantities. However, when water is a component, it is often regarded as the solvent, even if more of another component is present. For example, in an alcohol-water solution, the alcohol is regarded as the solute, and the water the solvent no matter how much of each is present.

Everyone is familiar with the concept of concentration. **Concentration** is quantity of solute in a given quantity of solvent or solution. For example, if a person usually drinks coffee with 2 teaspoons (tsp) of sugar per cup, how much sugar would he use in half a cup of coffee to get the usual sweetness? The sweetness depends on the concentration—the amount of sugar *per given volume of solution.* He would use 1 tsp of sugar (half of the normal amount) in half a cup of coffee (half of the normal amount).

EXAMPLE 11.1

If someone absentmindedly stirs more sugar than he likes into a cup of coffee, how can he make it less sweet?

Solution

Taking some sugar out of the solution is difficult, once the sugar has dissolved. The easy way to make the drink less sweet is to add more liquid. Increasing the volume makes less sugar *per unit volume,* so the coffee tastes less sweet.

EXAMPLE 11.2

Two cubes of sugar are dissolved in some water and then more water is added to fill a cup. A second cup has one lump of sugar dissolved in enough water to half fill the cup.

(a) Which cup, if either, contains more sugar?

(b) Which cup, if either, contains the sweeter-tasting solution?

(c) What is the difference between *quantity* and *concentration?*

Solution

(a) The first cup contains more sugar—two lumps is more than one.

(b) The contents of both cups taste equally sweet—both solutions have the same concentration.

(c) Concentration is a quantity of solute in a given volume of solution.

Basic Problems

Molarity is defined as the *number of moles of solute per liter of solution:*

$$\text{Molarity} = \frac{\text{number of moles of solute}}{\text{number of liters of solution}}$$

This definition is often shortened to "moles per liter," but condensing it in this way does not change the fact that it is really the number of moles *of solute* per liter of *solution*. The unit of molarity is **molar,** symbolized M. An italic capital *M* is sometimes used as a symbol for molarity; note that a nonitalic capital M means molar.

■ EXAMPLE 11.3

Calculate the molarity of a solution containing 7.50 mol of CH_2O in enough water to make 1.50 L of solution.

Solution

$$\text{Molarity} = \frac{7.50 \text{ mol}}{1.50 \text{ L}} = \frac{5.00 \text{ mol}}{1 \text{ L}} = 5.00 \text{ M}$$

There are at least three different ways of stating this concentration:

It is a 5.00 molar (5.00 M) solution.
The CH_2O is 5.00 M.
The concentration is 5.00 M.

Practice Problem 11.3 A solution is prepared using 3.55 L of water and 2.10 mol of a certain solute. The total volume is 3.75 L, and there is 19.7 mol of water. What is the molarity of the solute?

Molarity can also be defined as the number of *millimoles* (mmol) of solute per *milliliter* of solution.

$$M = \frac{\text{no. of moles of solute}}{\text{liter of solution}}$$
$$= \frac{\text{no. of millimoles of solute}}{\text{mL of solution}}$$

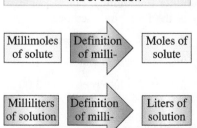

| Millimoles of solute | Definition of milli- | Moles of solute |

| Milliliters of solution | Definition of milli- | Liters of solution |

■ EXAMPLE 11.4

Calculate the molarity of 60.0 mL of solution containing 1.25 mmol of solute.

Solution

$$\frac{1.25 \text{ mmol}\left(\dfrac{1 \text{ mol}}{1000 \text{ mmol}}\right)}{60.0 \text{ mL}\left(\dfrac{1 \text{ L}}{1000 \text{ mL}}\right)} = \frac{1.25 \text{ mol}}{60.0 \text{ L}} = 0.0208 \text{ M}$$

Note that the number of millimoles per milliliter is equal to the number of moles per liter, and thus millimoles per milliliter is another way to define molarity. This equivalent definition makes many problems easier because quantities used in chemical laboratories are often measured in millimoles and milliliters.

Practice Problem 11.4   Calculate the molarity of a solution containing 4.50 mmol of NaCl in 3.80 mL of solution.

If quantities of solute and solution are given in units other than moles and liters or millimoles and milliliters, respectively, they can be changed to one of these sets of units to calculate the molarity.

EXAMPLE 11.5

Calculate the molarity of 50.0 mL of solution containing 7.50 g of CH_3OH.

Solution

Because molarity is defined in terms of moles of solute and liters of solution, the given quantities can be converted to moles and liters, respectively:

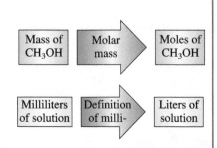

$$7.50 \text{ g } CH_3OH\left(\frac{1 \text{ mol } CH_3OH}{32.0 \text{ g } CH_3OH}\right) = 0.2344 \text{ mol } CH_3OH$$

$$50.0 \text{ mL}\left(\frac{1 \text{ L}}{1000 \text{ mL}}\right) = 0.0500 \text{ L}$$

$$M = \frac{0.2344 \text{ mol } CH_3OH}{0.0500 \text{ L}} = 4.69 \text{ M } CH_3OH$$

Alternatively, the number of moles can be changed to millimoles.

$$0.2344 \text{ mol}\left(\frac{1 \text{ mmol}}{0.001 \text{ mol}}\right) = 234.4 \text{ mmol}$$

$$M = \frac{234.4 \text{ mmol } CH_3OH}{50.0 \text{ mL}} = 4.69 \text{ M } CH_3OH$$

Practice Problem 11.5   Calculate the molarity of 11.6 mL of solution containing 0.750 g of $CaCl_2$.

Because molarity is a ratio, like speed and density, it can be used as a conversion factor. Wherever it appears, the symbol M can be replaced by the ratio moles per liter (mol/L) or millimoles per milliliter (mmol/mL). For example, a concentration of 3.11 M can be used as any of the following factors:

$$\frac{3.11 \text{ mol}}{1 \text{ L}} \qquad \frac{1 \text{ L}}{3.11 \text{ mol}} \qquad \frac{3.11 \text{ mmol}}{1 \text{ mL}} \qquad \frac{1 \text{ mL}}{3.11 \text{ mmol}}$$

In this way we can calculate the number of moles of solute present in 3.00 L of 1.50 M solution:

$$3.00 \text{ L}\left(\frac{1.50 \text{ mol}}{1 \text{ L}}\right) = 4.50 \text{ mol}$$

In this solution, the total quantity of solute is easy to visualize, as shown in Figure 11.1.

EXAMPLE 11.6

Calculate the number of liters necessary to contain 0.853 mol of 0.415 M solute.

Solution

$$0.853 \text{ mol}\left(\frac{1 \text{ L}}{0.415 \text{ mol}}\right) = 2.06 \text{ L}$$

Practice Problem 11.6 Calculate the number of millimoles of ethyl alcohol, C_2H_5OH, in 29.21 mL of 6.013 M solution.

[Moles of solute] → Molarity → [Liters of solution]

Dilution Problems

We can calculate the concentration of a solution that has been prepared by diluting a more concentrated solution by using the basic definition of molarity. For example, what concentration results when 0.750 L of 1.60 M NaCl is diluted with water to make 3.00 L of solution? When the solution is diluted with water, the *concentration* of NaCl is reduced, but the *quantity* of NaCl remains the same. (See Example 11.2.) We first calculate the original number of moles of NaCl and use that to calculate the final concentration:

$$0.750 \text{ L}\left(\frac{1.60 \text{ mol}}{1 \text{ L}}\right) = 1.20 \text{ mol}$$

Because only water—and no more solute—is added, there is 1.20 mol of solute in the final solution. Thus, the concentration of the final solution is

[Initial liters of solution] → Molarity → [Moles of solute]

$$M = \frac{1.20 \text{ mol}}{3.00 \text{ L}} = 0.400 \text{ M}$$

It is easy to understand that when the volume is quadrupled, the concentration is divided by four, from 1.60 M to 0.400 M.

EXAMPLE 11.7

Calculate the final concentration of NaCl after 1.25 L of 0.500 M NaCl is diluted (a) to 2.50 L with water and (b) with 2.50 L of water.

Solution

The fraction of a mole of NaCl in the original solution is

$$1.25 \text{ L}\left(\frac{0.500 \text{ mol}}{1 \text{ L}}\right) = 0.625 \text{ mol}$$

The number of moles of NaCl is not changed by the addition of water.

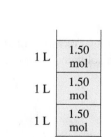

Figure 11.1 *Moles and Concentration of Solute in a Solution*

It is easy to see that 3.00 L of 1.50 M solution contains 4.50 mol of solute.

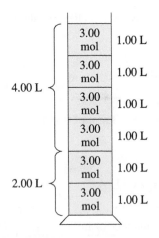

Figure 11.2 Combination of Two Solutions of Equal Concentration

(a) In this case, the final volume is 2.50 L, so the final concentration is

$$M = \frac{0.625 \text{ mol}}{2.50 \text{ L}} = 0.250 \text{ M}$$

(b) In this case, the final volume is almost exactly 1.25 L + 2.50 L = 3.75 L, so the final concentration is

$$M = \frac{0.625 \text{ mol}}{3.75 \text{ L}} = 0.167 \text{ M}$$

Practice Problem 11.7   A nurse must prepare 4.00 L of 0.250 M saline solution (NaCl). What volume of 6.00 M stock solution should the nurse dilute?

Combining two solutions is only a little more complicated.

EXAMPLE 11.8

Calculate the final concentration of a solution prepared by adding 2.00 L of 3.00 M sugar solution to 4.00 L of 3.00 M sugar solution.

Solution

Because the concentration of each solution is the same, the concentration of the combined solution is also 3.00 M (Figure 11.2). (The solutions would taste as sweet before and after mixing.)

Practice Problem 11.8   Show by calculation of the total number of moles of sugar in the combined solution of Example 11.8 that the concentration is still 3.00 M.

EXAMPLE 11.9

Calculate the final concentration after 1.25 L of 2.25 M NaCl is added to 3.50 L of 2.45 M NaCl and the resulting solution is diluted to 5.00 L.

Solution

The molarity of the final solution is equal to the total number of moles of solute divided by the final volume. Solute is contained in each solution, but not in the

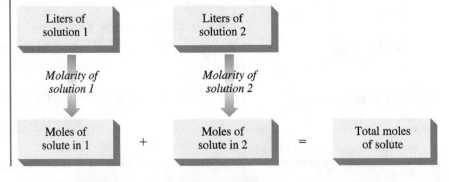

water used to dilute to 5.00 L. The number of moles of NaCl in the final solution is the sum of the numbers of moles in the two initial solutions:

$$1.25 \text{ L}\left(\frac{2.25 \text{ mol}}{1 \text{ L}}\right) = 2.813 \text{ mol} \qquad 3.50 \text{ L}\left(\frac{2.45 \text{ mol}}{1 \text{ L}}\right) = 8.575 \text{ mol}$$

The total number of moles of NaCl is $2.813 \text{ mol} + 8.575 \text{ mol} = 11.388 \text{ mol}$. The final volume is 5.00 L, and the final concentration is

$$\frac{11.388 \text{ mol}}{5.00 \text{ L}} = 2.28 \text{ M}$$

Practice Problem 11.9 Calculate the final concentration after 87.3 mL of 1.71 M sugar solution is combined with 71.7 mL of 3.11 M sugar solution and the resulting solution is diluted to 275 mL.

Numbers of Moles in Chemical Reactions

Molarities and volumes may be used to calculate the numbers of moles involved in chemical reactions (Chapter 10). The conversions used are shown in Figure 11.3, where they have been added to those of Figure 10.2.

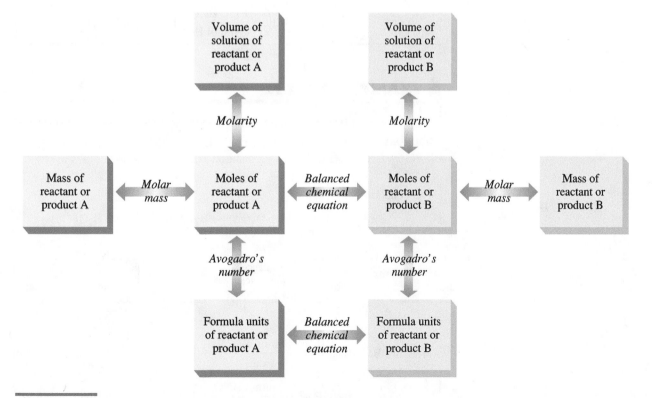

Figure 11.3 Conversions Including Those Involving Molarity

EXAMPLE 11.10

What volume of 1.50 M HCl is required to react with 34.6 mL of 2.44 M NaOH?

Solution

The reaction is

$$\text{NaOH(aq)} + \text{HCl(aq)} \rightarrow \text{NaCl(aq)} + \text{H}_2\text{O}(\ell)$$

Molarity can be expressed as millimoles per milliliter.

The number of millimoles of base is

$$34.6 \text{ mL}\left(\frac{2.44 \text{ mmol NaOH}}{1 \text{ mL NaOH}}\right) = 84.42 \text{ mmol NaOH}$$

That number of millimoles of base is equal to the number of millimoles of acid, according to the balanced equation given previously. The volume of acid required is therefore

$$84.42 \text{ mmol HCl}\left(\frac{1 \text{ mL HCl}}{1.50 \text{ mmol HCl}}\right) = 56.3 \text{ mL HCl}$$

EXAMPLE 11.11

What volume of 0.5000 M HNO$_3$ is required to react with 41.77 mL of 0.1603 M Ba(OH)$_2$?

Solution

The equation is

$$\text{Ba(OH)}_2(\text{aq}) + 2\,\text{HNO}_3(\text{aq}) \rightarrow \text{Ba(NO}_3)_2(\text{aq}) + 2\,\text{H}_2\text{O}(\ell)$$

$$41.77 \text{ mL Ba(OH)}_2\left(\frac{0.1603 \text{ mmol Ba(OH)}_2}{1 \text{ mL}}\right) = 6.6957 \text{ mmol Ba(OH)}_2 \text{ present}$$

$$6.6957 \text{ mmol Ba(OH)}_2\left(\frac{2 \text{ mmol HNO}_3}{1 \text{ mmol Ba(OH)}_2}\right) = 13.391 \text{ mmol HNO}_3 \text{ required}$$

The volume of 0.5000 M HNO_3 required is therefore

$$13.39l \text{ mmol } HNO_3\left(\frac{1 \text{ mL } HNO_3}{0.5000 \text{ mmol } HNO_3}\right) = 26.78 \text{ mL } HNO_3$$

Practice Problem 11.11 What volume of 0.1212 M $Ba(OH)_2$ is required to react with 41.74 mL of 0.2500 M HNO_3?

EXAMPLE 11.12

Calculate the number of moles of NaCl produced by reaction of 0.0452 L of 4.20 M HCl and 0.120 L of 2.17 M NaOH.

Solution

Because the quantities of two reactants are given, this problem involves a limiting quantity.

$$0.0452 \text{ L HCl}\left(\frac{4.20 \text{ mol HCl}}{1 \text{ L HCl}}\right) = 0.1898 \text{ mol HCl}$$

$$0.120 \text{ L NaOH}\left(\frac{2.17 \text{ mol NaOH}}{1 \text{ L NaOH}}\right) = 0.2604 \text{ mol NaOH}$$

$$NaOH(aq) + HCl(aq) \rightarrow NaCl(aq) + H_2O(\ell)$$

Because the reactants react in a 1:1 mole ratio, NaOH is in excess, HCl is in limiting quantity, and 0.190 mol of NaCl will be produced.

Practice Problem 11.12 Calculate the number of milligrams of NaCl that can be produced by the reaction of 22.4 mL of 2.00 M HCl and 1.74 g of NaOH.

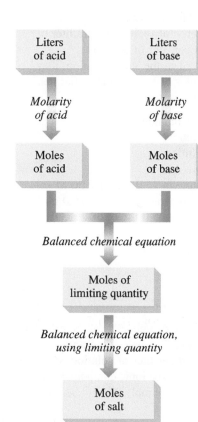

Liters of acid

Molarity of acid

Moles of acid

Liters of base

Molarity of base

Moles of base

Balanced chemical equation

Moles of limiting quantity

Balanced chemical equation, using limiting quantity

Moles of salt

The maximum molarity possible in an aqueous solution of an ionic compound is about 40 M (with $LiClO_3$ as the solute). Pure water itself contains 55.6 mol/L. Sometimes, knowing the maximum molarity is important for determining whether a calculated answer is reasonable, or for other purposes.

EXAMPLE 11.13

Two ionic solutes, called A and B, are dissolved in the same solvent. The ratio of the molarity of A to the molarity of B is 10^5. What can be deduced from this fact?

Solution

Chemists customarily represent the concentration of a substance by enclosing its formula or symbol in square brackets. For example, [A] represents the molarity of A. Then

$$\frac{[A]}{[B]} = 1 \times 10^5$$

The concentration of B in its solution must be very low because the concentration of A cannot be much greater than 10^1, at most.

Practice Problem 11.13 The ratio of molarities of A to B is 10^{-5}. What can be deduced from this fact?

Snapshot Review

ChemSkill Builder 6.1

❐ Molarity, the number of moles of solute per liter of solution, can be used as a factor to find the volume of a solution from the number of moles of solute or vice versa.

❐ Molarity may also be defined as the number of millimoles per milliliter of solution (but not the number of moles per milliliter of solution or the number of millimoles per liter of solution).

❐ If two or more substances are dissolved in the same solution, they may react or not. The numbers of moles of each solute in the final solution will be different in these two cases.

A. Calculate the concentration of a solution containing
   (a) 0.125 mol of solute in 0.375 L of solution.
   (b) 125 mmol of solute in 375 mL of solution.
   (c) 0.125 mol of solute in 375 mL of solution.
B. Calculate the number of millimoles of solute in 15.0 mL of 2.00 M solute.
C. Calculate the concentration of a solution prepared by adding 75.0 mmol of CH_3OH in 25.0 mL of aqueous solution to 45.0 mmol of CH_3OH in 25.0 mL and diluting to 200.0 mL.

11.2 Molarities of Ions

As shown in Section 11.1, the molarities of ionic compounds can be calculated just as the molarities of covalent compounds are. The molarity of an ionic compound is the number of moles of the *compound* per liter of solution. However, as discussed in Chapter 9, it is often useful to describe ionic compounds in solution as the separate ions. The molarity of any ion is simply the number of moles of *that ion* per liter of solution.

EXAMPLE 11.14

(a) Calculate the molarity of $AlCl_3$ if 0.220 mol of that compound is dissolved in enough water to make 0.500 L of solution.

(b) Calculate the concentration of each type of ion in that solution.

Solution

(a) $$\frac{0.220 \text{ mol } AlCl_3}{0.500 \text{ L}} = 0.440 \text{ M } AlCl_3$$

(b) The $AlCl_3$ is composed of Al^{3+} ions and Cl^- ions. The formula indicates that there are three times as many Cl^- ions as Al^{3+} ions. Thus,

$$0.220 \text{ mol } AlCl_3\left(\frac{1 \text{ mol } Al^{3+}}{1 \text{ mol } AlCl_3}\right) = 0.220 \text{ mol } Al^{3+}$$

$$0.220 \text{ mol } AlCl_3\left(\frac{3 \text{ mol } Cl^-}{1 \text{ mol } AlCl_3}\right) = 0.660 \text{ mol } Cl^-$$

The concentrations of the ions are

$$\frac{0.220 \text{ mol } Al^{3+}}{0.500 \text{ L}} = 0.440 \text{ M } Al^{3+}$$

$$\frac{0.660 \text{ mol } Cl^-}{0.500 \text{ L}} = 1.32 \text{ M } Cl^-$$

Practice Problem 11.14

(a) Calculate the molarity of $Al_2(SO_4)_3$ if 0.150 mol of that compound is dissolved in enough water to make 2.70 L of solution.

(b) Calculate the concentration of each ion in that solution.

When two different compounds containing an ion in common are placed in the same solution, if no reaction occurs, the numbers of moles of the common ion are added.

EXAMPLE 11.15

Calculate the concentration of each ion in a solution made by adding 41.4 mL of 1.03 M NaCl to 66.2 mL of 0.818 M $CaCl_2$ and diluting to 150.0 mL.

Solution

When these two solutions are combined, no chemical reaction takes place, but the final chloride ion concentration includes the chloride ions provided by both salts. The cation concentrations are not added because the cations are different. The number of moles of each ion is calculated as follows:

> Because no reaction takes place, the numbers of moles of Cl^- ion are merely added.

$$41.4 \text{ mL NaCl}\left(\frac{1.03 \text{ mmol NaCl}}{1 \text{ mL NaCl}}\right) = 42.64 \text{ mmol NaCl}$$

$$66.2 \text{ mL } CaCl_2\left(\frac{0.818 \text{ mmol } CaCl_2}{1 \text{ mL } CaCl_2}\right) = 54.15 \text{ mmol } CaCl_2$$

In 42.64 mmol of NaCl, there are

42.64 mmol Na^+ and 42.64 mmol Cl^-

In 54.15 mmol of $CaCl_2$, there are

108.3 mmol Cl^- and 54.15 mmol Ca^{2+}

The total numbers of millimoles are

42.64 mmol Na^+, $\qquad$ 150.9 mmol Cl^-, and 54.15 mmol Ca^{2+}

The final concentrations are

$$\frac{42.64 \text{ mmol } Na^+}{150.0 \text{ mL}} = 0.284 \text{ M } Na^+ \qquad \frac{150.9 \text{ mmol } Cl^-}{150.0 \text{ mL}} = 1.01 \text{ M } Cl^-$$

$$\frac{54.15 \text{ mmol } Ca^{2+}}{150.0 \text{ mL}} = 0.361 \text{ M } Ca^{2+}$$

Practice Problem 11.15 Calculate the concentration of each ion in a solution made by adding 10.0 mL of 0.800 M $(NH_4)_3PO_4$ to 14.9 mL of 1.44 M NH_4Cl and diluting to 50.0 mL.

We can calculate the concentrations of ions in solution after a chemical reaction takes place. In doing so, we often use net ionic equations (Chapter 9).

EXAMPLE 11.16

Calculate the concentration of each ion in a solution made by adding 24.0 mL of 1.50 M HCl to 42.7 mL of 0.212 M $Ba(OH)_2$ and diluting to 100.0 mL.

Solution

When these two solutions are combined, a chemical reaction does take place. The net ionic equation for the reaction is

$$H^+(aq) + OH^-(aq) \rightarrow H_2O(\ell)$$

The numbers of moles of H^+ and OH^- in the two initial solutions are 36.0 mmol H^+ and 18.1*0* mmol OH^- (determined by calculations similar to those in Example 11.15). Because the OH^- ion is in limiting quantity, the 18.1 mmol of OH^- will react with 18.1 mmol of H^+, leaving 17.9 mmol of H^+ in

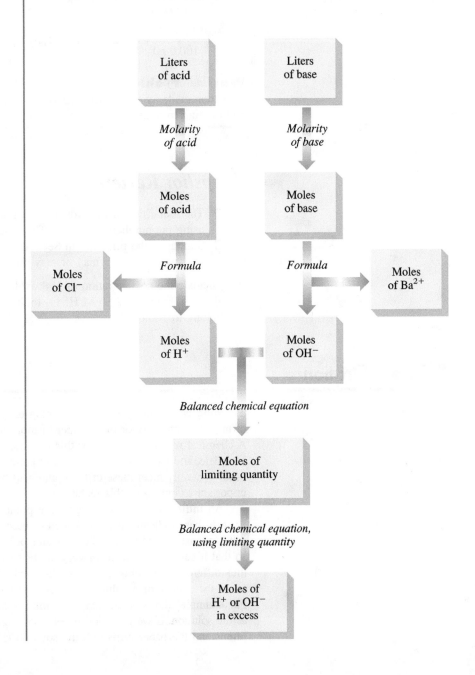

solution. The number of moles of water is of no interest; water is the solvent. The volume of water produced in the reaction is also of no interest. First, the volume of water produced is not significantly different from the sum of the volumes of H^+ and OH^- used up. Then, the final solution is diluted with water to 100.0 mL. The Cl^- and Ba^{2+} ions are spectator ions; their numbers of moles do not change when the initial solutions are combined. Thus, there are 9.052 mmol of Ba^{2+} and 36.0 mmol of Cl^- in the final solution, along with the excess 17.9 mmol of H^+. The concentrations are

$$\frac{17.9 \text{ mmol } H^+}{100.0 \text{ mL}} = 0.179 \text{ M } H^+ \qquad \frac{36.0 \text{ mmol } Cl^-}{100.0 \text{ mL}} = 0.360 \text{ M } Cl^-$$

$$\frac{9.052 \text{ mmol } Ba^{2+}}{100.0 \text{ mL}} = 0.0905 \text{ M } Ba^{2+}$$

Practice Problem 11.16 Calculate the concentration of each ion in a solution made by adding 15.5 mL of 2.50 M HCl to 12.6 mL of 3.13 M NaOH and diluting to 50.0 mL.

Snapshot Review

ChemSkill Builder 6.4

❑ The molarities of individual ions of an ionic solute are calculated using the numbers of moles of the individual ions.
❑ Similar to the principle in Section 11.1, if more than one ionic solute is present, the ions may or may not react.

A. Calculate the concentration of hydroxide ion in a solution prepared by adding 5.00 mL of 2.50 M HNO_3 to 20.0 mL of 0.750 M NaOH and diluting to 100.0 mL

11.3 Titration

Titration is a technique for determining either the concentration of a solution of unknown molarity or the number of moles of a substance in a given sample. A chemical reaction is used for this purpose, and the reaction must be fast, be complete, and have a determinable end point. The reactions of strong acids and bases generally meet these criteria, and acid-base titrations are among the most important examples of this technique.

An **indicator** is used to signal the point at which the titration is stopped. An acid-base indicator is a weak acid or base that has a different color from its salt. At least one of them—the indicator or its salt—must be intensely colored so that it can be seen even in very dilute solution. The color of the solution is thus different depending on the acidity or basicity of the solution it is in, and when the acidity of a solution changes sufficiently, a color change will occur. For example, the indicator called litmus is blue in basic solution and red in acidic solution. If we place a drop of a solution on a piece of paper treated with litmus and the paper turns red, the solution is acidic.

EXAMPLE 11.17

A common indicator, phenolphthalein, is colorless in acidic solution and red in basic solution. Describe the color changes when two drops of phenolphthalein solution are added to 100 mL of a colorless acidic solution and then the acid is gradually neutralized by adding drops of base to the continuously stirred solution.

Solution

The acidic solution is initially colorless and remains so when the indicator is added. As most of the base is added, no permanent color change takes place. When one drop or less of *excess* base is added, the solution will change to pink. The indicator, usually red in a basic solution, is present in very low concentration, and its red color looks pink in such a relatively large volume of solution.

Practice Problem 11.17   What happens to the color of the solution in Example 11.17 if acid is added after the last drop of base has been added?

The purpose of a typical titration is the determination of the concentration of a solution such as HCl, using a solution of NaOH of known concentration. Assume that 1 L of each solution is available (Figure 11.4a). Exactly 25.00 mL of the HCl solution is transferred with a **pipet** (Figure 11.4b) to a clean **Erlenmeyer flask** (Figure 11.4c), and two drops of an indicator are added to the solution. The indicator will show when the reaction is complete by changing color; that is, it will indicate when the **end point** has been reached. The end point is the point in the titration at which the mole ratio of reactants added is exactly equal to their mole ratio in the balanced chemical equation. That is the point at which we wish to stop the titration.

The NaOH solution is placed in a **buret** (Figure 11.4d). The tip of the buret is filled by allowing a small portion of the solution to run out the bottom, and then the level of the solution in the buret is read and recorded. Next, the NaOH solution is added from the buret to the Erlenmeyer flask—rapidly at first, then slowly as the reaction nears completion. When the last drop or half drop of NaOH solution completes the reaction, addition is stopped, and the final buret level is read and recorded. At this point, the number of moles of HCl originally in the solution and the number of moles of NaOH added to that solution are equal, just as they are in the balanced equation:

$$HCl(aq) + NaOH(aq) \rightarrow NaCl(aq) + H_2O(\ell)$$

The indicator enables us to tell when the reaction is complete because it has one color in the HCl solution and another in the NaOH solution (or it may be colorless in one solution and have a color in the other). As we add the NaOH solution from the buret, the color characteristic of that solution appears where the drop enters the HCl solution. As we swirl the flask rapidly to ensure mixing, that color disappears (Figure 11.4e). As the reaction proceeds further toward completion, it takes longer for the color due to the added base to disappear, even though we are adding smaller portions of NaOH solution. When we add the last drop of NaOH solution, the associated color remains for at least 1 min. We know then that the end point of the titration has been reached.

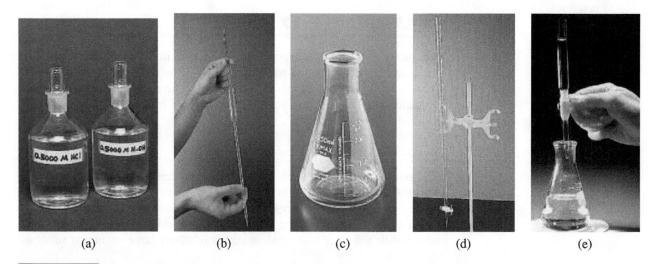

(a) (b) (c) (d) (e)

Figure 11.4 *Apparatus for Performing an Acid-Base Titration (not shown to scale)*
(a) Stock solutions of hydrochloric acid and sodium hydroxide. (b) A pipet is a piece of glassware shaped like a straw with an enlarged middle section. There is a mark about halfway up the top section. When the pipet is filled to the mark and then allowed to drain, the liquid delivered from the pipet will have the volume marked on the side. Common volumes are 5.000 mL, 10.00 mL, and 25.00 mL. The enlarged midsection allows more solution to be held, and the small top and bottom sections allow more exact volumes to be delivered. (c) An Erlenmeyer flask is shaped so that the contents do not spill out when the flask is swirled. (d) A buret is a uniform-bore tube with volume calibrations marked on its side. Readings are taken at the bottom of the meniscus, the curved surface of the liquid in the buret. The volume delivered from a buret is equal to the difference between the initial and final readings. The portion below the stopcock must be filled with liquid both before and after the titration to get an accurate volume. (e) One reagent is added from the buret to a measured volume of the other reagent in the Erlenmeyer flask.

> In titrations, it is the concentration of the *original* solutions that is of interest, not the concentrations in the *final* solution.

We can now calculate the concentration of the HCl solution. The volume of NaOH solution used is the difference between the initial and final buret readings. The concentration of NaOH is known, and thus the number of millimoles (or moles) of NaOH can be calculated. From the way a titration is run and the fact that the mole ratio of HCl to NaOH in the balanced equation is 1:1, the number of millimoles of HCl is equal to the number of millimoles of NaOH. The concentration of the HCl solution is calculated by dividing that number of millimoles by the number of milliliters of the HCl solution.

▌ EXAMPLE 11.18

An acid-base titration is performed as just described. Calculate the concentration of the HCl solution if the concentration of the NaOH solution is 2.000 M, the volume of HCl solution is 25.00 mL, the initial buret reading for the NaOH solution is 2.17 mL, and the final buret reading is 39.42 mL. (The lower numbers are toward the top of the buret.)

Solution

The volume of NaOH solution used is 39.42 mL − 2.17 mL = 37.25 mL. The number of millimoles of NaOH is

$$37.25 \text{ mL}\left(\frac{2.000 \text{ mmol}}{1 \text{ mL}}\right) = 74.50 \text{ mmol NaOH}$$

The number of millimoles of HCl is also 74.50 mmol because the titration was stopped when the numbers of millimoles of the two reactants were equal. The HCl concentration is therefore

$$\frac{74.50 \text{ mmol HCl}}{25.00 \text{ mL HCl}} = 2.980 \text{ M HCl}$$

Practice Problem 11.18 A titration is done to determine the concentration of NH_3 in a certain sample of household ammonia solution. The concentration of the HCl solution used is 1.500 M, the volume of HCl solution is 25.00 mL, the initial buret reading for the NH_3 solution is 1.73 mL, and the final buret reading is 42.36 mL. Calculate the molarity of the base.

The indicator for an acid-base titration is an intensely colored dye, which is itself an acid or a base. It must be intensely colored in at least one of the two solutions so that its color is visible when it is present in a very low concentration. We should not use too much of the indicator because it, rather than the acid or base of interest, would react with the other reagent; its quantity must be negligible, relative to the quantity of either reactant.

Why would we want to determine the concentration of an acid solution such as that of Example 11.18 when the acid gets converted to a salt in the process? The portion of acid used for the titration is indeed no longer useful, but the greater portion left in the stock bottle (see Figure 11.4a) is the same concentration as that initially present in the flask. Thus, the titration allows us to determine the concentration of the major portion of the original solution.

EXAMPLE 11.19

Calculate the concentration of H_2SO_4 solution that is completely neutralized in an acid-base titration if the concentration of NaOH solution is 1.500 M, the volume of H_2SO_4 solution is 25.00 mL, the initial buret reading for the NaOH solution is 1.28 mL, and the final buret reading is 45.19 mL.

Solution

The volume of NaOH solution used is 45.19 mL − 1.28 mL = 43.91 mL. The number of millimoles of NaOH is

$$43.91 \ \text{mL}\left(\frac{1.500 \ \text{mmol NaOH}}{1 \ \text{mL}}\right) = 65.865 \ \text{mmol NaOH}$$

The balanced equation for this reaction is

$$H_2SO_4(aq) + 2\,NaOH(aq) \rightarrow Na_2SO_4(aq) + 2\,H_2O(\ell)$$

The number of millimoles of H_2SO_4 is

$$65.865 \ \text{mmol NaOH}\left(\frac{1 \ \text{mmol } H_2SO_4}{2 \ \text{mmol NaOH}}\right) = 32.933 \ \text{mmol } H_2SO_4$$

The concentration of the H_2SO_4 solution is

$$\frac{32.933 \ \text{mmol } H_2SO_4}{25.00 \ \text{mL}} = 1.317 \ \text{M } H_2SO_4$$

EXAMPLE 11.20

Two different indicators are used to show the two end points (one for each ion-izable hydrogen atom) when H_2SO_3 is titrated with NaOH. In one laboratory, the labels fell off the indicator bottles. To determine which indicator was which, a student titrated 25.00 mL of 1.317 M H_2SO_3 with 21.96 mL of 1.500 M NaOH, using one of the indicators. Write the equation for the chemical reaction that occurred.

Solution

The numbers of millimoles of acid and base are calculated from the volumes and molarities given:

$$25.00 \ \text{mL } H_2SO_3\left(\frac{1.317 \ \text{mmol } H_2SO_3}{1 \ \text{mL } H_2SO_3}\right) = 32.925 \ \text{mmol } H_2SO_3$$

$$21.96 \ \text{mL NaOH}\left(\frac{1.500 \ \text{mmol NaOH}}{1 \ \text{mL NaOH}}\right) = 32.94 \ \text{mmol NaOH}$$

Because the numbers of millimoles of acid and base are equal, the acid and base react with each other in a 1:1 ratio. The balanced equation is therefore

$$NaOH(aq) + H_2SO_3(aq) \rightarrow NaHSO_3(aq) + H_2O(\ell)$$

Practice Problem 11.20   What volume of 1.500 M NaOH would be required to completely neutralize 25.00 mL of 4.176 M H_2SO_4?

EXAMPLE 11.21

Calculate the number of millimoles of Na_2CO_3 present in a sample if it takes 27.17 mL of 2.500 M HCl to convert the sample to NaCl, CO_2, and H_2O.

Solution

$$Na_2CO_3(s) + 2\,HCl(aq) \rightarrow 2\,NaCl(aq) + CO_2(g) + H_2O(\ell)$$

$$27.17\ \text{mL HCl}\left(\frac{2.500\ \text{mmol HCl}}{1\ \text{mL HCl}}\right)\left(\frac{1\ \text{mmol Na}_2\text{CO}_3}{2\ \text{mmol HCl}}\right) = 33.96\ \text{mmol Na}_2\text{CO}_3$$

Practice Problem 11.21 Calculate the number of millimoles of $NaHCO_3$ in a sample if it takes 27.17 mL of 2.500 M HCl to convert the sample to NaCl, CO_2, and H_2O.

EXAMPLE 11.22

An unknown acid with only one ionizable hydrogen atom per formula unit, represented as HA, is prepared in the laboratory. Calculate the molar mass of the acid if it takes 33.48 mL of 0.5000 M NaOH to neutralize a solution prepared by dissolving 3.172 g of the acid in water. The reaction may be represented as follows:

$$HA(aq) + NaOH(aq) \rightarrow NaA(aq) + H_2O(\ell)$$

Solution

The number of moles of base is calculated first:

$$33.48\ \text{mL NaOH}\left(\frac{1\ \text{L}}{1000\ \text{mL}}\right)\left(\frac{0.5000\ \text{mol NaOH}}{1\ \text{L NaOH}}\right) = 0.01674\ \text{mol NaOH}$$

The number of moles of acid is

$$0.01674\ \text{mol NaOH}\left(\frac{1\ \text{mol HA}}{1\ \text{mol NaOH}}\right) = 0.01674\ \text{mol HA}$$

The molar mass is the number of grams per mole:

$$\frac{3.172\ \text{g HA}}{0.01674\ \text{mol HA}} = 189.5\ \text{g/mol}$$

 Snapshot Review

ChemSkill Builder 6.2

❒ A titration is a controlled reaction used to determine the number of moles of one substance by treatment with a known number of moles of a second substance. The known number of moles is calculated as a volume times a molarity of the solution of known concentration. The number of moles of the other substance may be used to calculate its concentration, its molar mass, or other quantities.

A. A titration of HCl and NaOH used 10.00 mL of 3.000 M HCl and 29.42 mL of NaOH. (a) How many millimoles of HCl was used? (b) How many millimoles of NaOH did that HCl react with? (c) What was the original concentration of the NaOH?

Key Terms

Key terms are defined in the Glossary.

buret (11.3)
concentration (11.1)
end point (11.3)
Erlenmeyer flask (11.3)

indicator (11.3)
molar (11.1)
molarity (11.1)
pipet (11.3)

solute (11.1)
solvent (11.1)
titration (11.3)

Symbols/Abbreviations

M (molar) (11.1) M (molarity) (11.1)

Summary

The concentration of a solute depends on the quantities of both the solute and the solution (or solvent). Molarity is defined as the number of moles of solute per liter of solution. Molarity is calculated by dividing the number of moles of solute by the volume of the solution in liters, or alternatively, by dividing the number of millimoles of solute by the milliliters of solution. Because molarity is a ratio, it can be used as a conversion factor to change the volume of solution into the number of moles of solute, or vice versa.

If an aqueous solution is diluted with water, the number of moles of solute does not change, but the molarity does. The final concentration of such a solution is calculated by dividing the number of moles of solute by the final volume. (The number of moles might have to be calculated from the initial volume and concentration.) If two solutions of the same solute are mixed, the total number of moles present in the final solution is the sum of the numbers of moles in the two original solutions. The *molarities* are *not* added.

The number of moles of a reactant involved in a reaction can be calculated from molarity and volume; that number of moles can then be used to calculate the number

of moles of product. The number of moles of product can then be changed to a final molarity if a final volume is known (Section 11.1).

The individual ions of an ionic compound may be regarded as separate solutes. The number of moles of each ion is calculated from the number of moles of the compound and the formula of the compound. If solutions of two compounds containing one ion in common are mixed, the number of moles of that ion is determined by adding the numbers of moles of the ion in the original solutions. In contrast, if solutions of ions that react with each other are mixed, the numbers of moles of the ions that react are subtracted from the original numbers of moles present, as in a problem involving a limiting quantity. The molarities of the ions in the final solution will be related to the numbers of moles of the ions remaining in that solution (Section 11.2).

The experimental technique of titration is often used to determine the number of moles of a reactant in a given sample of an unknown, using a measured volume of a (standard) solution of known concentration. The color change of an indicator shows when the reaction has been completed. The concentration and volume of the standard solution give the number of moles of solute in the standard solution, and then the number of moles of the unknown substance may be calculated from the balanced chemical equation. If an unknown substance is dissolved

in a measured volume of solution, its molarity can be calculated from its volume and the calculated number of moles (Section 11.3).

Items for Special Attention

■ Do not confuse quantities and concentrations.

■ Be sure to use mol as an abbreviation for mole—*not* M or m, which are used for other quantities related to moles.

■ Remember that the volume of *solution,* not the volume of solvent, is used in the definition of molarity.

■ Concentrations are *not* added when solutions are mixed.

■ In molarity problems involving two compounds, be sure to distinguish between those in which a reaction does not occur and those in which one does occur.

Answers to Snapshot Reviews

11.1 A. (a), (b), and (c) All three solutions contain the same quantity of solute and all have the same volume. Their concentration is 0.333 M.

B. $15.0 \text{ mL}\left(\dfrac{2.00 \text{ mmol}}{1 \text{ mL}}\right) = 30.0 \text{ mmol}$

C. There is a total of 120.0 mmol in the final solution.

$\dfrac{120.0 \text{ mmol}}{200.0 \text{ mL}} = 0.6000 \text{ M}$

11.2 A. The substances react according to the net ionic equation

$$H^+(aq) + OH^-(aq) \rightarrow H_2O(\ell)$$

There are present

$5.00 \text{ mL}\left(\dfrac{2.50 \text{ mmol H}^+}{1 \text{ mL}}\right) = 12.5 \text{ mmol H}^+$

$20.0 \text{ mL}\left(\dfrac{0.750 \text{ mmol OH}^-}{1 \text{ mL}}\right) = 15.0 \text{ mmol OH}^-$

The 12.5 mmol H^+ reacts with 12.5 mmol OH^-, leaving 2.5 mmol OH^- in solution. The concentration of OH^- is $(2.5 \text{ mmol})/(100.0 \text{ mL}) = 0.025 \text{ M}$.

11.3 A. (a) 30.00 mmol HCl   (b) 30.00 mmol NaOH

(c) $\dfrac{30.00 \text{ mmol}}{29.42 \text{ mL}} = 1.020 \text{ M}$

Self-Tutorial Problems

11.1 (a) If exactly one-thousandth of a 2.000-L sample of 3.000 M solution is poured into a small beaker, what is the concentration of the solution in the beaker?

(b) How many milliliters of solution are in the beaker?

(c) How many millimoles of solute are in the beaker?

(d) What is the concentration in millimoles per milliliter in the beaker?

11.2 Calculate the molarity of a solution of 1.70 mol of solute in

(a) 1.00 L of solution   (b) 2.00 L of solution

(c) 5.00 L of solution   (d) 0.500 L of solution

11.3 What is the difference between (a) "dilute the solution to 40.0 mL with water" and (b) "dilute the solution with 40.0 mL of water"?

11.4 What is the final concentration when 25.0 mL of 1.22 M sugar solution is added to 35.0 mL of 1.22 M sugar solution?

11.5 Calculate the concentration of each of the following solutes:

(a) 0.365 mol solute in 0.4000 L of solution

(b) 365 mmol solute in 0.4000 L of solution

(c) 0.365 mol solute in 400.0 mL of solution

(d) 365 mmol solute in 400.0 mL of solution

11.6 If 3.13 mL of a solution is poured from 100.0 mL of a 0.693 M sample, what is the concentration of the 3.13-mL portion?

11.7 (a) If two dozen couples get married at city hall on a certain weekend, how many brides are there? How many grooms?

(b) What is the concentration of the cation in a 2.0 M solution of NH_4NO_3? What is the concentration of the anion?

11.8 What is the concentration of each ion in the following solutions?

(a) 1.0 M NaCl   (b) 1.0 M $MgCl_2$

(c) 1.0 M $CrCl_3$ (d) 1.0 M $LiNO_3$

(e) 1.0 M $Co(NO_3)_2$ (f) 1.0 M $Al(NO_3)_3$

(g) 1.0 M $Al_2(SO_4)_3$ (h) 1.0 M $(NH_4)_2SO_4$

11.9 What is the final volume of solution if 2.2 L of solution is diluted (a) with 3.3 L of solvent or (b) to 3.3 L with solvent?

11.10 Which of the following combinations of solutions will result in a chemical reaction, which will result in a combination of the number of moles of a common ion, and which will result in a mere dilution?

(a) Na_2SO_4(aq) + $Ba(NO_3)_2$(aq)

(b) $Ba(NO_3)_2$(aq) + KNO_3(aq)

(c) KCl(aq) + $AlCl_3$(aq)

(d) Na_2CO_3(aq) + HCl(aq)

(e) LiOH(aq) + KNO_3(aq)

(f) KOH(aq) + LiOH(aq)

11.11 (a) A chemist titrates 25.00 mL of $NaHCO_3$ with 31.77 mL of 2.000 M HCl. What is the purpose of the titration? What answer does she get?

(b) A chemist titrates 4.13 g of an acid, HA, with 35.72 mL of 2.000 M NaOH. What is the purpose of the titration? What answer does she get?

11.12 In which of the following combinations of solutions will there be a chemical reaction? Which have ions in common? In which are the ions all different and unreactive?

(a) HCl(aq) + K_2CO_3(aq)

(b) NaCl(aq) + $LiNO_3$(aq)

(c) LiCl(aq) + KNO_3(aq)

(d) Na_2SO_4(aq) + KBr(aq)

(e) $CuCl_2$(aq) + KCl(aq)

(f) NaOH(aq) + H_2SO_4(aq)

Problems

11.1 Definition and Uses of Molarity

11.13 Calculate the molarity of a solution containing (a) 0.123 mol of solute in 0.7000 L of solution. (b) 123 mmol of solute in 700.0 mL of solution.

11.14 Calculate the molarity of a solution containing 1.17 mol of solute in 943 mL of solution.

11.15 Calculate the molarity of a solution containing 79.4 mmol of solute in 122.5 mL of solution.

11.16 Calculate the molarity of a solution containing 0.5050 mol of solute in 400.0 mL of solution.

11.17 Calculate the molarity of 29.7 mL of a solution that contains 6.11 g of methyl alcohol, CH_3OH.

11.18 Calculate the volume of 0.881 M solution that contains 0.175 mol of solute.

11.19 Calculate the number of milliliters of 1.38 M NaCl solution that contains 122 mg of NaCl.

11.20 Calculate the number of grams of $NaNO_3$ in 0.0112 L of 3.09 M $NaNO_3$ solution.

11.21 Calculate the molarity of 886 mL of a solution that contains 149 g of ethyl alcohol, C_2H_5OH.

11.22 Calculate the number of moles of solute in 0.8122 L of 2.163 M solution.

11.23 Calculate the number of millimoles of solute in 41.0 mL of 2.611 M solution.

11.24 Calculate the number of grams of $AlCl_3$ in 1255 mL of 0.909 M $AlCl_3$ solution.

11.25 What is the final concentration if 225 mL of 0.500 M solution is diluted (a) with 1.100 L of solvent or (b) to 1.100 L with solvent?

11.26 Calculate the volume of 3.171 M solution that contains 25.5 mmol of solute.

11.27 Calculate the number of milliliters of 3.83 M NaCl solution that contains 14.7 g of NaCl.

11.28 Calculate the molarity of a solution prepared by diluting 20.8 mL of 2.11 M solution to 50.0 mL.

11.29 Calculate the volume of solution prepared by diluting 69.7 mL of 2.13 M solution to 1.51 M.

11.30 Calculate the volume of 2.50 M solution required to make 6.00 L of 0.450 M solution by dilution with water.

11.31 Calculate the molarity of a solution prepared by diluting 75.00 mL of 2.132 M solution to 125.0 mL.

11.32 Calculate the volume of solution prepared by diluting 6.929 mL of 3.555 M solution to 0.8229 M.

11.33 Calculate the volume of 3.00 M solution required to make 75.00 mL of 1.600 M solution by dilution with water.

11.2 Molarities of Ions

11.34 Calculate the concentration of each ion in each of the following solutions:

(a) 0.344 M $Al_2(SO_4)_3$

(b) 1.61 M $(NH_4)_3PO_4$

(c) 0.0808 M $Ba(OH)_2$

(d) 3.75 M KBr

(e) 3.09 M $NaClO_3$

11.35 In which one(s) of the following combinations of solutions is a reaction expected?

(a) $KC_2H_3O_2(aq)$ + HCl(aq)

(b) $CaF_2(aq)$ + $HNO_3(aq)$

11.36 Calculate the concentration of each ion in each of the following solutions:

(a) 2.50 M HNO_3 (b) 3.00 M $Co(ClO_3)_3$

(c) 2.10 M $CuSO_4$ (d) 0.136 M $Ca_3(PO_4)_2$

(e) 3.11 M $(NH_4)_2SO_3$

11.37 Calculate the concentration of each ion in 0.715 M $Al_2(SO_4)_3$ solution.

11.38 Calculate the concentration of each ion in 0.128 M (a) $Hg(NO_3)_2$ solution, and (b) $Hg_2(NO_3)_2$ solution.

11.39 Calculate the concentration of each ion in solution after 12.3 mL of 0.816 M $BaCl_2$ is mixed with 14.3 mL of 0.806 M $AlCl_3$ and the resulting solution is diluted to 50.0 mL.

11.40 Calculate the *total* concentration of all the ions in each of the following solutions:

(a) 3.25 M NaCl (b) 1.75 M $Ca(ClO_3)_2$

(c) 12.1 g of $(NH_4)_2SO_3$ in 615 mL of solution

11.41 If 0.217 mol of Li_2SO_4 and 0.217 mol of K_2SO_4 are dissolved in enough water to make 650.0 mL of solution, what is the concentration of each ion in the solution?

11.42 Calculate the concentration of each ion in solution after 35.3 mL of 2.17 M $MgCl_2$ is mixed with 21.4 mL of 0.500 M $AlBr_3$ and the resulting solution is diluted to 100.0 mL.

11.43 If 0.500 mol of $Al_2(SO_4)_3$ and 0.500 mol of Na_2SO_3 are dissolved in enough water to make 250.0 mL of solution, what is the concentration of each ion in the solution?

11.44 Assuming that the final volume is the sum of the initial volumes, calculate the concentration of each ion in solution after

(a) 30.00 mL of 4.000 M NaOH is added to 60.00 mL of 1.250 M HCl.

(b) 30.00 mL of 4.000 M NaCl is added to 60.00 mL of 1.250 M HCl.

11.45 Calculate the concentration of each type of ion in solution after 30.0 mL of 3.35 M NaCl and 70.0 mL of 1.35 M Na_2SO_4 are mixed. Assume that the final volume is 100.0 mL.

11.46 What is the concentration of each type of ion in solution after 23.69 mL of 3.611 M NaOH is added to 29.10 mL of 0.8921 M H_2SO_4? Assume that the final volume is the sum of the original volumes.

11.47 Calculate the concentration of each type of ion in solution after 50.0 mL of 4.00 M NaCl and 50.0 mL of 2.50 M NaBr are mixed. Assume that the final volume is 100.0 mL.

11.48 What is the concentration of each type of ion in solution after 42.00 mL of 3.000 M NaOH is added to 50.00 mL of 2.535 M $HClO_3$? Assume that the final volume is the sum of the original volumes.

11.49 Find the concentration of each type of ion in solution after 25.0 mL of 0.919 M $CoCl_2$ is diluted to 100.0 mL.

11.50 Find the concentration of each type of ion in solution after 10.0 mL of 0.650 M Na_3PO_4 is diluted to 50.0 mL.

11.3 Titration

11.51 Calculate the concentration of an H_2SO_4 solution if 25.00 mL is completely neutralized by 21.73 mL of 4.000 M NaOH solution.

11.52 Calculate the concentration of a phosphoric acid solution if 25.00 mL is completely neutralized by 31.17 mL of 4.000 M sodium hydroxide solution.

11.53 Calculate the concentration of an H_3PO_4 solution if 25.00 mL is converted to Na_2HPO_4 by 39.13 mL of 2.000 M NaOH solution.

11.54 Calculate the concentration of a sulfuric acid solution if 25.00 mL is converted to sodium sulfate by 17.42 mL of 3.150 M sodium hydroxide solution.

11.55 When 2.818 g of potassium hydrogen phthalate (symbolized here as KHPh; molar mass = 204.2 g/mol) is titrated with KOH solution, it takes 31.74 mL of the base to achieve the end point. Calculate the concentration of the KOH solution.

$$KHPh(aq) + KOH(aq) \rightarrow K_2Ph(aq) + H_2O(\ell)$$

11.56 How many millimoles of $AgNO_3$ will react with 21.29 mL of 2.500 M $CaCl_2$?

11.57 How many millimoles of H_2SO_4 will react completely with 12.88 mL of 1.500 M NaOH?

11.58 How many millimoles of CaO(s) can be "dissolved" with 25.00 mL of 4.000 M HCl?

11.59 How many millimoles of $Ca(OH)_2(s)$ will react with 29.17 mL of 4.000 M $HClO_3$?

11.60 How many millimoles of $AgNO_3$ will react with 17.13 mL of 0.203 M $AlCl_3$?

11.61 An antacid tablet contains 31.3 g of $NaHCO_3$. What volume of 2.84 M stomach acid (HCl) can this tablet neutralize?

11.62 An antacid tablet contains $NaHCO_3$. What mass of this compound is required to neutralize 178 mL of 2.91 M stomach acid (HCl)?

General Problems

11.63 Calculate the concentration of each type of ion in solution after 37.22 mL of 1.000 M HCl is added to 19.29 mL of 4.107 M NaOH. Use a net ionic equation in solving this problem. Assume that the final volume is equal to the sum of the volumes of the two original solutions.

11.64 Calculate the number of milligrams of Na_2CO_3 in 725 mL of 715 mM solution.

11.65 Calculate the concentration of H^+ ion produced when H_2S is bubbled into 0.300 M Cu^{2+} solution, causing precipitation of all the copper(II) ion as CuS. Assume no change in the volume of the solution.

$$Cu^{2+}(aq) + H_2S(g) \rightarrow CuS(s) + 2\,H^+(aq)$$

11.66 Calculate the concentration of acetic acid produced by reaction in 1.00 L of solution of

(a) 2.0 mol $KC_2H_3O_2(aq)$ + 1.0 mol HCl(aq)

(b) 3.0 mol $KC_2H_3O_2(aq)$ + 2.0 mol HCl(aq)

11.67 Calculate the concentration of each ion in solution after 47.33 mL of 1.807 M NaOH is mixed with 39.19 mL of 0.5093 M H_2SO_4 and then diluted to 100.0 mL.

11.68 Calculate the concentration of formaldehyde (CH_2O) in a solution prepared by mixing 125 mL of 6.13 M CH_2O and 175 mL of 4.34 M CH_2O and diluting the mixture to 500.0 mL with water.

11.69 Calculate the concentration of CH_2O in a solution prepared by mixing 1.25 L of 3.00 M CH_2O and 719 mL of 1.75 M CH_2O and diluting the mixture to 2.50 L with water.

11.70 If 5.033 g of potassium hydrogen phthalate, an acid salt having one ionizable hydrogen atom and a molar mass of 204.2 g/mol, is used to neutralize 39.17 mL of NaOH solution, calculate the concentration of the base.

11.71 Calculate the concentration of each ion in solution after 30.8 mL of 4.65 M NaOH is mixed with 21.9 mL of 0.750 M H_3PO_4 and then diluted to 100.0 mL.

11.72 Calculate the sodium ion concentration after 20.0 mL of 3.00 M NaOH is mixed with 30.0 mL of 1.00 M HCl and diluted to 100.0 mL.

11.73 Calculate the final sugar concentration after 2.25 L of 3.00 M sugar solution is diluted to 5.00 L with (a) water and (b) 1.00 M NaCl solution.

11.74 Vinegar contains several acids. Calculate the total concentration of acids in a 20.0-mL sample of vinegar if it takes 37.88 mL of 0.2000 M NaOH to neutralize the acids. Assume that each acid contains only one ionizable hydrogen atom per formula unit.

11.75 Calculate the concentration of each of the ions in solution with concentrations greater than 0.500 M after

(a) 1.25 M HCl is mixed with an equal volume of 1.25 M NaCl.

(b) 1.25 M $HC_2H_3O_2$ is mixed with an equal volume of 1.25 M $NaC_2H_3O_2$.

11.76 The label has fallen off a bottle of a solid organic acid. If 26.2 mL of 2.00 M NaOH is needed to completely neutralize 2.36 g of the acid, determine if the acid is oxalic acid ($H_2C_2O_4$), benzoic acid ($HC_7H_5O_2$), or bromobenzoic acid ($HC_7H_4O_2Br$).

11.77 Calculate the acetic acid concentration and the acetate ion concentration (a) after 0.150 mol of acetic acid and 0.100 mol of sodium acetate are dissolved in enough water to make 1.00 L of solution and (b) after 0.250 mol of acetic acid and 0.100 mol of sodium hydroxide are dissolved in enough water to make 1.00 L of solution.

11.78 Calculate the hydrogen ion concentration and the chloride ion concentration (a) after 0.150 mol of hydrochloric acid and 0.100 mol of sodium chloride are dissolved in enough water to make 1.00 L of solution, (b) after 0.250 mol of hydrochloric acid and 0.100 mol of sodium hydroxide are dissolved in enough water to make 1.00 L of solution and (c) compare your results to those of Problem 11.77.

11.79 Calculate the concentration of each ion in solution after 94.3 mL of 2.14 M $MgCl_2$ is mixed with 82.8 mL of 0.700 M $AlCl_3$ and then diluted to 500.0 mL.

11.80 When lithium nitride is treated with water, it reacts with the water to form hydroxide ions and ammonia. What concentration of hydroxide ions is present if 0.110 mol of solid Li_3N is treated with water and then diluted to 100.0 mL?

11.81 Calculate the percentage of $CaCO_3$ in a 5.000-g sample of limestone if 24.24 mL of 2.500 M HCl is required to react completely with the $CaCO_3$. Assume that the rest of the limestone sample is inert.

11.82 In a certain experiment, 10.00 mL of 1.500 M H_3PO_4 was titrated to a certain end point with 27.61 mL of 1.630 M NaOH. Write the equation for the chemical reaction that occurred.

11.83 After a 10.0-g sample containing Na_2CO_3 and inert substances was treated with 32.74 mL of 5.000 M HCl, it took 4.20 mL of 1.000 M NaOH to neutralize the excess HCl. Calculate the percent of Na_2CO_3 in the sample.

11.84 After a 10.00-g sample containing Na_2CO_3 and inert substances was treated with 41.04 mL of 3.000 M HCl, it took 4.22 mL of 1.000 M NaOH to neutralize the excess HCl. Calculate the percent of Na_2CO_3 in the sample.

11.85 When an alkali metal oxide is treated with water, it reacts with the water to form hydroxide ions. What concentration of hydroxide ions is present if 0.250 mol of solid Li_2O is treated with water and the final volume is 500.0 mL?

11.86 In a certain experiment, 25.00 mL of 2.500 M H_3PO_4 was titrated to a certain end point with 39.66 mL of 3.152 M NaOH. Write the equation for the chemical reaction that occurred.

11.87 What volume of 3.152 M NaOH would be required to completely neutralize the H_3PO_4 in the previous problem.

11.88 (a) Calculate the concentration of each type of ion in 58.99 mL of a solution in which 9.404 mmol of Na_2SO_4 and 29.11 mmol of NaOH had been placed.

(b) Calculate the concentration of each type of ion in solution after 47.92 mL of 1.000 M NaOH is added to 11.07 mL of 0.8495 M H_2SO_4. Assume that the volume of the final solution is the sum of the volumes of the two original solutions.

(c) Explain how parts (a) and (b) are related.

11.89 Calculate the concentrations of acetate ion and acetic acid in solution after 10.0 mL of 1.50 M $HC_2H_3O_2$ and 10.0 mL of 0.850 M NaOH are mixed. Assume that the final volume is 20.0 mL and that the excess acetic acid yields no acetate ions to the final solution (because it is a *weak* acid).

$$OH^-(aq) + HC_2H_3O_2(aq) \rightarrow C_2H_3O_2^-(aq) + H_2O(\ell)$$

11.90 Calculate the concentrations of ammonium ion and ammonia in solution after 30.0 mL of 1.35 M NH_3 and 30.0 mL of 0.750 M HCl are mixed. Assume that the final volume is 60.0 mL and that the excess ammonia yields no ammonium ions to the final solution (because it is a *weak* base).

$$H^+(aq) + NH_3(aq) \rightarrow NH_4^+(aq)$$

11.91 (a) Calculate the concentration of each type of ion in 111.23 mL of a solution containing 49.68 mmol of NaCl plus 28.43 mmol of NaOH.

(b) Calculate the concentration of each type of ion in solution after 78.11 mL of 1.000 M NaOH is added to 33.12 mL of 1.500 M HCl. Assume that the volume of the final solution is the sum of the volumes of the two original solutions.

(c) Explain how parts (a) and (b) are related.

11.92 Calculate the concentration of each ion in solution after 27.3 mL of 3.08 M NaCl is mixed with 19.1 mL of 0.877 M $CaCl_2$ and then diluted to 100.0 mL.

11.93 Calculate the molar mass of an unknown acid, HA, if a 12.11-g sample of the acid takes 38.38 mL of 5.000 M NaOH to neutralize it.

11.94 Calculate the molar mass of an unknown acid, H_2A, if a 12.11-g sample of the acid takes 38.38 mL of 5.000 M NaOH to neutralize it.